CONGRÈS INTERNATIONAL DE GÉOGRAPHIE

NORDEN 1960

INTERNATIONAL GEOGRAPHICAL CONGRESS

GUIDEBOOK
DENMARK

Contributions to problems
discussed in Symposia and Excursions

Edited by

NIELS KINGO JACOBSEN

1960

KØBENHAVNS UNIVERSITETS GEOGRAFISKE INSTITUT

CONTENTS

XIX International Geographical Congress, „Norden" 1960
Programme for Section Denmark   Page

Papers:

NATIONAL COMMITTEE OF DENMARK

Chairman:

Nielsen, Niels, Professor, Dr.: Department of Geography, University
of Copenhagen,
Copenhagen.

Secretary:

Schou, Axel, Professor, Dr.: Department of Geography, University
of Copenhagen,
Copenhagen.

Members:

Vedel, A. H., Vice-Admiral, Dr.: The Royal Danish Geographical
Society,
Copenhagen.

Feilberg, C. G., Professor, Dr.: Department of Geography, University
of Copenhagen,
Copenhagen.

Humlum, Johs., Professor, Dr.: Department of Geography, University of Århus,
Århus.

Aagesen, Aage, Dr.: School of Economics,
Copenhagen.

Please notice the address:

Det Kongelige Danske Geografiske Selskab, Kejsergade 2, Kbhvn. K.

———————

The Danish programme comprises four symposia and four excursions held partly before and partly after the Congress Sessions in
Stockholm August 6th—13th, 1960.

Symposia:

Symposia, with restricted numbers of participants, will be held
in the form of meetings with lectures and discussions on special subjects as well as local excursions.

Excursions:

The excursions are intended to demonstrate areas and phenomena
typical of Denmark.

Agrarian Geography (Symposium)

Date: July 29th–August 3rd, 1960 (6 days).

Place: Horsens.

Topics:

1. Intensive agriculture.
2. Population.
3. Settlement.
4. Types of ownership.
5. Land-reclamation.
6. Soil stability and soil destruction.

Papers read:

Pakistan: Ahmad, Kazi S.: Reclamation of Water-Logged and Saline Lands in West Pakistan.

Israel: Amiran, D.: Recent Techniques of Integrated Rural Settlement in Israel.

France: Blanc, A.: Évolution contemporaine de l'économie agricole en Lorraine.

France: Brunet, P.: Un cas particulier de l'influence des villes sur l'extension des Friches: Paris et les vallées briardes.

Germany: Endriss, G.: Flurbereinigung und Dorfauflockerung im Raum von Freiburg im Breisgau (Regierungsbezirk Südbaden des Landes Baden–Württemberg in der Bundesrepublik Deutschland).

France: Gay, F.: Vicissitudes de l'emploi de la troisième sole de l'essolement triennal en Champagne Berrichonne.

Canada: Hills, T. L.: Reclamation in the St. Lawrence Lowlands.

Participants:

Ahmad, Kazi S. (Pakistan). *Akin, W. E.* (U. S. A.). *Amiran, D.* (Israel). *Birch, I. W.* (U. K.). *Blanc, A.* (France). *Brunet, P.* (France). *Chen, Cheng-Siang* (China). *Dufour, J.* (France). *Endriss, G.* (Germany). *Fairbairn, E.* (New Zealand). *Gay, F.* (France). *Hart, J. F.* (U. S. A.). *Helburn, N.* (U.S.A.). *Hills, T. L.* (Canada). *Jacobsen, N. Kingo* (Denmark). *Kampp, Aa. H.* (Denmark). *Kuhlman, H.* (Denmark). *Montgomery, C.* (Sweden). *Nielsen, Niels* (Denmark). *Pardo, L. P.* (Spain). *Schaub, K.* (U. S. A.). *Schou, Axel* (Denmark). *Siddiqi, S. I.* (Pakistan). *Takeuchi, J.* (Japan). *Troll, C.* (Germany). *Tschudi, Aa. Brun* (Norway).

Programme:

July 29th: Opening. Paper sessions.

July 30th: Excursion: East Jutland. Highly developed farming area.

July 31st: Excursion: South-West Jutland. Regional planning in marine foreland. Agricultural development in the salt-marsh areas. Land-reclamation from the sea.

August 1st: Paper sessions.

August 2nd: Excursion: Central and Western Jutland. Old types of soil destruction with modern recolonization. Recent wind-erosion.

August 3rd: Excursion: Fyn. Agriculture and horticulture. Small holdings and large-scale farming.

Visits will be arranged to different types of farms, small holdings, big family-farms, manors, horticultural settlements, dairies, and other agricultural factories, centres for organization, coldstores, etc., in order to give an outline of the geography of Danish agriculture.

Leaders:

Professor Niels Nielsen, chairman, in cooperation with Professor Axel Schou, Niels Kingo Jacobsen, Aa. H. Kampp, and Hans Kuhlman, Department of Geography, University of Copenhagen, Copenhagen.

Physical Geography of Greenland (Symposium)

Date: July 31st–August 3rd, 1960 (4 days).

Place: Copenhagen.

Topics:
1. Arctic climatology.
2. Glaciology in the coastal region.
3. The Greenland Ice Cap.
4. Periglaciology.
5. Arctic Geomorphology.

Papers read:

Austria: Ambach, W.: Investigations of the Heat Balance in the Area of Ablation on the Greenland Ice Cap.

France: Bauer, A.: Précision des mesures d'ablation. Expédition Glaciologique Internationale au Groenland.

U. S. A.: Benson, C. S.: Stratigraphic Studies in Snow and Firn of the Greenland Ice Sheet.

Denmark: Danish Geodetic Institute: Work in Greenland.

Denmark: Danish Meteorological Institute: Weather Service in Greenland and Climatological Observations.

Denmark: Dansgaard, W.: The Origins and the Velocities of Ice Bergs determined by 0^{18} and C^{14} Analyses.

Denmark: Fristrup, B.: Recent Investigations in Greenland.

Denmark: Fristrup, B.: Studies of Four Glaciers in Greenland.

U. S. A.: Gerdel, R. W.: Some Climatological Studies on the Greenland Ice Cap.

U. S. A.: Goldthwait, R. P.: Regimen of an Ice Cliff on Land in Northwest Greenland.

Denmark: Greenland Geological Survey: Investigations in Greenland.

U. S. A.:   Griffith, Th.: Some Glacial Investigations in the Thule Area, Greenland.

Germany: Hochstein, M.: Magnetic Measurements on the Greenland Ice Cap.

Germany: Hofmann, W.: Tellurometer Measurements on the Greenland Ice Cap during the International Glaciological Greenland Expedition (EGIG), Summer 1959.

U. K.:   Jackson, C. J.: Summer Precipitation in the Queen Elisabeth Islands.

Denmark: Larsen, H. Valeur: Runoff Studies from a Glacier in SE-Greenland 1958.

U. K.:   Lister, H.: Accumulation and Firnification in North Greenland.

France: Malaurie, J.: Gélification, éboulis et ruissellement sur la côte nord-ouest du Groenland.

U. S. A.:   Marshall, E. W.: Structure and Stratigraphy of Ice Island T-3 and Ellesmere Ice Shelf.

Germany: Mälzer, H.: Nivellement of the Greenland Ice Cap.

Denmark: Møller, J. Tyge: Glaciers and Periglacial Phenomena in the Upernivik Island, West Greenland.

U. S. A.:   Nobles, L.: Structure of the Ice Cap Margin, Northwestern Greenland.

U. S. A.:   Nutt, David & Per Scholander: Gases in Greenland Icebergs.

Switzerland: Quervain, M. R. de: On the Work carried out by the Group »Glaciology Indlandsis« of the International Glaciological Expedition 1959/60 (EGIG).

U. S. A.:   Scholander, Per: see above: David Nutt.

Participants:

Ambach, W. (Austria). *Anstey, Robert* (U. S. A.). *Barry, Roger* (U. K.). *Bauer, A.* (France). *Benson, G. S.* (U. S. A.). *Boyd, L. A.* (U. S. A.). *Brockkamp, B.* (Germany). *Dansgaard, W.* (Denmark). *Davies, W.* (U. S. A.). *Fristrup, B.* (Denmark). *Gajzágé, A.* (Hungary). *Gerdel, R. W.* (U. S. A.). *Goldthwait, R. P.* (U. S. A.). *Griffiths, Th.* (U. S. A.). *Hochstein, M.* (Germany). *Hofmann, W.* (Germany). *Jackson, C. J.* (U. K.). *Jaeckel, G.* (Germany). *Larsen, H. Valeur* (Denmark). *Lister, H.* (U. K.). *Lloyd, M. Trevor* (Canada). *Malaurie, J.* (France). *Marshall, E. W.* (U. S. A.). *Mälzer, H.* (Germany). *Møller, J. T.* (Denmark). *Nobles, L.* (U. S. A.). *Nutt, David C.* (U. S. A.). *Percin, F. de* (U. S. A.). *Quervain, M. R. de* (Switzerland). *Seebass, F.* (Germany). *Smith, D. J.* (U. K.). *Tuck, J.* (U. S. A.). *Wood, W.* (U. S. A.).

Leaders:

Børge Fristrup, chairman, in cooperation with Jens Tyge Møller, Department of Geography, University of Copenhagen.

Regional Geography of Denmark (Excursions)

Dates: July 20th–26th, July 28th–August 3rd, August 15th–21st, August 23rd–29th (cancelled), 1960 (7 days).

Place: The excursions start and terminate in Copenhagen.

Route:

1st day: Registration, introduction, and excursion in the Copenhagen area. Departure for Ålborg by boat at night.

2nd day: Morning excursion in Vendsyssel: Raised sea-beds at different levels. Reclamation of bog lands. Dune landscapes and soil devastation by blowing sand.
Afternoon excursion: 1) Denmark's biggest prehistoric stone-settings at Lindholm Høje. 2) The interplay between limestone plateau and raised Stoneage-sea. 3) The tunnel-valley at Mariager. Stay for the night at Århus.

3rd day: Morning excursion: Young moraine landscapes in Eastern and Central Jutland. Visit to a farm in Ask (Eastern type). Continuing to Himmelbjerget.
Afternoon excursion: Main stationary line of the Würm Glaciation. Melt-water plains and old moraines of the Riss Glaciation. Visit to a farm in Faurholt (Western type). The Agricultural Museum in Herning. Stay for the night at Herning.

4th day: Morning excursion: Lagoon landscapes west of Ringkøbing. The spit of Holmslands Klit.
Afternoon excursion: Newly developed farm colony on former heath at Sønder Vium. The fishing port of Esbjerg.
Stay for the night at Ribe.

5th day: Morning excursion: The marine foreland south of Ribe. Older endiked salt marshes, young foreland and land-reclamation, tidal-flat areas in the region between the old land and the Frisian islands. Crossing the Wadden Sea on the dam to the isle of Rømø.
Afternoon excursion: Cross-section of North Slesvig from Tønder to Åbenrå. Driving through the outwash plain of Tinglev to the young moraines and tunnel-valleys along the eastern coast. Fjord landscape at Kolding.
Stay for the night at Middelfart.

6th day: Morning excursion: Farm land of great fertility in Western Fyn. Dead-ice landscapes (plateau-hills). Market gardening around Odense. Visit to Hans Christian Andersen's home.
Afternoon excursion: Industrial development east of Odense. The small town of Kerteminde.
Stay for the night at Nyborg.

7th day: Morning excursion: Crossing of Store Bælt by ferry to Sjælland. Trelleborg Viking settlement. Glacial landscapes around the diked area of Lammefjord.

Afternoon excursion: Fjord landscapes on Sjælland. Old villages. Arrival in Copenhagen.

Leaders:

Viggo Hansen and Kr. M. Jensen, Department of Geography, University of Copenhagen.

Urban Development and its Effect (Symposium)

Date: August 15th–20th, 1960 (6 days).

Place: Copenhagen. This symposium was cancelled.

Coastal Geomorphology (Symposium)

Date: August 15th–20th, 1960 (6 days).

Place: Esbjerg and Århus.

Topics:
1. Relief features of tidal-areas.
2. Salt-marsh development.
3. Simplification of moraine shorelines.
4. Coast-type systematics.

Papers read:

U. K.:   Barnes, F. A.: see below: C. A. M. King.

France: Guilcher, A. and King Cuchlaine A. M.: Preliminary Observations on the Beaches of the West Coast of Ireland.

U. K.:   King, Cuchlaine A. M.: see above: A. Guilcher.

U. K.:   King, Cuchlaine A. M. and Barnes, F. A.: Changes in the Configuration af the Inter-Tidal Beach Zone of the South Lincolnshire Coast since 1951.

U. K.:   King, Cuchlaine A. M. and Barnes, F. A.: Morphological Development of Salt Marsh near Gibraltar Point, Lincolnshire.

Participants:

Barnes, F. A. (U. K.). *Beck, J.* (Denmark). *Bruun, Per* (U. S. A.). *Guilcher, A. J.* (France). *Gullentops, F.* (Belgium). *Hsi-Lin, T.* (Singapore). *Jacobsen, N. Kingo* (Denmark). *Jakobsen, Børge* (Denmark). *Kidson, C.* (U. K.). *King, C. A. M.* (U. K.). *Kuhlman, H.* (Denmark). *Larsen, B. Valeur* (Denmark). *McIntire, W. G.* (U. S. A.). *Meesenburg, Horst* (Denmark). *Møller, J. T.* (Denmark). *Nielsen, Niels* (Denmark). *Olsen, H. A.* (Denmark). *Pruitt, E. L.* (U. S. A.). *Ruellan, F.* (France). *Russell, R. J.* (U.S.A.). *Schou, Axel* (Denmark). *Smith, H. T. U.* (U. S. A.). *Steers, J. A.* (U. K.). *Stephens, N.* (N. Ireland). *Trask, P. D.* (U. S. A.). *Valentin, H.* (Germany). *Vann, J. H.* (U. S. A.). *Whittow, J. B.* (Uganda).

Programme:

August 15th: Registration and paper session.
Afternoon excursion to the isle of Mandø in the Wadden Sea (tidal-flat topography).

August 16th: Morning excursion to the isle of Rømø (reclamation works, salt-marsh formation, dunes, beach).
Afternoon excursion to the young salt marshes outside the sea-dike at Råhede and Rejsby (natural formation of salt marsh, tidal-flat topography, experimental fields for land-reclamation).

August 17th: Morning excursion to the dune areas in the region Blåvands-huk-Skallingen (»fossil« shorelines, dune topography, evolution stages of dune vegetation).
Afternoon excursion: Skallingen (salt-marsh development, tidal-creek topography, experimental fields, tidal-flats, salt-pans, surge overflow-plains).
Returnal to Esbjerg by boat through the channel Hobo-Dyb to Grå-dyb with a visit to the Søren Jessen High-Sand or returnal by bus (dune-area of Blåbjerg and the embanked lagoon of Fiil Sø).

August 18th: Morning excursion to the salt-marsh area at Tønder (late-glacial sub-surface, various types of post-glacial sedimentation. Recent sedimentation and reclamation works).
Afternoon: Paper session.

August 19th: Removal from Esbjerg (the west coast with tidal-flats, dunes and lagoons) to Århus (the east coast with forms of erosion and accumulation in a moraine landscape practically without tidal influence).
Morning excursion to the Lille Bælt region.
Afternoon excursion via Vejle to Århus.

August 20th: The Djursland Peninsula. Stages in the simplification of moraine shorelines, caused by abrasion, accumulation, upheaval, and embankments.

Leaders:

Professor Axel Schou in cooperation with Professor Niels Nielsen, Børge Jakobsen, Niels Kingo Jacobsen, J. Tyge Møller, and Hans Kuhlman, Department of Geography, University of Copenhagen.

COASTAL
GEOMORPHOLOGY

The organization of research work in South-West Jutland

By Niels Nielsen

Abstract

    An outline of Skalling-Laboratoriet and De Danske Vade- og Marsk-undersøgelser as a Danish centre for the studies of landscape elements characteristic of West Jutland and the coasts of Western Europe: tidal-flat, salt-marsh and dune.

Skalling-Laboratoriet was founded in the summer of 1930 as a modest field laboratory on the peninsula Skallingen. The object was to create a centre for the studies of the combination of landscape elements characteristic of West Jutland and of the coasts of Western Europe: tidal-flat, salt-marsh and dune.

The laboratory on Skallingen was in function until it was laid in ruins by military operations in 1944. In the years 1947-1949 it was reconstructed farther to the north, immediately to the south of the village Ho; however, the buildings kept the name *Skalling-Laboratoriet*. They comprise a number of wooden houses with habitation for about ten scientists, a kitchen and rooms for research work.

In 1938 a branch of Skalling-Laboratoriet was established in the port of Esbjerg, whose authorities placed at our disposal a house previously used in the service of the port. While the laboratory on Skallingen is almost exclusively adapted to field-work, the building in Esbjerg is provided with laboratory equipment in view of the execution of sedimentological and biological experiments and hydrographic analyses. This laboratory has room for four scientists. Further, it possesses a motor boat with equipment for work in the Wadden Sea.

Both the laboratory on Skallingen and that in Esbjerg principally serve scientific purposes; however, they are also used as centres for students' courses, and they receive and house foreign guests.

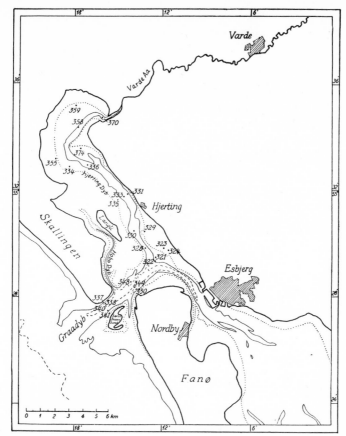

Fig. 1. The Graadyb tidal area, localities and sample stations 1941.
K. Hansen, Medd. f. Skall.-Lab. XIV.

Since 1930, Skalling-Laboratoriet has treated a great number of research objects, among which may be mentioned:

1): natural formation of salt-marsh;
2): biological conditions in dune, salt-marsh and tidal-flat;
3): sand-drift and sand-deposition;
4): tidal processes;
5): transport of materials;
6): soil conditions;
7): habitation;
8): general coastal evolution;
9): formation of channels.

The results of these investigations have been published in »Meddelelser fra Skalling-Laboratoriet«, volumes I-XVI. Thanks to annual

Fig. 2. Dense *Obione*-marsh near the coast, especially on the edge of the little creek *Obione* is very high. B. Jakobsen, Medd. f. Skall.-Lab. XIV.

grants from the *Carlsberg Foundation* and to the favourable attitude which we have met from the part of the Esbjerg authorities and from a number of other institutions it has been possible to carry on these researches and to maintain the two laboratories.

These many-sided researches have enabled us to accumulate, in the course of the years, a certain quantity of knowledge of the processes determining the evolution along the coast of South-West Jutland — the morphological as well as the biological processes — and the intimate collaboration between scientists with different spheres of interests proved to be very fruitful because the close connection between the physical processes and conditions and the biological-ecological conditions provided results of a rather far reaching significance.

During the years 1938-1941 we succeeded in carrying through comprehensive hydrographical examinations of the tidal-area between Esbjerg and the frontier to Germany; we also established a systematic, quantitative analysis of the sediment-drifting and, especially, of the sedimentation in the areas close to the coast, more particularly the beach meadows.

The experiences gained through our researches naturally resulted in an attempt of planning and carrying through a number of practical works. To this effect was established, in 1941, at the instigation of the Ministry of Public Works the so-called *Vadehavsudvalg* with the object of executing certain researches and practical works in the Wadden Sea especially in relation to the conditions reigning around

Fig. 3. Profile of the salt-marsh, foreland type. Notice the alternating layers of sand and clay. N. Kingo Jacobsen, Medd. f. Skall.-Lab. XV.

the dam which, at that time, was under construction between the mainland and Rømø.

In the years following the second World War appeared, from various circles, a wish of carrying out the necessary measures for land-reclamation and for rationalization of the economical life and the habitation conditions in this region; to this purpose was appointed, in 1953, the *Samordningsudvalg* (Co-Operation Commission) under the auspicies of the Ministry of Agriculture. However, the competent authorities realized that it was indispensable, in the first place, to carry out a fundamental research work to be combined with a rational, experimental work in order to arrive at the methods which would serve the purpose.

The management of this preliminary work was entrusted to Professor *Niels Nielsen;* the Tønder county and the Danish government granted a 5-year appropriation towards the execution of the preliminary researches; these started the 1st of August 1953, and by the end of the year 1958 the programme had almost been carried through.

The work was organized as follows: a co-operation was established between Skalling-Laboratoriet, which undertook the solution of the tasks in the northern part of the Wadden Sea, and *De Danske Vade- og Marskundersøgelser,* which was in charge of the investigations

Fig. 4. Exact measurement of sedimentation 1931-1935. Block of salt-marsh clay from sample-area on Skallingen. The light layer at 30 mm. of the scale is red-coloured sand laid out 1.8.1931. Niels Nielsen, Medd. f. Skall.-Lab. I.

in the region from the isle of Mandø to the frontier. Two centres were established with their seat in Skærbæk and in Tønder, respectively, and combined with the laboratories in Esbjerg and on Skallingen.

The daily management of the two departments in Southern Jutland was delegated to *Børge Jakobsen,* M. Sc., and *Niels Kingo Jacobsen,* M. Sc., respectively, with the assistance of a considerable number of young scientists and students. In the Skærbæk department the studies of the tidal-flats were concentrated, while the Tønder department had the task of examining the diked-in salt-marsh areas (polders; Danish: kog). Both departments were provided with the necessary equipment of instruments, means of transport and utensils, and working rooms were hired in both Skærbæk and Tønder. The treatment of the material has for the greater part taken place in the Geographical Institute at the University of Copenhagen, who has placed special rooms at our disposal for this purpose. Further, the necessary team of unskilled labourers was engaged for the execution of digging-work etc.

The results of our combined efforts have been represented in reports to the Danish Ministry of Agriculture, and our researches

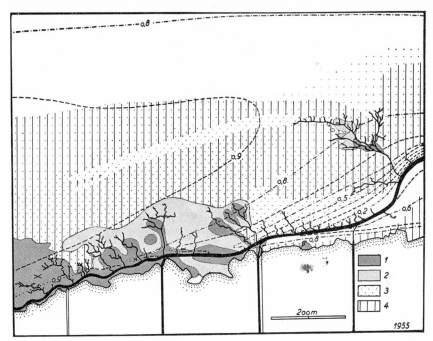

Fig. 5. Vegetation map, showing a tidal flat facing west, situated at the Højer
canal. The curves are indicated in metres in proportion to DNN.
1. A dense vegetation with *Glyceria (Puccinellia)* as a predominant plant; further, *Spartina* and *Salicornia* occur.
2. A more sparse vegetation cover consisting of the same plants.
3. *Spartina* in a rather sparse growth.
4. *Salicornia.*
The map shows to which extent the plants — especially *Glyceria* — are dependent on a good drainage; thus, at many places along the well developed priels
the annel grass descends below high tide level. Mean high tide level is here about
95 cm. above DNN. B. Jakobsen & Kr. M. Jensen, Medd. f. Skall.-Lab. XV.

are published in the Royal Danish Geographical Society's publications. All the fundamental material is filed in the Geographical
Institute of the University.

After 1958 the above-mentioned works have been divided into
various enterprises: The research-work proper is continued with the
four stations as bases. We have established a special experimental
field for land-reclamation close to the village Rejsby and a special
department for surveyings under the leadership of *Jens Tyge Møller*,
M. Sc.

In the region surrounding the Rømø Dam we have initiated a close
co-operation with *Statens Vandbygningsvæsen* (The Department of
Hydraulic Engineering); here we have carried on the studies which
started in the period 1939-1941 with the purpose, among others, of

Fig. 6. The ditching-plough, drawn by a caterpillar-tractor. The ditch is dug so as to have an obliquely declining border; the material is thrown to both sides, forming a slightly curved field ridge. B. Jakobsen, Kr. M. Jensen & Niels Nielsen, Medd. f. Skall.-Lab. XV.

Fig. 7. The lee-bank behind a fascine fence. This bank provides good conditions for the growth of *Salicornia*. The erection of the fascine fence took place in the autumn 1953, and the photo was taken in the summer 1954. B. Jakobsen & Kr. M. Jensen, Medd. f. Skall.-Lab. XV.

Fig. 8. Air photo of the canal area at the mouth of the Rejsby river.
B. Jakobsen & Kr. M. Jensen, Medd. f. Skall.-Lab. XV.

following the morphological alterations which inevitably arise when a dam is built across a tide-water area.

After the achievement of our research programme we have now succeeded in organizing a number of big land-reclamation enterprises. As one of the first steps towards the realization of this scheme it was decided, in 1958, to make an attempt of preparing a basis of a new polder between the frontier and Emmerlev. We have entered into negociations with the competent authorities in Schleswig-Holstein in view of a co-operation in order to establish a corresponding polder between the Danish-German frontier and the Hindenburg Dam. The Danish polder has been planned to be about 1.000 hectares. The establishments are supposed to be finished about 1961. However, we shall not be able to determine the date of diking until we have followed, for some years, the tempo of the land-formation. The land-reclamation at the frontier is under supervision of a special commission, of which Professor *Niels Nielsen* is chairman.

Another big land-reclamation enterprise is going on on both sides of the Rømø Dam. Here, an area of about 1.000 hectares is under treatment, and the development is absolutely satisfactory with formation of new land to a considerable extent on both sides of the dam along the coast of the mainland. This land-reclamation is under the

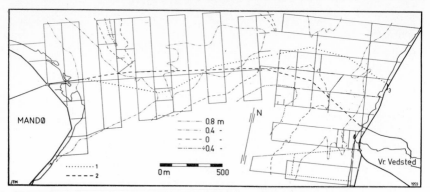

Fig. 9. Sketch-map of the surveying along the ebb-road to Mandø.
J. Tyge Møller, Folia Geogr. Danica VIII:2.

leadership of *Statens Vandbygningsvæsen,* who is in charge of the work of securing and maintaining the Rømø Dam.

A third land-reclamation field, of an extent of 100-150 hectares, is the above-mentioned experimental field at Rejsby. Among the great number of problems which we have encountered should be mentioned the drainage across the tidal-flats. In this relation too the Rejsby field has proved to be very useful; here we have carried through a number of systematical investigations of the possibilities of constructing drainage channels.

In the years 1958 and 1959 a special examination has been carried out of the area between Mandø and the mainland, where we are facing a series of problems of a particular character, attached to the maintenance of the transport on an ebb-road. From ancient time the connection has been kept up by means of horse-drawn vehicles; however, the motor-traffic of our time is so heavy that it destroys the surface of the tidal-flat and, thereby, gives rise to changes which cause certain worries.

LITERATURE

Meddelelser fra Skalling-Laboratoriet I-XVI, 1935-1959. København.

The Coastline of Djursland
A study in East-Danish shoreline development

By Axel Schou

Abstract

The peninsula of Djursland on the east coast of Jutland in the centre of Denmark proper has been analysed in relation to shoreline development. All stages of simplification are represented ranging from initial moraine coasts to totally simplified equilibrium forms.

The geomorphological analysis should be compared with the results of investigations concerning wave force, see Sofus Christiansen: Wave-Power and the Djursland Coast. Geografisk Tidsskrift, vol. 59, 1960. Concerning placenames, see map p. 31 in this paper.

Geomorphology and coastal dynamics

Coast types as well as shoreline development are results of an interplay between two distinctly different complexes of phenomena, the geological structures of the land area and the marine activities of the surrounding seas. Concerning geological structure Denmark is an area of glacial accumulation formed by deposition in the varying marginal zones of the Pleistocene ice cap. The terrestrial nuclei which form the skeleton of the Danish landscape pattern consist of the enormous quantities of boulders, gravel, sand and clay, all forming a pattern of moraine landscapes and glaciofluvial plains.

During the Riss-Saale glaciation the area of Denmark proper was completely covered by an ice cap. In the last glacial period, the Würm-Weichsel glaciation, the extreme limits of the ice cap never extended far enough to cover the southwestern part of the peninsula of Jutland. That it did not do so is to a very large measure the explanation of the great difference between West Denmark and East Denmark today, as to both relief features and coast types. The main stationary line of the last ice sheet through Jutland (fig. 1) is a geomorphological borderline of distinct significance. Southwest of this line old moraine landscapes of the Riss-Saale glaciation lie between the vast outwash plains of the last glacial period and the whole region is characterized by its flat topography. East and north of the line young moraine landscapes are predominant: large-featured hills with steep slopes and great differences in level in the marginal zones alternate with smooth moraine flats and small local outwash plains.

The peninsula of Djursland is situated in the centre of the Denmark-proper area that lies east of the main stationary line (fig. 1); as regards geological substratum and surface layers it is a typical Danish region in which nearly all Danish relief forms are represented.

Concerning dimensions as well as types of marine activity there are pronounced differences between the North Sea and the inner Danish seas (the Kattegat, the Danish Straits and the Baltic). For example, in the North Sea the maximum height of waves is 5 m., whereas the highest waves observed in the Baltic are only 3 m. The tidal range at the North Sea coast near the Danish-German border is 2 m., in Esbjerg the difference between the tide levels is only 1.5 m., and farther north at the west coast of Jutland this value diminishes. At the Scaw spit near the entrance to the inner Danish seas the tidal range is insignificant. This means that in the Kattegat and the Baltic only a very small tidal wave is generated. The tiny tidal amplitudes which can be calculated here are normally covered entirely by non-periodical level changes mainly caused by wind pressure. Finally, it should be noted that west winds are predominant, as illustrated by the direction resultant of wind work (DRW) calculated for the island of Anholt in the Kattegat (fig. 1).

The different marine environments have created highly differing coast types in West Denmark and East Denmark. This means that the west coast of Jutland is exposed to strong wind and wave activity, the fetch in the NW-direction being more than 1500 km. as a maximum and 500 km. as a minimum, the depths increasing to 10 m. very near the coast. As glacial deposits offer only slight resistance to wave attack, mature stages in the simplification of the shoreline are reached at all exposed localities. The west coast of Jutland with its north-south direction approaches a straight line because of marine activity caused by westerly winds. The direction of the coastline was not determined by the initial relief, but is due to the forces of the sea. The sea has cut cliffs through all earlier hills and built bars before the former intermediate bays. An almost uninterrupted zone of dune landscapes has developed along the west

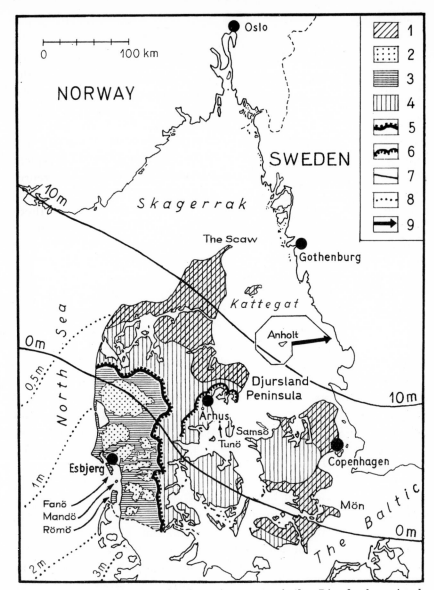

Fig. 1. *The physical-geographical environment of the Djursland peninsula.*

1. Area where limestone rocks form the substratum under the Quaternary deposits.
2. Old moraine landscapes, Riss/Saale glaciation.
3. Outwash plains of the Würm/Weichsel glaciation.
4. Predominant young moraine landscapes, Würm/Weichsel glaciation.
5. Main stationary line of the last glaciation.
6. Terminal moraine in the Djursland peninsula.
7. Lines of equal elevation since the Stone Age (Litorina-Tapes epoch).
8. Lines of equal tidal amplitude.
9. Direction resultant of wind work.

coast, continuing southward on the west coasts of the islands of Fanö, Mandö and Römö. Owing to the tides there are salt marsh coasts along the southwestern part of the shoreline of Jutland.

The East-Danish coast type is much more varied than the West-Danish type described above. East Denmark being of an archipelago nature, the fetches reach all dimensions, and the water depth is highly variable, which means that the complex of morphogenetic agencies is to be found in a rich variety of combinations. The resulting form-complexes are also influenced by the post-glacial isostatic and eustatic level changes which are still active. North Denmark is still in a state of emergence but with little velocity, about 1 mm. a year. The southern part of the country has sunk since the Stone Age and is still sinking at a similar rate. It must be added that human activities of many kinds: harbour building, reclamation and coast protection are factors of great importance in this densely inhabited land.

The Djursland peninsula

The existence of this peninsula on the east coast of Jutland is partly the result of uplift of the limestone substratum between fault lines. Djursland is a horst formation of the bedrock where resistant Cretaceous limestone withstood erosion by the ice sheets of the glacial periods. The shoreline of the northeast corner is bordered by limestone cliffs. The subterranean dislocations which are so characteristic of Central Europe were also contributory to the shoreline configuration of Denmark (see fig. 5).

Nevertheless, Denmark's shoreline is mainly governed by the surface relief of the moraine deposits of the Würm glaciation. Where these accumulations of moraine material are of considerable thickness they form projections on the coastline. This is the case on the south coast of the Djursland peninsula (fig. 2), where the hilly landscapes are explained as marginal moraines formed along the front of a glacier, which during the final Baltic stage of the Würm-Weichsel glaciation following the Baltic depression moved from south to north and had its extreme limit here. The bays, Kalvö Vig and Æbeltoft Vig, are submerged central depressions formed by erosion under the ice lobes of this glacier snout.

The peninsula of Djursland is a significant example of various types of Danish moraine coasts as well as various stages in shoreline development. The north coast is exposed to an open sea area with a maximum fetch of about 300 km., while the south coast faces the islands of Samsö and Tunö, north of the Funen archipelago, where the maximum fetch is not more than 25 km. Governed by these circumstances marine erosion and beach drifting have been very effective along the north coast which is totally simplified, while the southern shoreline still retains all typical features of the initial moraine coast.

For coastal research concerning bay closing, tombolo building, spit growth, and the formation of cuspate forelands a region of this kind offers the best chances.

With regard to coastal features and stages of shoreline simplification nine different types may be distinguished in the Djursland peninsula (fig. 2).

   I. Initial moraine coast — Kalvö Vig, South Djursland.

  II. Young simplification stage of a moraine coast —Æbeltoft Vig, South Djursland.

 III. The equilibrium moraine cliff shoreline of the west coast of Helgenæs, a beach drift source-locality.

 IV. The beach drift drain-locality of Begtrup Vig.

  V. Mature, simplified festoon-shaped East Djursland shoreline.

 VI. Totally simplified part of the East Djursland shoreline.

VII. Earlier (»fossil«) shorelines of the Litorina strait of Kolindsund.

VIII. Tectonically determined limestone cliff coast, Northeast Djursland.

 IX. Old simplified complex shoreline of North Djursland.

I. Kalvö Vig, a »Bodden« coast in initial stage.

The bay of Kalvö, being a submerged central depression, has the dimensions of the ice-lobe which generated the initial cavity in the surface relief by glacial erosion. Concerning the shoreline configuration many details may be explained as results of the landscape-creating activities of the glaciers during the Baltic stage, the last phase of the Würm-Weichsel glaciation. The bay west of the Hestehave woods, southwest of the town of Rönde, is the deepest, »drowned« part of a subglacially eroded valley formed by meltwater flowing upwards as a result of hydrostatic high-pressure, with a northern direction in an ice tunnel during the last glaciation. Now this valley contains a small consequent river course running in a southerly direction to the bay. Other indentations of the shoreline, for example

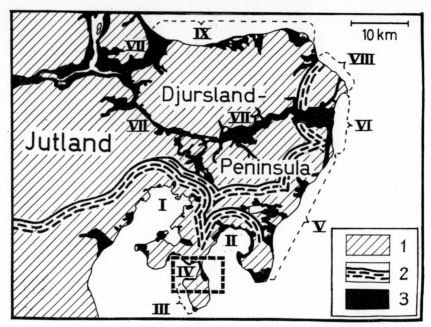

Fig. 2. *Geomorphological map of the Djursland peninsula.*

1. Young moraine landscape, Würm/ Weichsel glaciation.
2. Marginal moraines.
3. Coastal plains formed by marine accumulation combined with up-heaval of land (3—5 m.) and re-clamation. The frame indicates the area shown in fig. 3 C.
I. The bay of Kalvö Vig.
II. The bay of Æbeltoft Vig.

III. The totally simplified cliff shore-line of Helgenæs.
IV. The bay of Begtrup Vig.
V. The mature simplified festoon-shaped east coast.
VI. The totally simplified east coast.
VII. The earlier "fossil" shorelines of the strait of Kolindsund.
VIII. The limestone cliffs.
IX. The old simplified north coast.

Knebel Vig, may be explained as relief cavities originated by resist-ing dead ice in the late-glacial period, when the surrounding area was flooded by meltwater which caused sedimentation around the ice lumps. The sheltered position of the bay in the angle between the east coast of Jutland and the south coast of Djursland combined with the narrow inlet explains the fact that wave activity is only small and the resulting shoreline simplification insignificant. The post-Litorina 2.5 m. land upheaval is responsible for the dead cliff shoreline and the bordering narrow coastal plains, for example on the north coast of Egens Vig. However, even if the wave activity is weak it has caused small-dimensioned but typical beach drift pheno-mena in exposed localities. The island of Kalvö thus was welded to the mainland by a tombolo which was later stabilized by isostatic uplift as well as by human activity, construction of road and fortifications necessitated by the existence of the medieval castle of Kalvö, of which the tower ruin still remains on the former island. Similar tomboloes have developed at Sködshoved, near the south entrance to the bay as well as at Dejred Öhoved at the entrance of Knebel Vig. As a whole the Kalvö Vig shoreline may be characterized as an initial moraine coast only slightly modified by wave activity and level changes.

II. *Æbeltoft Vig, a »Bodden« coast modified by shoreline simplification.*

Compared with Kalvö Vig, this bay is more open and exposed to effective wave attack from the southeast, the fetch in this direction being 60 km. As a consequence the shoreline simplification caused by beach drifting has progressed to a certain degree. The lake Bogens Sö at the west coast is a lagoon lying between the elevated cliff shoreline of the Litorina sea and the delimiting beach ridge plain. In contradiction to Kalvö Vig the shoreline at the head of Æbeltoft Vig is not in conformity with the initial relief contours indicated by the elevated Litorina shoreline. The smoothly rounded curve may be explained as an approximation to the ideal equilibrium formation of a bay exposed to beach drift dynamics. Promontories like Bogens Hoved on the west coast and Ahl Hage on the east coast are of quite different origin, the former being caused by the resistance of moraine accumulation, the latter being a cuspate foreland (fig. 7). The diminishing grain size north along the Ahl Hage beach, in conjunction with the occurrence of recurved spits on the north coast of this foreland, demonstrates that in accordance with the general laws of bay closure beach drift into the bay is responsible for the formation of this cuspate foreland, which acts as a breakwater providing the necessary shelter effect for the harbour of Æbeltoft. The Ahl Hage foreland is based on an extensive submarine sand accumulation, Sandhagen, clearly shown on airphotos (fig. 7). The existence of this extensive accumulation on the eastern shoreline is governed by the strong beach drift along this shoreline with its western exposure.

III. *The west coast of Helgenæs, a totally simplified cliff shoreline.*

The southernmost prominence of Djursland, Helgenæs peninsula, does not profit from the sheltered conditions which characterize the Kalvö Vig region described above. The west coast of Helgenæs in particular is exposed to effective wave attack generated by the

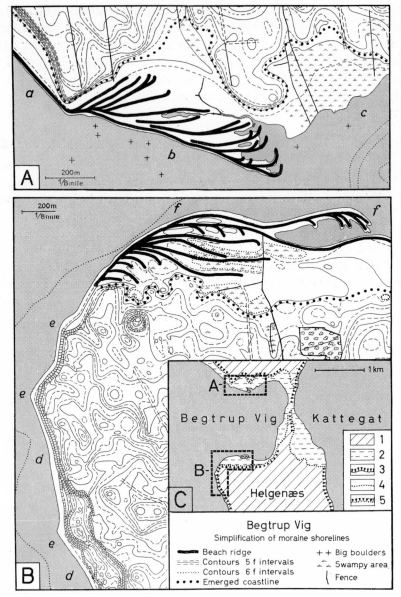

Fig. 3. *Begtrup Vig. Stages in shoreline simplification.*

A. Bay closing stages. Strands Gunger. a. Bay totally closed by coastal plain
development combined with upheaval of land (3 m.). b. Mature closing stage.
Spit complex under growth before the elevated Stone Age cliff shoreline.
Surveying 1954, (cfr. airphoto 1945, fig. 4). c. Former bay, filled up by vegetational growth, sedimentation of fine-grained material and upheaval of land
but without beachridge development until now.

B. Stavsöre. d. Northern part of the simplified Helgenæs west coast. e. Precipice
of the shoreline caused by slides of Tertiary plastic clay. f. Old spit complex
structures in the coastal plain. g. Recurved spits in the growing stage.

C. Begtrup Vig, localization map (cfr. framed area in map fig. 2).

1. Young moraine landscape. 2. Coastal plain. 3. Cliffs. 4. Shoreline of the stone
age sea. 5. Dead cliffs.

Fig. 4. *North coast of Begtrup Vig.* A recurved spit complex has developed before a former bay of the Litorina Sea. The west part of the shoreline is totally simplificated. Airphoto 1945. Concerning explanation of topographical features and stages of shoreline simplification cfr. fig. 3 A.

On the offshore outside the spit complex the white shade indicates sand masses brought into the bay by beach drifting caused by westerly winds. The bottom in this shallow-water area shows a surface with tunnels and ridges formed by moderate swell. The eastend of this sandplatform has a steep slope the shape of which is due to current action caused by wind pressure in the narrow opening of the bay between this sedimentation platform and the corresponding one at the south coast. On these platforms future bayclosing spit complexes may develop with orientation in continuation of the NW-SE running shoreline shown in the left part of the photo. The seashore limiting line of the fieldpattern area indicates the shoreline of the Litorina Sea.

dominant westerly winds over a sea area with water depths of more than 20 m. and a fetch of about 20 km. As a result of the marine activity the moraine cliff shoreline from the south cape Sletterhage to Stavsöre at the entrance to the bay of Begtrup is totally simplified, demonstrating the equilibrium form of the locality carved by erosion, the orientation of the shoreline NNW-SSE being very nearly at a right angle to the resultant of wave-work (fig. 1, p. 31). This cliff shoreline is retreating without altering its orientation. Small prominences of the shoreline are caused by earth slides which occur as a result of the retreating of the cliffs after wave attack, in particular in places where lenses of Tertiary plastic clay in the moraine are exposed in the cliff face (fig. 8). The sliding clay masses often exhibit stepped fractures. As a result of these cliff-forming processes large masses

of boulder clay are delivered to the littoral zone and exposed to
beach drifting. The coastal stretch is overnourished; in Per Bruun's
terminology it is called a source-locality of beach drift material.

IV. Begtrup Vig, bay closing in different stages.

This bay was a sound in the Litorina age, Helgenæs being at that
time an island, which later was welded to the Djursland peninsula
by a tombolo (fig. 3, C) which afterwards became stabilized partly
by the post-Litorina uplift and partly by the building of fortifications on the strategically important tombolo. Exposed to the
westerly winds the beach drift into the bay is very considerable. At
the southern entrance the bay acts as a drain-locality for the beach
drift along the west coast of Helgenæs. Here sand masses have built
up a platform on which beach ridges and recurved spit systems are
formed at Stavsöre (fig 3, B) as the youngest part of a beach ridge
plain constructed in front of the elevated Litorina cliff shoreline.
Lagoons in various stages of filling up by sand accumulation and
vegetational growth may be seen (fig. 3, B, e, f).

The analoguous process is to be seen at the northern entrance
to the bay (fig. 3, A). Here the cliffs of Mols Hoved act as a source
of beach drift material. South of the village of Strands typical stages
in bay closure can be demonstrated in the airphoto (fig. 4). At
locality a the former bay of the Litorina age is now closed by a bar
and the shoreline is simplified totally. Farther to the east at b, a bay
is in the mature stage of closing. A spit complex is in a phase of
rapid growth (fig.9). This system of beach ridges is a result of accumulation processes in the 20th century. It is possible to indicate
the future locality of bay closure. The airphoto shows distinctly
that enormous masses of sand have been moved into the bay mouth
where they now form the foundation for further spit formation. It
is to be foreseen that these submarine accumulation platforms at the
north and south shore of Begtrup Vig will combine and form a base
on which spit systems from north and south and bar islands in the
central part may finally be welded together, forming a bar across
the entrance of the bay.

V. The mature simplified, festoon-shaped coast of East Djursland.

The east coast from Hasenöre to Havknude exhibits the festoon-
shape that is typical of mature stages in shoreline simplification.
The prominences Brokhöj (34 m.), Jærnhatten (49 m.), Glatved-
Limbjerg (40 m.) and Havknude (14 m.) are moraine hills, at Glat-

ved with a content of limestone boulders. The resistance of these moraine nuclei is a result of the dimensions of the Quaternary accumulations. The festoon parts of the coastline consist of shingle ridges built up between the moraine nuclei as bar-islands (fig. 5) and tomboloes separating lagoons from the sea by the closure of bays and straits between the former moraine islands. Some of these barred parts of the former sea area still exist as lakes, for example Nörresö, east of Rugaard, and lake Draaby, farther to the south. In other cases the lagoons are overgrown, now forming swampy areas like Gungerne east of Boeslum, separated from the sea by a beach ridge plain with a covering of dune sand. The recent beach ridges along this shoreline have a maximum level of 2.5 m. above Danish Ordnance Datum. Old elevated beach ridges rise to a level of 7.5 m. Earlier coastal features often are truncated by the recent shoreline development, for example at Katholm, where Havknude represents a former island in the Litorina sea. It was separated from the mainland by a strait which today is still identiable as a low-lying area east of Katholm woods.

VI. The totally simplified part of the Djursland east coast.

The northern part of the east coast of Djursland, from Havknude to Fornæs, is totally simplified. A beach ridge plain, Hessel Hede, grew out from the south at the entrance of the Litorina strait of Kolindsund, which is now followed by the course of the river Grenå, the mouth of which has been deflected in a northernly direction by the growth of the spit system. As a consequence of the strong wind activity the Hessel Hede area has been covered by blown sand, this deposit disguising the structures of the original beach ridge plain. The conifer plantation established as a shelter against dangerous wind erosion also hides the surface relief. Like many other Danish harbours the original Grenå harbour was localized to the mouth and the lower course of the river. The need for deeper harbour basins caused by the increasing size of ships has been met by the construction of the modern harbour of Grenå at the sea coast, sheltered by a large pier from the heavy beach drift from the south.

The old stage of simplification which is indicated by the ruler-straight course of the shoreline stretch described here may be explained by the fact that calculations of wave force show a maximum value in this locality of the east coast. The adjustment of the shoreline orientation to the terminant direction at a right angle to the resultant vector of wave force is nearly complete (see fig. 1, p. 31).

Fig. 5. *Accumulation locality of the Djursland coastline* (cfr. fig. 2, section V). Festoon-shaped beach ridge plain built up between the moraine nuclei Glatved and Havknude, the latter to be seen in the distance. The shingle ridges are built up by stone material from the boulder clay and the glaciofluvial deposits. Axel Schou phot. 1955.

VII. The earlier (»fossil«) shorelines of Kolindsund.

The Litorina strait of Kolindsund mentioned above once used to run eastwards through a depression, originally a subglacial valley which in the Litorina age separated the northern part of Djursland as an island from the mainland. A part of this strait remained as a lake which was reclaimed in the 19th century. Its former basin is now a cultivated plain, characterized by the pattern of draining ditches and the surrounding reclamation canal, running along the dead cliffs of the »fossil« Litorina sea shoreline. In other places the former strait now remains as swampy areas, the most extensive one being the bay of Pindstrup Mose, from which the peat is used as fuel in the plywood and veneer manufacturing plant which has been built here. Concerning extension of the former strait, see fig. 2.

VIII. The limestone cliffs.

At Fornæs, near the lighthouse it is possible at low water to observe a wave-cut platform abraded in solid limestone with a thin veneer of beach deposits, this fact indicating the existence of the underground horst on which the localization and existence of the Djursland peninsula depend. Farther to the north the Danian limestone rises to a higher level and forms a shoreline of steep cliffs running NW-SE. The vertical clean-cut cliff walls of Sangstrup Klint

Fig. 6. *Erosion locality of the Djursland coastline* (cfr. fig. 2, section VIII).
The limestone cliff of Sangstrup at low water summer conditions. The abrasion
plane exposed in the foreground. At the top of the cliff the glacially eroded
surface of the Danian limestone can be seen covered by a thin layer of moraine.
Axel Schou phot. 1955.

and Karleby Klint form the abrupt limit of the landmass of Djursland here at the northeast corner of the peninsula. In the lower parts
of the cliffs wave-cut caves are proofs of the force of marine attack.
The abrasion plane cut in the limestone is overstrewn with boulders
that are being washed out from the fallen parts of moraine masses
which cover the glacially smoothened surface of the limestone beds.
In the breaker zone these boulders are eroding pot holes in the wave-
cut platform, an illustration of the dynamics of abrasion. Surface
forms caused by the chemical solvent action of sea water may have
some effect too; shallow depressions along the fissure lines of the
chalk might be explained in that way (fig. 6).

In Djursland limestone cliffs are only to be seen at this locality,
but they are typical elements of the coastal landscapes of Denmark,
particularly in the eastern part of the country where the limestone
cliff dimensions are greater than here. This is caused partly by the
high position of the Senonian and Danian sediments, partly by the
dislocation of the limestone beds by ice pressure in the glacial age.

North of the limestone cliff of Karleby Klint a depression forms
the limit of this coastal type. The adjacent northern shoreline is
characterized by the moraine cliff of Gerrild Klint, and here the
typical north coast type of shoreline starts with a smooth 90-degree
curve, which may be explained as the ideal equilibrium form of
coastlines with a finite length, to use the terminology of Per Bruun.

IX. The old simplified North Djursland shoreline.

In contradiction to the south coast of Djursland the shoreline of the north coast is quite independent of the initial moraine relief. The main east-west orientation is to some extent tectonically determined, as the underground limestone horst forms the eastern prominence. It is the most simplified stretch of the Djursland coastline, developed partly by the closure of all original bays and sounds, partly by erosion in the moraine deposits. The equilibrium form of the recent shoreline is an approximation to the terminant direction at right angles to the wave force vector (see fig. 1, p. 31), the great fetch of 300 km. with northern orientation being the dominant factor in the calculation of this value indicating the strength and orientation of wave action. The smooth curved connection of the northern shoreline of Djursland with the east coast of Jutland may be explained as an adaptation to the equilibrium shoreline of bay heads, according to Per Bruun's hypothesis.

A geomorphological analysis shows that this simplified shoreline consists of elements of different origins. The western part, Hevring Hede, is a recurved spit complex built out from east to west, closing the northern entrance to the former strait that separated the northern part of Djursland from Jutland during the Litorina transgression. To a certain degree blown sand has disguised the initial structures of this marine foreland, but in many places the fan-shaped pattern of the beach ridge plain is still indicated by the configuration of the contours in the ordinance sheet, scale 1:20.000. The heavy wind activity of this coastal stretch causes severe wind erosion in the farm lands, in particular in localities with light sandy soils, first and foremost in spring when precipitation often is very small.

The eastern part of the north coast at Knudshoved consists of several moraine nuclei connected by tomboloes, in this way separating former sea areas and lagoons, which later became barred foreland partly by the accummulation of blown sand and partly by vegetational growth.

Like other beach drift shorelines the north coast of Djursland is unfavourable to navigation. The need for a fishing harbour has been met by the construction of the Bönnerupstrand harbour of the island-harbour type. This particular harbour construction with sand-tight moles surrounding a basin which is connected with the shoreline by a bridge which presents only a minimum of hindrance to the beach drift. This particular Danish harbour type has been adopted with slight modification in many similar localities. Quarrying for

Fig. 7. *Ahl Hage, a cuspate foreland at the entrance to the bay of Æbeltoft Vig* (cfr. fig. 2, II). The foreland has developed on a wide platform of sand, Sandhagen, built up by beach drifting into the bay. The whole foreland complex acts as a breakwater for the harbour of Æbeltoft constructed in the bay behind it. The grain size of the beach material is diminishing from south to north. The dark shade in the interior of the foreland indicates the conifer plantation established to protect the agricultural area against blown sand.

The Danish Geodetic Institute copyright.

gravel and stone which is an industry of importance, has caused a need for loading facilities, which has been met by constructing extensive piers on the broad off-shore, dimensioned as to length in order to reach areas with depths sufficient for the necessary navigation.

There is a significant discrepancy between the recent shoreline and the old mature shorelines of the Litorina age. Elevated Litorina cliff shorelines bordered by coastal plains occur for example south of Bönnerup and southeast of Stavnshoved, with an orientation quite

Fig. 8. *The Helgenæs west coast, a source-locality for beach drift.* Lenses of Eocene plastic clay in the moraine cause earthslides when exposed in the cliff, and overlying boulder clay masses are brought into the littoral zone. The coarse-grained materials, shingle and pebbles are transported by beach drifting along the coast, while the fine-grained sand and clay particles are taken away by current action (cfr. fig. 3 B).

Axel Schou photo.

different from the shoreline of today. The recent shoreline is thus a complex of accumulation localities and recent cliffs representing an old stage of simplification, the orientation partly governed by the earlier coastline, partly by the recent dynamics.

Even if the Djursland shoreline is of rather limited extent, about 100 km. long, it is possible there to find typical examples of all Danish coast types except the real tidal salt marsh, which to merely a small degree may said to be represented by some flat shores of the beach meadow type in sheltered bays where wave activity proceeds far from the shoreline. Concerning dimensions the Djursland coastal complex cannot rival certain localities in other parts of Denmark. The limestone cliffs in the island Mön rise to 100 m. above sea level, the Römö beach in southwest Jutland is ten times as extensive as any Djursland beach and, compared with the West Jutland dune landscapes, the sand agglomerations on the north coast of Djursland are only insignificant. Anyhow, Djursland is a typical part of Denmark as regards physical geographical features, and in particular with regard to shoreline development.

Fig. 9. *Strands Gunger at the north coast of the bay of Begtrup Vig, a drain-locality for beach drift* (cfr. fig. 3 A). A recurved spit complex has developed before the former cliff shoreline of the Litorina sea. The recurved spits as well as the windblown tree on the cliff edge in the foreground indicate the west-east orientation of the direction resultant of wind work.

Axel Schou photo.

LITERATURE

Bruun, Per (1946–47): Forms of Equilibrium of Coasts with a Littoral Drift. Geogr. Tidsskr. 48. København.

Bruun, Per (1951): Littoral drift along sea shores. Ingeniøren 10. København.

Bruun, Per (1954): Coastal stability, København.

Christiansen, Sofus (1958): Bølgekraft og kystretning. With a Summary: Wave-power and shoreline orientation. Geogr. Tidsskr. 57. København.

Guilcher, A. (1954): Morphologie littorale et sous-marine.

Guilcher, A. and others (1957): Les cordons littoraux de la Rade de Brest. Extrait du Bull. d'Information du Comité Central d'Oceanogr. et d'Etude des Côtes IX: 1.

Jessen, Axel (1920): Stenalderhavets Udbredelse i det nordlige Jylland. The extension of the Stone Age Sea (Tapes-Litorina Sea) in Northern Jutland. D. G. U., II Rk. Nr. 35.

Johnson, D. W. (1919): Shore Processes and Shoreline Development.

Kannenberg, Ernst-Günther (1951): Die Steilufer der Schleswig-Holstein-ischen Ostseeküste. Kiel.

King, Cuchlaine A. M. (1959): Beaches and Coasts. London.

Köster, R. (1958): Die Küsten der Flensburger Förde. Schr. des Naturwis. Vereins f. Schleswig-Holstein. Kiel.

Munch-Petersen, I. (1918): Bølgebevægelse og Materialebevægelse langs Kyster. (Wave movement and beach drifting). Fysisk Tidsskr. 16. København.

Munch-Petersen, I. (1933): Materialwanderungen längs Meeresküsten ohne Ebbe und Flut. Hydrologische Konferenz der Baltischen Staaten. Leningrad.

Price, W. Armstrong (1953): The Classification of Shorelines and Coasts. Contribution No. 15. Dept. of Oceanogr., The A.&M. College of Texas.

Schou, Axel (1945): Det marine Forland (The Marine Foreland). Folia Geogr. Danica IV. København.

Schou, Axel (1949): Atlas of Denmark I. The Landscapes. København.

Schou, Axel (1949): Danish Coastal Cliffs in Glacial Deposits. Geogr. Annaler. Stockholm.

Schou, Axel (1952): Direction Determing Influence of the Wind on Shoreline Simplification and Coastal Dunes. Proc. XVII Int. Congress.

Schou, Axel (1956): Die Naturlandschaften Dänemarks. Geogr. Rundschau 11.

Steers, J. A. (1945): The Coastline of England and Wales. Cambridge.

Wave-Power and the Djursland Coast

By Sofus Christiansen

Abstract

For some localities of the Djursland coast an essay is made to estimate the influence of the fetch on wave-power. Variations of fetch and coastal material seem to be of major importance for the configuration of the coast, while vertical movements seem to be quite insignificant. For geomorphological description of the Djursland Coast, see Axel Schou: The Coastline of Djursland. Geografisk Tidsskrift, vol. 59, 1960.

The coastline of the peninsula Djursland in the eastern part of Jutland shows a diversity of morphology, which is unusual in so small a region. It is for that reason difficult to establish a standard of reference from which the coast can be morphologically analysed. In this article an essay of using numerical expressions of total wave-work fit for specially selected localities is shown. The method by which the expressions used is derived was published earlier (*S. Christiansen,* 1958), and is based on a formula for effect of wave-work $E = W^4x \ HxF$. In the formula E means total wave-energy from a given direction, W is windforce after the Beaufort-scale, H the frequency of wind from the direction considered, and F the fetch given in km. The formula was worked out by *Per Bruun* (1955) and is based on both practical experience and theoretical calculations. From the named formula a vector for every compass-direction is determined; these are later geometrically added forming a direction-resultant. Use of geometrical addition of vectors based on other calculations was earlier made by *M. Musset* (1923), *A. Schou* (1945), *S. Y. Landsberg* (1956) and others.

The wind-observations on which the statistics used in this work are based, were made 1879-1925 from the Fornæs Lighthouse. Of course the wind varies somewhat in the region dealt with, but errors introduced in calculations on behalf of this are considered insignificant, especially as maximum-error in observations of wind-direction is as much as $22\frac{1}{2}°$. The advantage of using the calculations shown below is therefore not the exactness of the expression of wave-work, but the fact that the calculations involve an estimation of the influence of the fetch. As stated already by many workers in coastal matters, variations of fetch at least in closed waters are significant.

The southern part of Djursland, the morphology of which is mainly glacial, is characterized by the three glacial-depression-bays: Kalvö Vig, Begtrup Vig and Æbeltoft Vig (fig. 1).

For *Kalvö*, the direction-resultant of wave-work (DR) is shown in illustration. The dimension given in arbitrary units amounts to »1.2«. The direction of the DR means, that the beach-drifting of the bay has a net-movement towards the inner part — as is usually the case for bays. It must therefore be expected, that an accretion of material can be found round the small island of Kalvö. It must be noticed however, that the marine foreland of the region partly is due to the postglacial upheaval of land.

The coastline south of *Strands* has a DR which is larger than that of Kalvö and a direction more to the south. This is caused by the somewhat larger areas of water, which magnify the work of waves. The accumulation of material is for that reason larger than for Kalvö Vig. As a sign of accumulation, a very nice complex recurved-spit is seen. It is of some use as a natural break-water for fishing-dinghies.

Measured in the same units, the wave-power of *Örby* is still a little larger. The resistance against wave-attack of this landscape has been so small, that the glacial forms of the initial coastline are hardly recognizable. In fact, the coastline is almost linear, and it will most likely maintain its form. The wave-power of this coast will show but slight variation, and the recession of the coastline will consequently be almost constant per unit of length. Not much doubt can be raised about the perception that the coast by this locality has developed one of the plane-equilibrium-forms described by *Per Bruun* (1946). It can be noticed, that in accordance with the more violent movement of coast-material, the average grain-size of it is larger than that of the localities previously mentioned. Some of the pebbles are indicator-boulders revealing a glacial drift from the bottom of the Baltic between Sweden and Estonia (quartz-porphyries).

The form of *Æbeltoft Vig* is probably a constant one too, but in this case recurved. *Per Bruun* postulated (1946) a special recurved plane-equilibrium-form. The postulate was met with strong criticism. If lines indicating the dominant fetch are drawn from points along the beach, the lines are most often orthogonal to the coast. This means that such points of beach (often) can be regarded as,

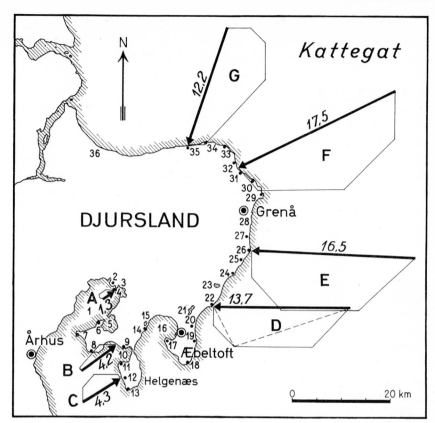

Fig. 1. *Direction resultants of wave work (DR) along the Djursland coastline.*
A. Kalvö. B. Strands. C. örby. D. Jærnhatten. E. Katholm. F. Gerrild. G. Bönnerupstrand. 1. Kalvö Vig. 2. Hestehave. 3. Kalvö. 4. Egens Vig. 5. Knebel Vig.
6. Dejred Öhoved. 7. Sködshoved. 8. Mols Hoved. 9. Strands Gunger. 10. Begtrup
Vig. 11. Stavsöre. 12. örby. 13. Sletterhage. 14. Bogens Hoved. 15. Bogens Sö.
16. Æbeltoft Vig. 17. Ahl Hage. 18. Hasenöre. 19. Brokhöj. 20. Gungerne, Boeslum.
21. Draaby Sö. 22. Jærnhatten. 23. Nörresö, Rugaard. 24. Glatved-Limbjerg.
25. Katholm Skov. 26. Havknude. 27. Katholm. 28. Hessel Hede. 29. Fornæs.
30. Sangstrup Klint. 31. Karleby Klint. 32. Gerrild Klint. 33. Knudshoved.
34. Stavnshoved. 35. Bönnerupstrand. 36. Hevring Hede.

Hede = moor. Hoved = cape, point. Klint = cliff. Skov = wood. Sö = lake.
Vig. = bay. ö = island.

forming a curve of equilibrium. Supposed the inlet of the bay is
narrow, there is a tendency for the bay to develop a half-circled
coastline. Probably this is the case of Lulworth Cove, Dorset, and
of Æbeltoft Vig too. The inlet of the latter seems to be too wide to
make the explanation valid; however it is in fact greatly narrowed
by the presence of a low-water area, which excludes all waves of
larger magnitude.

The east coast of Djursland differs in total from the coasts already treated. *Jærnhatten* (i. e. the »Iron-hat«, an old fashioned helmet) is a morainic cliff developed by strong wave-power. The large fetch from east results in a DR from that direction. A small truncated foreland is situated in front of the cliff (fig. 2). Eventually the form of this can be explained by splitting the DR in two composants. These will be orthogonals to each of the two sides of the foreland. The sides of the foreland can then be regarded as equilibrium coasts. Of course the splitting is only allowable if the two sides are individual coasts; this can be the case if the bottom really indicates a diversion in this place. In fact the problem of cuspate forelands is still not definitely solved (the »Dungenessproblem«).

The magnitude of DR by *Havknude* and especially by the cliffs of *Sangstrup* and *Gerrild* shows a maximum for the region treated in this work. In spite of this the coastline around the points mentioned is far from the straightline-form developed by Örby. The cause of this is a resistance against abrasion of the east coast which by far exeeds that of the average moraine-coast. In the case of Jærnhatten the resistance was conditioned by the large amount of wave-work required to move the masses of material concentrated in the cliff and in the bottom before it. Farther to the north, the cliffs are not solely consisting of glacial deposits, but are fundamented on »limsten« (a limestone belonging to the Cretacious system). Because of the varying resistance against erosion, the east coast of Djursland has developed the characteristic »festoon«-form.

The north coast has no reinforcements of limestone and is for the larger part built up by accumulation of beach-material. This is why the coastline by *Bönnerup* in spite of its smaller DR-values is made far more straight-lined than was the east coast. On account of the beach-drifting — as indicated by the DR from the east — a small harbour by Bönnerup is built according to the »island«-principle.

Calculations of wave-power of the north coast are impeded by the distribution of the fetch. Fetch of significance are found in only few directions, but in those cases they are far larger (300 km.) than is usually seen in inner waters. The difficulty by so large fetches is, that the material of observations does not show if an observed wind-force is accompanied by the correlated maximum height of waves (or of wave-energy). With a small fetch the problem is not overwhelming, because of the observation-frequency, which is 4 hours. In 4 hours lesser windforces will over a small fetch be able to raise maximum wave-height. Evidently, this can not be expected, when the fetch is 300 km. Wave-power must therefore by Bönnerup by a conservative estimate be about 1200-1500 »units«. Incidentally one is from the wind-observation tables mystified by the relatively frequent winds of force 10. The explanation of their abundance must be the human tendency to prefer »easy numbers«.

Four factors seem to determine the development of coasts: 1) the initial form, 2) the structure of the coast (mass of material, kind of material and grain-size), 3) wave-power and 4) vertical movements of coast.

The importance of the initial form is clearly seen by comparing the coastline of Strands by that of Örby. Though identical in regard of most things their initial forms make them so different, that the former is a young coast, while the other has reached maturity.

Effect of difference in structure is easily seen from the fact, that the eastern coasts of Djursland have not yet reached maturity as has the Örby coast. Limestone seems to exert a resistance against abrasion at least 3-4 times as great as boulder-clay. By comparing the two coasts it must however be noticed, that they differ in length. The length of a mature coast can under certain conditions be regarded as an expression of stage in development — or in many cases being almost the same, an expression of the available wave-power.

Vertical movements seem to be of no importance in the region concerned. From measurements the north coast is seen to rise, the south coast to be sinking. When differences in initial forms are considered, this statement cannot be drawn from the morphology. Effects of the very slow vertical movements are at Danish coasts at least by no means dominating the fast work of waves on the loose deposits. By this reason systematics of Danish coasts cannot be based on the Davis-Johnson system. Generally the principle of Gulliver seems to be more fit.

LITERATURE

Bruun, Per (1947): Forms of Equilibrium of Coasts with a Littoral Drift. Geogr. Tidsskr. 48. København.

Bruun, Per (1955): Coast Stability. København.

Christiansen, Sofus (1958): Bølgekraft og kystretning. (With an English Summary). Geogr. Tidsskr. 57. København.

Danmarks Klima, Climatic Record of Denmark (1933): The Danish Meteorological Institute. København.

Landsberg, S. Y. (1956): The Orientation of Dunes in Britain and Denmark in Relation to Wind. Geogr. Journ. CXXII:2. London.

Schou, Axel (1945): Det marine Forland. Fol. Geogr. Dan. IV. Medd. f. Skall.-Lab. IX. København.

Coastal Research and its Economic Justification

By Per Bruun

Abstract

Proper and thorough planning of coastal engineering projects is discussed and the economic justification of research work indicated. Examples are given concerning navigational problems, coastal protection problems, and harbor sediment problems.

This paper is written as a causerie. No attempt has been made to base its reasonings and conclusions on a dollar-and-cents basis, but rather it stresses the importance of common sense, good science, good technology and — most important — good conscience. »All that you do — do with all your might. Anything done half is never done right«.

»We have no time for that sort of thing and furthermore we have no confidence in it«, has been the standard excuse for lack of proper and thorough planning of many coastal engineering projects whether they comprised a navigation problem, a coastal protection problem or a harbor sediment problem. The result was in one case a continuous struggle to keep an inlet free from deposits as a result of inadequate dredging — the use of inadequate equipment at inadequate time intervals. Another result was inadequate coastal protection planning — taking chances in some respects and over-dimensioning in other respects, thereby leaving the arena to engineering philosophy instead of to engineering science.

The question of *why we do coastal research* is, therefore, not difficult to answer: It is necessary to know and understand the coastal phenomena in order that we can:

because if we do not do just that the result we come up with may look as foolish as the above figure.

Coastal research includes a great number of subjects ranging from the emplacement of huge breakwaters on the ocean bottom for the purpose of checking ocean waves and sand drift to the planting of proper vegetation in marsh areas and on dunes for checking sediment transport by water or wind. The employees involved in this research programme are recruited from a great variety of fields in arts and science: geology, geography, soil mechanics, coastal engineering, hydraulic engineering, oceanography, physics, mathematics and meteorology. In order that a coastal set-up shall be a complete and fully effective organization it must include people from all of these fields, which in mutual good understanding »carry the ball« of coastal research.

A discussion on the economic justification of such research requires a discussion of the applied sides of research aspects, but it should never be forgotten that without fundamental research applied research of any importance is impossible.

Man's interference with coastal development is most powerfully manifested in »the jetty« — the huge monsters jutting far out into the ocean as »artificial promontories« built either as vertical impermeable monolithic block jetties or as sloping rubble mound or block jetties which are permeable for water to some extent but will not allow the passage through them of wave motion or littoral drift material.

Jetties are not a new invention. They were built thousand of years ago. The ancient port at Alexandria with the famous lighthouse Pharos had rubble mound jetties. Jetties for the ancient harbor at Tyre which were discovered recently have massive stone breakwaters which in construction showed a notable advance over the work at Pharos as there were two walls of hewn stone, keyed together with metal dowels — the space between the walls being filled with some kind of concrete. The Greek harbor jetties were founded upon beds of tipped impervious material with masonry forming the superstructures. Roman harbor jetties as e. g. found at Ostia were much more substantial than anything previously existing both in design and in construction. One reason was the Roman cement which contributed to stability and lasting qualities. Methods of constructing underwater works were involved and all Roman jetties and breakwaters were built of masonry founded at sea bed level. A structural technique — based on experience — was already highly developed.

Medieval ports using monolithic rock or rubble mound design and mostly having a wharf on the protected side were built in Italy, Great

Fig. 1. Typical Storm at Catania Harbor, Algiers (H. F. Cornick).

Britain, France, Holland, and Germany. Realizing through costly experience the forces hidden in wave action, harbors were almost without exception established in protected estuaries, bays and waterways.

With the rapid development of navigation in the 19th century it became necessary to construct harbor jetties out into the open sea in countries such as France, Great Britain, Italy and Spain. The design varied from place to place, but the desire for saving materials usually resulted in attempts being made to build the jetties with as steep slopes as possible — frequently as block constructions founded on rubble mound layers on the bottom. Such jetties were often subject to extremely strong wave action and heavy damages occurred. It is no wonder that attempts at a rational approach to design of jetties based on wave forces started in these countries.

The first research concentrated on measuring wave forces in the prototype (England, Italy and France), and it became clear that there is a wide difference between wave forces exerted by deep water, shallow water, and breaking waves — the latter giving rise to extremely high shock pressures of explosive character thanks to an air pocket often associated with the breaking phenomena.

A mathematical approach to the problem of wave forces by trocoidal waves on a vertical wall was presented in 1928 by *Sainflou* whose theory was later tested by *Cagli* in full-scale measurements of wave action at Genoa (Italy), and by *Rouville* and *Petry* at Dieppe

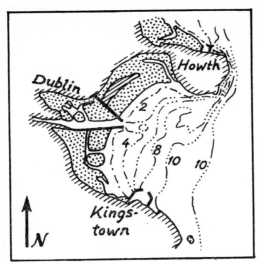

Fig. 2. Harbors at Dublin, Ireland.

(France). Based on these full-scale tests diagrams were developed which proved useful for practical design.

Meanwhile research is still not satisfactory for the shallow area where trocoidal characteristics are changed to solitary and breaking wave characteristics, and where, moreover, the direct influence of wind cannot be neglected. Most harbor jetties are located in this particular area of changing and irregular wave characteristics and most research in prototype and in hydraulic model (*Bagnold, Cagli,* and the *U. S. Corps of Engineers*) therefore has been concentrated on forces by waves which were breaking or about to break. There is considerable scatter in the results of these tests, model tests indicating comparatively much higher shock pressures than prototype tests with irregular wave trains (Dieppe, France). The collapse of or heavy damage to extremely expensive breakwaters such as those at Antofagasta (Chile), Catania (Algiers — Fig. 1), Alderney (England), and Bilboa (Spain), could probably have been avoided if wave mechanics had been explored beforehand and certain precautions taken against too heavy forces by breaking waves. Other jetties, e. g., the Dover Admiralty Pier, has stood even the heaviest wave action. It is indeed surprising that research in this particular and economically well-justified field so far has hardly involved a total expense exceeding the cost of a hundred meter's length of one of the collapsed heavy duty breakwaters. Much research work is awaiting proper action while the USSR recently announced comprehensive research on waves and wave forces to be carried out from a breakwater where rooms for research equipment were built into the breakwater itself.

Regarding the detailed design, costly experience has shown that attempts in only »estimating« the proper size of blocks (whether natural or artificial) and other pertinent factors for the stability of the jetty are often quite costly and difficulties gradually developed in regard to meeting the costs of numerous mishaps. Because of the complexity of this problem all rational approaches must be considered as semi-theoretical in as much as experience coefficients play an important role in their composition (Iribarren, Kaplan, Hudson, Hedar, U. S. Waterways Experiment Station).

Let us, from a purely engineering, wave mechanics and structural field, move into coastal morphology founded by the geographers *(Davis (9), Johnson (17), v. Richthofen)* and utilized later by the engineers who needed its results in order to understand and predict the natural development of certain coastal areas for which harbors or other coastal developments were planned. The importance of coastal research in practical life is clearly demonstrated in the harbors built at Dublin, Ireland (Fig. 2). Unsuccessful attempts at maintaining desirable depths in the estuary of the Liffey River lead to the construction of the harbor at Howth and later to the development of Kingstown harbor further south. The physical situation is that flood currents with the normal 10 ft. tidal range run north while ebb currents run south. Both currents make turns into the bay part of the river entrance. Prevailing winds are from the south and west, but the biggest waves enter the area from the east.

The bay area is greatly bothered by deposits of river and littoral drift sediments. With the construction of the harbor at Howth less trouble was expected. Meanwhile, it was unfortunate that elementary principles of coastal morphology and littoral drift technology were not considered, and the heavy sand drift from the north along the concave shoreline toward the northwest caused large deposits along the western jetty, eventually covering it completely. The third attempt in establishing a harbor was the construction of the harbor at Kingstown area, and even if the flood currents from the southeast on the lee side of the promontory at Howth. Because of this location littoral drift materials from the north do not penetrate into the Kingstown area, and even if the flood currents from the southeast carry considerable amounts of solids these materials are not deposited in the harbor entrance, partly because of an advantageous configuration of same and partly because the slow outgoing ebb-

Fig. 3. Miami Beach, Florida.

currents in the entrance are able to hinder penetration of materials into the harbor itself.

These harbors were all built in the 19th century when the field of coastal morphology was in its infancy. It is, therefore, not fair to blame the design engineers for their mistakes which nevertheless were of rather elementary nature. Meanwhile similar mistakes have been made in the 20th century, e. g. in Italy where uncritical use of the Italian engineer *Cornaglia's* »neutral depth« theory for sand transport toward or away from the shore led to a number of great failures e. g. Maurizio Harbor. The Danish version of the same theory, the so-called »Headland-Theory« (Pyntteori) also led to a couple of rather expensive and not very successful experiments at Hirtshals and Hanstholm which are North Sea Coast headlands. Attempts are now being made to correct these mistakes.

Proper research in and knowledge about coastal morphology could have decreased the amount of trouble and saved tax-payers the cost of expensive corrective measures.

Coastal morphology takes into consideration not only the development of planforms (4, 9, 14, 25, 27) but the development of beach and bottom profiles as well (4, 23). In order to evaluate the stability of a beach and its »foundation«, the offshore bottom, knowledge about their reactions to wave and current activity is necessary. These problems have been studied for years by coastal researchers. It is now known that beach and bottom profiles are subject to seasonal fluctuations depending upon the change in wave action from one time to another. It is also realized that their slopes cannot develop beyond a certain maximum steepness, but on the other hand it has been clarified that they are »tough-stable« and do not collapse suddenly like a piece of structural engineering, e. g. a bridge or a piece of aerodynamic engineering such as an airplane (as was claimed in Denmark by a coastal committee in 1942 regarding the stability of the Thyborøn barriers. The claim resulted in inadequately planned protection on one side and the taking of unnecessary risks on the other side. Further unnecessary precautions were taken by over-dimensioning other elements, such as the time factor). A »glass of cold research ice water« would have permitted a more thorough and better justified plan from the very beginning. This is now all realized and is being corrected. The author of this article has no desire of keeping the channel open or to close it but find that whatsoever be suggested the project shall be well thought, well reasoned and tested technically as well as economically.

Speaking about sedimentation, the simplest problems are those in rivers and canals which should be mentioned briefly because of their relation to coastal problems. It is no wonder that important developments within this field were the result of research work in India, the United States and the USSR where enormous flood, irrigation and drainage problems call for proper planning, therefore, the assistance of research. China however is the country which has experienced the great flood disasters. Millions of Chinese have through the years lost their lives in floods caused by inadequate river regulation and drainage caused not least by uncontrolled sedimentation in rivers. The Chinese have now become very active in this research where basic knowledge of physics and mathematics is so important and this fits into the Chinese mind.

British engineers in India made the first contributions to the practical sedimentation technology introducing the so-called »regimen theories« as a basis for design of drainage canals (Sir *Claude Inglis*). Engineers in India and *Thomas Blench* in the United States later followed up behind this line while the USSR and Germany took more interest in the physical aspect of channel stability. *Meyer-Peter's* work in Switzerland, *Shield's* work in Germany and *Kalinske's* work in the U. S. A. further developed this field which went into its purely physical and final development stages by the work of *Einstein* and *Chien* in the U. S. A. (13) The results were: better

Fig. 4. Palm Beach Inlet, Florida. North to the right.

planning, fewer mishaps and, therefore, huge savings. One of the bad examples of planning which ignores sedimentation laws was the construction of a huge hydraulic power plant in the Congo. Shortly after its completion the plant choked up with sediment deposits and the project had to be re-worked (by model experiments).

Let us from this introduction return to sediment problems on sea-shores where they are mainly concentrated around harbor and coastal protection works.

Sedimentation problems on seashores and their relation to man-made structures can most effectively and conveniently be explained by the terminologies »Source and Drain«.

A *source of materials* is a coastal zone, submerged or emerged, which delivers materials to other coastal areas. A source might be an area where erosion takes place, a shoal in the sea e. g. located on the downdrift side of a (newly) jetty-improved inlet, the shallow area in front of an inlet which has been closed, a river which trans-ports sand material to the coastal zone, or sand drift from dunes to the beach. Artificial nourishment of any kind to a beach is also a source.

A drain of materials is a coastal zone where materials are deposited. Natural drains include marine forelands of any kind such as spits, recurved spits, tombolos, cuspate forelands, angular forelands, etc. The drains may also be a bay, an inlet or a shoal. Artificial drains include man-made constructions such as jetties, groins, dredged sand traps, inadequately designed and inadequately constructed harbors etc.

In practical coastal engineering and littoral drift technology the following rules are valid.

(1) a coastal protection should be built in such a way that it functions as a drain. It should, therefore, have a source but not a drain on the updrift side. If there is a drain the coastal protection in question cannot be expected to work satisfactorily unless materials are supplied artificially to the shore in question.

(2) a harbor (or an improved inlet) on a littoral drift coast should not act as a drain. It is, therefore, desirable that it has no source area or only a limited source area on the updrift side or on either side of it. It is best if it has a drain on the updrift side or on both sides.

Without making themselves fully clear on the importance of »sources« and »drains«, geographers, geologists and engineers have, with great eagerness, studied these phenomena for decades; the geographers concentrating on the coastal morphology aspects (17, 25, 27); the geologists most often on the mineralogical aspects and the engineers on the total amount of nuisance caused by inadequate understanding, therefore, lack of respect for nature's source and drain rules and regulations (1, 4, 7, 24).

Let us consider a few of these cases. Fig. 3 is an aerial photograph of Miami Beach, Florida, which is provided with a great number of wooden or steel groins. There is, however, very little beach left and statistics indicate that only approximately 15 per cent of the visitors to this famous beach and seaside resort ever swim in the ocean. The 85 % prefer to stay on the dry side of the shoreline or else enjoy swimming in the numerous swimming pools which have now been built. The natural conclusion seems to be that Miami *Beach* is not a very attractive beach for ocean bathing, and the reasons for this apparently are a too little and not a very attractive beach, steep offshore bottom, dangerous currents at the vertical wall groins and too much loose shell material (up to 50 %) in the beach sand.

Using coastal engineering terminologies the reasons could also be expressed as a result of lack of any source of material for the groin system in question. It has probably cost several millions of dollars

Fig. 5. Leeside Erosion on the Southside of a Group of Groins at Bovbjaerg, North Sea Coast, Denmark.

to build up coastal protection at Miami Beach mainly based on groins and vertical sea walls, and the outcome as described is that only little beach is left. If a source of suitable material for beach nourishment had been located in the bay and this material had been dumped on the beach we would still have had and could still maintain a beach at Miami Beach instead of great amounts of coastal protection junk.

Another example, Fig. 4, is an aerial photograph of Palm Beach, Florida, after the inlet was dredged and the jetties which were built in 1918-1925 had blocked the southward littoral drift almost completely. The consequence was heavy erosion on the southside of the inlet. Through a number of years attempts were made to combat this erosion by construction of a great number of groins, but being without any source of material the groins failed. Modern development in the coastal protection field was later responsible for artificial nourishment from the bay and finally (1958) a by-passing sand plant was put in operation on the north side of the inlet and is supposed to pump 200.000-250.000 cu. yd. of sand fill across the inlet per year. Further south it is the intention to nourish the beach from dredging operations in the bay. It would probably have been better if groins had never been built.

It is a well-known fact that groups of groins function as drains and for this reason will always have adverse effects on the downdrift shore. If groins were not drains they would not work at all (24). It may, nevertheless, not be fully recognized that groins will usually cause considerably more erosion than accretion! A good example of such tremendous disadvantage to the overall picture is illustrated by Fig. 5 showing the last groin in a group of 130-250 meter long groins on the Danish North Sea coast at Bovbjerg. The groins in question have stabilized the beach where they were built, but on the leeside (southside) they have caused erosion of the shoreline of up to 10 meters per year in farmland. It is now the intention to build more groins on the 2 kilometer non-protected downdrift shore extending to the next group of groins which consist of only five partly abandoned shorter structures. Meanwhile the result will only be an extension and activation of the erosion problem further south.

This again points with adequate clearness to the fact that artificial nourishment of beaches is to be much preferred as shore protection because it is entirely free of skirmishing »boundary conditions«. Meanwhile in order to utilize artificial nourishment it will be necessary to develop better and more suitable dredging equipment as e. g. nuclear powered submarine dredges such as suggested by the author in an article in the »Shore and Beach« (American Shore and Beach Preservation Association) in June 1959.

Harbors are not supposed to work as drains for littoral drift materials. They are supposed to work contrarily. They can, however, be built in such a way that they present marvelous »olympic gold medal drains« because of not being designed correctly. The harbor of Madras, India, (Fig. 6) presents a very instructive case (7). Its breakwaters extend outward about 1000 meters from the original low-water shoreline (1876). Up to 1913, a large triangular area of sand about 260 acres (105 hectares) in extent had accumulated on the southside of the harbor; on the northside considerable shoreline recession had taken place. The old entrance to the harbor was centrally situated between the breakwaters facing east and the sand drifting northward found slack water between the pier heads in which to settle with the result that before the entrance was closed it was shallowing up at the rate of about 1 ft. per year. In 1902 a northeast entrance project was started including a 400 meter long sheltering arm completed in 1911. The result of this closing of the old entrance and extension of the eastern arm was continued deposits along the whole eastern jetty face which would have become more and more pronounced if it had not been checked by comprehensive dredging operations. Another advantageous result of the described »remodeling« was that the harbor became smooth enough for working cargo into and out of lighters alongside the ships and piers in practically all kinds of weather. Later another sheltering arm was built at the southern corner of the harbour, where accumulating sand is checked by a suction-dredge (mounted on the arm) which pumps the spoil into hopper barges moored inside the harbor. All the expensive nuisance described above could have been avoided with proper planning, but the hydraulic model technique was unknown when the harbor was first built in the 1870—1880 period.

The same is true for Zeebrügge harbor in Belgium which was completed in 1907. It has the configuration of a big northward curved »nail« (Fig. 7). 5-6 ft./sec. (1.5-2 m.) and heavy silt laden flood currents from the southwest carried 3—4 million cu. meters of silt per year into the harbor to be deposited on the leeside of the jetty in a big eddy current. Attempts were made to flush this material away by a 400 m. wide »clair-voie« (opening) at the land end of this jetty, but the result was an increase rather than a decrease in the deposits. The opening was, therefore, closed and after World War II hydraulic model experiments were carried out partly in Holland and partly in Belgium to solve this problem. Fig. 7 is a photograph of a floodtide situation demonstrating the current pattern. By constructing a large semi-circular breakwater to fill out the eddy area, deposits in the harbor will decrease about 50% which, in turn, will present a tremendous saving in maintenance costs of the harbor. The remainder of the material bypasses the harbor with the tidal currents.

In somewhat similar model experiments with the Karlsruhe river harbor in Germany special jetty configuration se-

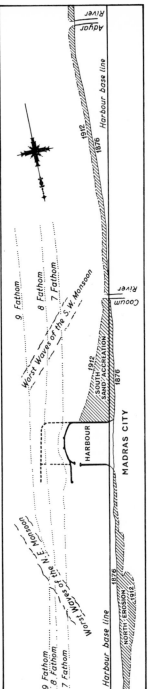

Fig. 6. The Harbor of Madras, India (H. F. Cornick).

cured by-passing of heavy bed-load transport in the river flow.

The harbor at Abidjan, Ivory Coast, Africa, presents a similar problem which was properly solved by model experiments in the Netherlands. A cut was made to connect the ocean with a lagoon to accommodate vessels of 27 ft. draft (Fig. 8). Sand coming from the west is deposited by the flood current at »M«; the ebb current, which is strongly concentrated at that point transports it in the direction of »P«, where part of it settles in a deep hole in the sea bottom.

In this case, as well as in many other cases of research, man was successful in making nature his servant and this is so much better than making nature an opponent or enemy. This philosophy is true for artificial »man made« harbors with jetties, breakwaters, wharfs, etc. as well as for natural harbors which man has tried to improve in different ways. This last mentioned subject has been given much thought by coastal morphologists, whether they were geographers, geologists or engineers, and deserves special mention because of its relationship to one of the most interesting subjects in coastal research.

The ancient Egyptian, Phoenician, Greek, Roman and Viking naval fleets were based in estuaries, bays, fiords and lagoons and we find similar installations today at such places. Now, as thousands of years ago, the tidal estuary, river or inlet is a cultural factor of immense importance.

It is customary to talk about »nature's delicate balance« which man cannot touch without bringing about adverse effects. The fact is that everything in nature is in a process of development and man by interfering with this development can influence the natural process in one way or another and the accompanying effects will usually be adverse in certain ways, but advantageous in other respects.

Inlets have always been »problem children« and this is particularly true for those inlets which have resulted from breakthroughs on littoral drift shores — and this is the greater part of them (3).

Lack of understanding of inlet-physics led to misuse of inlets, particularly when they were loaded with more navigation responsibility than they were able to carry on their sand and water shoulders. The result was an endless succession of failures. There is hardly an inlet on the United States barrier east coast (or on the Danish North Sea coast) which has not caused all kinds of trouble including irregular shoaling or deepening, uncontrollable meandering, erosion or accretion, unprovoked movements, or even sudden »disappearances«, furthermore, headaches, backaches and ulcertrouble. This is true whether the name of the inlet is Ponce De Leon, Great Egg,

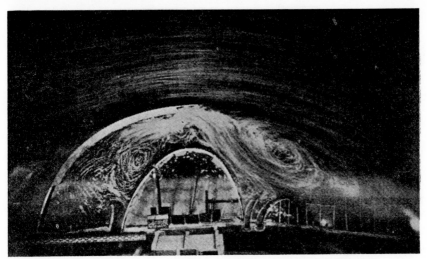

Fig. 7. Model Experiment with Zeebrugge Harbor, Belgium (Waterbouwkundig Laboratorium, Antwerp).

Man-Killer (Matanzas) or Thyborøn. The reason why they were »problems« was that they were not »understood«, and for a long time their various »doctors« were representatives from all branches of life including butchers and lawyers (but not coastal researchers who were able to handle the problem from a physical point of view). *Brown* (3) and *O'Brien* (22) were responsible for the first real progress which later was followed up by the work of others on an entirely physical basis (2, 5, 6, 8, 12). It is now known that an inlet in alluvial material is not only a »difficult hole in something else« but that it — as everything else in nature — depicts a balance between the acting forces. Based on analysis of many inlets (5) it seems possible to express the stability of an inlet »Stab« as:

$$\text{»Stab«} = F\left(t_s, \frac{O}{M}, \frac{Qm}{M}\right)$$

where t_s is the so-called »stability shear stress« between flow and bottom. ($t_s = \frac{Pg V^2}{C^2}$, where p = density of water; g = acceleration of gravity; V = mean velocity of flow; and C = Chezy's friction coefficient). O = the so-called »tidal prism« which is the total amount of water flowing through the inlet in one half tidal cycle, usually referring to spring tide, flood or ebb conditions; and M = the amount of littoral drift material brought to the inlet entrance per year. Regarding Qm, see below.

Considering first the t_s, a great number of analyses of inlets have

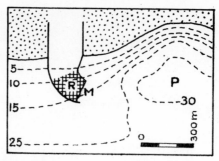

Fig. 8. Abidjan Harbor, Ivory Coast, Africa.

shown that the cross-sectional area of the inlet gorge, which is the smallest cross-section in the inlet channel, can be considered explicitly as a function of different factors such as maximum flow, configuration and shape of the cross-section flow characteristics, shear stress between flow and bottom, soil conditions, suspended load and littoral characteristics, wave action, freshwater head flow, and finally the »time history« of the inlet channel. These factors are interrelated and further analyses have shown that the shear stress t is the most practical and useful parameter (5). The question of inlet stability has therefore become a »structural design problem« in which detailed computations of flow (12) must be compared with »the allowable« or »the ultimate strength« of the bottom (»the determining shear stress«, t_s) which in turn depends upon the factors mentioned above. t_s for »average conditions« is about 0.39 kg/m²; for heavy littoral drift conditions, 0.47 kg/m²; and for light littoral drift conditions, about 0.32 kg/m². It is hopeless to endeavor to maintain an inlet with free flow over an alluvial material bottom with lesser values of t_s.

Meanwhile satisfactory $\frac{O}{M}$ and $\frac{Qm}{M}$ ratios are as important as an adequate t_s. Consideration of a great many inlets (5) have revealed that those having a $\frac{O}{M}$ ratio in excess of 300 have a higher degree of stability while inlets with $\frac{O}{M}$ ratios < 100 have a more predominant transfer of sand on (shallow) bars across the inlet and less significant tidal currents, for which reason they are rather unstable and usually characterized by narrow, frequently shifting channel(s) through shoals. It is not possible to say where the transition $\frac{O}{M}$ ratio between stable and unstable inlet channels lies because the littoral drift irregularity, in quantity as well as in direction, most likely will make it impossible to establish such fixed ratio. Meanwhile, numerous mis-haps could have been avoided if such (in fact) rather elementary problem had been investigated and taken into consideration properly before actual construction work commenced, but regardless of where you go in the world the philosophy seems to have been that »every-body shall have his private inlet exactly where he (not nature) pleases« (28).

The question of an adequate $\frac{O}{M}$ ratio automatically brings to light the fact that littoral drift material — even with the most advanta-geous t_s and $\frac{O}{M}$ — cannot pile up infinitely on either side of the inlet's seashore or on sea and/or bay shoals. It is necessary to get rid of this material by passing the material across the inlet channel either by natural or artificial means.

If nature itself in numerous cases did not by-pass sand across inlets, passes, and channels on seashores a number of »marine fore-lands«, including barriers, spits and entire peninsulas would not exist. A typical example of nature's strategy is found in Florida which was built up of sand washed down by rivers and streams from the Appalachian Highland and carried southward, crossing estuaries and tidal inlets, for final deposition in the huge barrier and ridge systems which we call Florida. In fact northern Florida seems to be the world's largest recurved spit system (25, 28).

The two main principles in by-passing or sand by natural action are:

> By-passing on an offshore bar,   and
> By-passing by tidal flow action.

Most cases present a combination of these two methods.

A submerged bar in front of an inlet or harbor entrance on a littoral drift coast will often function as a »bridge« upon which sand material is carried across the inlet or entrance (6). Every channel dredged through the bar will, therefore, be subject to depo-sits.

By-passing by tidal flow action takes place when littoral deposits are spoiled out of the inlet by ebb currents in the downdrift direc-tion. Both bar and tidal flow by-passing include cases of irregular transfer of large amounts of materials in migrating sand humps or by change in the location of channels.

Research (6) has revealed that one can distinguish between inlets or entrances with predominant bar by-passing and inlets with predominant tidal flow by-passing by considering the ratio $\frac{M}{Qm} = r$ between the magnitude of littoral drift (M in cu. yd. per year) and the quantity of flow through the inlet or entrance (Qm in cu. yd. per sec. under spring tide conditions).

If this ratio is >200-300 bar by-passing is predominant; a ratio <10-20 indicates that conditions for predominant tidal flow by-passing exist. Meanwhile, whether or not such by-passing actually takes place depends on whether or not it is possible to use the tidal flow for transferring material in the downdrift direction. This depends, among other things, upon the inlet configuration. Inlets exist which, due to strong tidal currents, jet material so far out into the ocean that it is lost forever to the shore. Characteristic examples of this situation are Ft. Pierce Inlet and Bakers Haulover Inlet in Florida where inlet ebb currents up to 7-8 ft./sec. may occur, particularly at the Haulover Inlet (28). Similar current velocities may exist in Thyborøn channel after a storm when the tide is running out shooting material out into the North Sea.

By-passing problems can be solved by careful planning including model experiments as e. g. carried out for the harbors at Abidjan, Lagos, the Volta River and many others. Failures and heavy maintenance costs have in this way been avoided. Establishment of sand traps including devices for artificial (mechanical) by-passing is an example of man's »cut-through« of the problems when other solutions were not convincing or possible as e. g. at Palm Beach Inlet, Florida (Fig. 4).

The sediment transport field is still in a state of rapid development with the radioactive tracing technique being the newest invention. Two different types of radioactive labeling are now in use: the direct labeling and the artificial labeling. The direct labeling can be realized either by neutron activation of sediment constituents (as with the phosphorus — 32 St. Peter quartz sandstone from Kentucky) or by absorption into or the depositing on the sediment's surface of a radioisotope as e. g. radioactive gold Au 198 (used in California), and radioactive silver Ag 110 (used in Portugal). The artificial labeling is employed by the solution of a radioisotope in melted glass which when ground and property screened is supposed to reproduce the properties of the sediment. The best traces seem to be the isotope Scandium (Sc) 46 which has been used in rivers (the Thames) as well as in the sea (off the Norfolk coast). The Russian luminophore method uses fluorescing materials.

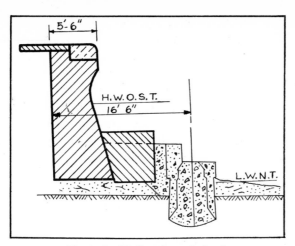

Fig. 9. Sea Wall at Bray, Ireland.

The Sc-tracing technique was developed particularly in Great Britain (10, 11, 15). An example of the use of Sc 46 is the now classic Thames River experiment carried out in 1954 and 1955 by the Hydraulics Research Establishment, Wallingford. The isotope Scandium 46 was selected as a suitable gamma-ray source, with a convenient half-life of 85 days. The Thames experiment was arranged with the object of demonstrating with certainty whether or not landward transport of silt takes place in the Thames Estuary. The tracer material had a density similar to that of Thames mud, and consisted of soda glass containing about 1.5 per cent of scandium oxide. Material corresponding to 30 curies was injected in the main shipping channel abreast of the entrance to the tidal basin of Tilbury Docks at the upper end of Gravesend Reach, 26 miles below London Bridge. No dredging of the shoal area at the lower end of Gravesend Reach during the period of 18 days immediately preceding injection was carried out, so that the radioactive material would not be unduly attracted there. Immediately prior to the time of the test a systematic blank survey was made of background readings on Geiger counters on the bed of the estuary between 8 and 38 miles below London Bridge. The scandium glass was mixed with natural mud and released from containers on the river bottom after which detection started. One of the surprising results obtained during the next three weeks of tracing was that in the tidal basin at Tilbury Docks (12 miles above the injection point) where siltation necessitates considerable dredging, the activity gradually increased to 3 times the background value during the first fortnight. From the total number of observations it became quite clear that silt can move toward the head of the estuary in these reaches when it is known that close to the bed there is a net landward movement of water. This, in turn, indicates that dredged material should be pumped ashore behind the high water line. This change of practice compared to the present dumping in the outer part of the estuary practice would not be expected to have an immediate effect on the river because regime is a delicate balance between accretion and erosion, and as material was removed, it would be partly replaced by material eroded from the mud flats and by fine silt from the coast washed into the estuary on flood tides, some of which would deposit in the estuary instead of being washed seaward on the ebb as hitherto. Gradually, however, the balance would change until eventually a considerable improvement would occur, with a corresponding reduction in the amount of dredging required. The economic importance of this would be enormous.

Similar techniques are now under development for the seashore, the USSR, Great Britain, and Portugal having the lead so far.

The conclusion of the abovementioned on sediment transport in streams as well as in the sea is not an unusual one; it is much better to have nature as your friend than as your enemy.

Typical examples of a somewhat different method of making nature a real enemy are presented in the numerous vertical coastal protection sea walls built everywhere in the world whether they are heavy gravity walls of English type or steel sheet-pilings such as e. g. the Florida shores are cluttered with — many of which are turned over or are in other ways worn out because of misunderstood use and inadequate design (28). Fig. 9 shows a gravity wall at Bray, Ireland. It was built in 1884-86 with cross-section as shown by heavy full lines. Meanwhile its vertical face contributed to an increase of erosion at the same time as oversplashed water and inadequate drainage aggravated its stability. It, therefore, became necessarry to put a sheet-piling apron in front of the wall, but its vertical face had the same adverse effect as the original wall. Finally it was necessary to put one more (caisson) apron in front of the other apron and all of this became very expensive. Today Florida continues the same mistakes made in Ireland 70 years ago. Fig. 10 shows a photograph of Jacksonville Beach in Florida, and it clearly demonstrates what happens when an equal amount of misunderstanding of the problem and lack of proper planning made up the prevailing background for the design. Some miles of similar seawall collapsed in that way in

Fig. 10. Jacksonville Beach.

Florida, and more will collapse in the near future because Florida has been due for a serious hurricane flood for several years now.

The statistical approach to storm flood tide analysis was »born« in Holland. In 1939 *Wemelsfelder* published a statistfical analysis of high tide data from the Dutch coast. His method when adjusted to and interpreted in agreement with the local situation allows estimation of the frequency of high tides and also, using great care, extrapolation outside the zone of present experience. Such frequency analysis now in progress in Florida and elsewhere where storm tides are common are of great importance, e. g., for the determination of the insurance values of real estate in coastal areas. In Florida, despite the lack of adequate data, the available information clearly shows that the possibilities of flooding are high and, unfortunately, very much under estimated. At many coastal communities and developments even the most elementary considerations with respect to safety of life and damage to property have been disregarded and the inhabitants are living on »borrowed time«. Those who »developed« the coastal areas in question are not easy to find but may occasionally appear behind the so-called »free press« when they believe that this will help them force their dollarbased desires and inadequate projects through.

The above examples all consider »wet parts« of the coastal research fields. Other parts are only half wet or perhaps all dry. A company built a rubble mound breakwater pier somewhere in the United States. This pier was supposed to carry pipelines for fuel oil.

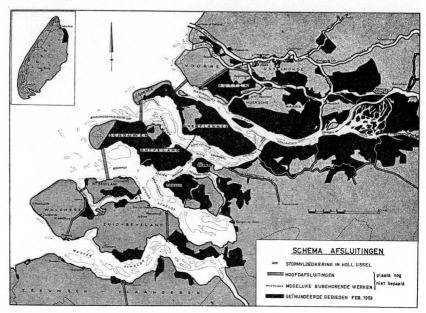

Fig. 11. Layout of the Delta Project, Netherlands (J. van Veen).

It was called to attention that a conservative rigged pipeline would not be a proper solution under the given circumstances, but it was built in that »headed-for-trouble-way« anyway and became an expensive »baby« for this reason. A little research — such as suggested — would have saved the company tens of thousands of good American dollars.

Half wet coastal work includes reclamation of land in swampy areas and in marshland. Here again it is true that the intelligent method of procedure is to let selected plants do reclamation work instead of hauling in all the dirt over perhaps long distances. Examples of such reclamation work are found in the British and Dutch Spartina Grass marshland and in the Danish reclamation work on the North Sea coast.

The dry counterpart to this vegetation reclamation are the measures against sand drift by proper plants as e. g. *ammophila* species (helme). Where formerly wind blew away dunes and piled up sand on roads and agricultural land proper plantings have been able to build up dunes and dykes where they were wanted for coastal protection reasons such as the Danish West Coast sand dykes. In the United States, Cape Hatteras National Park is now using mechanical planting machines pulled by crawler type tractors and developed by

its own research. The practical dunes
planting research by the National Park
Service is expected to be able to decrease
the unit price of planting to about 50% of
the cost of conservative methods of planting by hand.

Plants have been imported to Florida
from North Carolina and Denmark and
are doing fine, but more research is necessary to find plants which will fit the different climatological zones.

Let me finish this »sermon« on coastal
research by mentioning one of the largest
— if not the largest — coastal engineering
research projects the world has ever seen,
which is the research programme associated with the Dutch »Delta-Project«. This
huge undertaking was initiated after the
1953 flood-disaster which killed approximately 2.000 people and caused a billion
dollars worth of damage (2.000.000.000
fls).

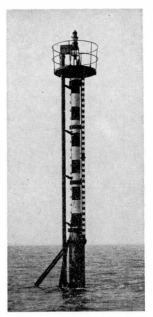

Fig. 12. Symbol of Modern
Coastal Research — Dutch
Survey Pole in the North
Sea (Delta-Werken).

The contours of the Delta-Project are shown in Fig. 11 (14). It
includes three big dams in the river entrances and two smaller ones
further inland. The waters of the Delta area will be divided into two
separate basins by means of dams. The southern basin will be
entirely cut off from the sea and become a freshwater lake. The
northern one, which comprises the mouths of the Rhine and Meuse
Rivers, will continue to be connected with the sea because the waterway to Rotterdam must remain open to shipping. Tidal waves will,
therefore, still be able to penetrate inland by way of this basin but
they will only cause high tides in the waterway itself.

In order to secure the best and most economical result from this
huge project the cost of which may be as high as one billion dollars
worth (almost 2.000.000.000 fls) before it is completed in the course
of approximately 25 years the Dutch have undertaken an extensive
research programme including research on tides, tidal currents and
density currents in the Delta area itself and in the connecting areas.
Furthermore, detailed studies of wave action and sand movement
are under way using the most modern techniques including the
establishment of permanent automatically operated »pole-stations

(Fig. 12) out in the North Sea which are loaded with instruments such as wind recorders, tide recorders, wave recorders, current recorders, etc.

Perhaps the most intriguing part of the enormous research programme is the tidal research including the influence of structures on the penetration of tides whether they are of astronomic type or are mainly storm tides (12). In the Netherlands no less than three different methods of tidal prediction are now in use: the hydraulic model, the computation method, and the electric analogue method. Each method has its typical merits and limitations. For some purposes one may be more suitable than the other. Perhaps a coastal researcher in the applied sciences will get the most impressive look he can ever have by visiting Prof. *Thijsse's* Dutch Nordoostpolder »Open Air Laboratory« where up to 30 models from the Netherlands and elsewhere may be seen at one time.

If you ask the Dutch if all this research pays they will most likely answer that »they simply cannot afford not to do it«. Furthermore, you should remember that the »Lord made the world but the Dutch built Holland«.

Conclusion.

From the above causerie of examples of economic justification for coastal research it may appear that the author of this paper is inclined to believe that coastal research is something which we should always do considering it at least from a face-saving point of view.

This it not the idea at all. He honestly considers it as being entirely irresponsible and foolish not to *plan ahead* because nobody can defend or afford to spend $25.000.000 for a second-class product if he can secure a first-class product for $20.000.000 or perhaps $30.000.000 with the additional $5.000.000 well spent for urgently needed improvements.

A designer's »sense of responsibility« should always be related to knowledge about his safety factor which he studied carefully before proceeding and not to overdimensioning of boundary conditions and design related to lack of adequate knowledge about the problem.

REFERENCES

1. *Abecasis, Carlo Krus* (1955): »The History of a Tidal Lagoon Inlet and its Improvements (the case of Aveiro, Portugal)«, Coastal Engineering V.

2. *Bretting, A. E.* (1958): »Stable Channels«, Acta Polytechnica, Scandinavia 245.

3. *Brown, E. I.* (1928): »Inlets on Sandy Coasts«, Proceedings, American Society of Civil Engineers, Vol. 54.

4. *Bruun, Per* (1954): »Coast Stability«, Copenhagen.

5. *Bruun, P. and Gerritsen, F.* (1958): »Stability of Coastal Inlets«, Proceedings, American Society of Civil Engineers, Vol. 84, No. WW3, and Proceedings of the VIIth International Conference on Coastal Engineering, »Coastal Engineering«, No. VII.

6. *Bruun, P. and Gerritsen, F.* (1959): »Natural By-Passing of Sand at Coastal Inlets«, Proceedings, American Society of Civil Engineers, Vol. 85, No. WW5.

7. *Cornick, H. F.* (1959): »Dock and Harbour Engineering«, London.

8. *Corps of Engineers, U. S. Army* (1959): »Bibliography on Tidal Hydraulics«, Committee on Tidal Hydraulics Report No. 2.

9. *Davis, W. M.* (1912): »Die beschreibende Erklärung der Landformen«, Berlin-Leipzig.

10. Dept. of Scientific and Industrial Research (1957): »Hydraulic Research«, Wallingford, Berks, England.

11. Dept. of Scientific and Industrial Research (1958): »Hydraulic Research«, Wallingford, Berks, England.

12. *Dronkers, J. J.* and *Schönfeld, J. C.* (1955): »Tidal Computations in Shallow Water«, Proceedings, American Society of Civil Engineers, Vol. 81.

13. *Einstein, H. A.* (1950): »The Bed-Load Function for Sediment Transportation in Open Channel Flows«, U. S. Dept. of Agriculture, Technical Bulletin No. 10260.

14. *Ferguson, H. A.* (1959): »Hydraulic Investigations for the Delta Project«, Proceedings, American Society of Civil Engineers, Vol. 85, No. WW1.

15. *Inglis, Sir Claude* and *Allen, F. M.* (1957): »The Regimen of the Thames Estuary as Affected by Currents, Salinity and River Flow«, Proceedings, Institution Civil Engineers, Vol. 7.

16. *Jakobsen, B.* and *Jensen, Kr. M.* (1956): »Undersøgelser vedrørende landvindingsmetoder i Det danske Vadehav«. Geografisk Tidsskrift 55. Meddelelser fra Skalling-Laboratoriet XV. Copenhagen.

17. *Johnson, D. W.* (1919): »Shore Processes and Shoreline Development«. New York.

18. *Johnson, J. W. (1953):* »Sand Transport by Littoral Currents«, Proceedings Vth Hydraulic Conference.

19. *Johnson, J. W.* (1951–1958): »Coastal Engineering«, Nos. I, II, III, IV, V, VI, Proceedings, Coastal Engineering Conferences, (Berkeley, California).

20. *Lane, E. W.* (1955): »Design of Stable Channels«, Proceedings, American Society of Civil Engineers, Vol. 120.

21. *Nielsen, Niels* (1960): »The organization of scientifical research work in South-West Jutland«. Geografisk Tidsskrift 59. Copenhagen.
22. *O'Brien, M. P.* (1931): »Estuary Tidal Prisms Related to Entrance Areas«, Civil Engineering.
23. *Saville, Thorndike, Jr.* (1950): »Model Study of Sand Transport Along an Infinitely Long, Straight Beach«, Transactions, American Geophysical Union, Vol. 31.
24. *Schijf, J. B.* (1959): »Generalities of Coastal Protection«, Proceedings, American Society of Civil Engineers, Vol. 85, No. WW1.
25. *Schou, Axel* (1945): »Det marine Forland« (The marine Foreland). Copenhagen.
26. *Shepard, F. P.* and *Inman, D. C.* (1951): »Sand Movement on the Shallow Inter-Canyon Shelf at La Jolla, California«, Beach Erosion Board, Technical Memorandum No. 26.
27. *Steers, J. A.* (1945): »The Coastline of England and Wales«.
28. *University of Florida* (1958): »Selected Papers from Proceedings of Sixth Conference on Coastal Engineering«.
29. *Veen, J. van* (1936): »Onderzoekingen in de Hoofden«, published by Ministerie van Waterstaat. 's-Gravenhage.
30. *Veen, J. van* (1948): »Dredge, Drain, Reclaim«. The Art of a Nation. The Hague.
31. *Veen, J. van* (1950): »Eb- en Vloedschaar Systemen in de Nederlandse Getijwateren«. Tijdschrift Koninklijk Nederlandsch Aardrijkskundig Genootschap. Amsterdam.

The influence of the Rømø Dam on the sedimentation in the adjacent part of the Danish Wadden Sea.

By H. A. Olsen.

Within a period of a few years the bottom configuration of the Danish Wadden Sea must be considered, in broad outline, as being in equilibrium. In the course of a longer period the situation of the tidal streams may be more or less displaced; new channels and gullies may appear and old ones disappear. Contrary to this, the vast tidal flats may remain for long periods without being subjected to considerable alterations of the level and of the aspect; however, in case of a change of the natural conditions, as for instance the immigration of a vegetation on high-lying tidal flats close to the coast, the result is a disequilibrium, which has partly a constructive power: the formation of new salt-marshes; partly a destructive tendency: erosion on the windward side of these new salt-marches *(B. Jakobsen,* 1954).

The construction of the Rømø Dam represented an artificial interference in the natural conditions of the Wadden Sea; as a result of this the tidal flats and the channels immediately began to change and to adapt themselves to the new conditions. This offered a favourable occasion for studying the destructive effect and constructive effect of the forces — effects which may normally be difficult to trace, but which now appear in overdimensioned form, until a new state of equilibrium has been established.

In the following is given an exposé of the factors influencing the sedimentation in the Wadden Sea and, further, of the effects which the Rømø Dam has had on the sedimentation to the south of the dam. Special interest has been taken in the informations which can be drawn from these examinations.

The factors which determine the sedimentation.

The factors which are of decisive importance to the sedimentation and to the process of salt-marsh formation can be divided into the following groups:

  a) *Astronomical and meteorological forces* which determine the transport of material;

  b) *Geographical conditions* which are of special importance to the sedimentation;

  c) *Biological forces* which are of essential importance for retaining the sediment.

a): *The astronomical forces* produce *the tide,* the currents of which transport the suspended material, and are thus the first condition for the salt-marsh formation. In the channel Pajdyb to the south of the Rømø Dam (fig. 1) the mean high-water level has been calculated to be +0,96 m. DNN (Danish Ordnance Datum) for the period from July 1942 to December 1943. In the channel Rømø Leje 2 km. to the north of the dam the range of the tide has been calculated to be 1,78 m. in the period from July to December 1956.

The meteorological forces are air pressure, wind and ice formation. From a meteorological point of view the air pressure and the wind are inseparable; however, in the Wadden Sea *the air pressure* is of special importance, as the difference of pressure influences the level of the tide; consequently, the conditions of flooding (i.e. the depth of the water and the size of the waves) act on the sedimentation conditions.

The wind produces waves which are able to suspend the material and to keep it in suspension and, further, to accumulate masses of water. By this accumulation the depth of the water is altered, a fact which contributes to the influence on the size and the shape of the waves. Thanks to equalization currents the accumulation of water is moreover able to hamper or to intensify the tidal streams. All these factors influence highly the sedimentation.

The ice formed in the Wadden Sea will at low tide ground on the high tidal flats and freeze to the bottom. By transport of these ice floes at high tide certain quantities of earth are moved to an even higher level, causing ice-borne sediments. The amount of this sedimentation is often overestimated, because the accumulations of ice after a short thawing become quite black owing to silt on the

surface. It seems to deposit an enormous quantity of material, whereas in fact, the greater part of the deposit is still ice. An examination
of the remainders after the thawing of all the ice will prove that
an ice pack for instance 2 m. high only leaves about 5 cm. of silt
at best; such a sedimentation will have an uneven surface, exposed
to attacks from wave action; therefore, a certain loss of material
is supposed to take place. It often happens that even on high-lying
tidal flats ice packs are removed by spring gales and disappear into
the Wadden Sea. Observations during many years have shown that
the ice disappears in a single tidal period from the Wadden Sea.
Only the grounded ice remains. This signifies that in reality the
ice causes loss of material.

b): *The geographical conditions*, i.e. the pattern of morphological
elements, even of a minor character, are of the greatest importance
for the sedimentation. Later in this paper it will be demonstrated
how variations of the sedimentation may be attributed to various
influences of a geographical nature.

c): *The biological forces* have essentially importance for the
fixation of the sedimented material, but also for the reshaping of
the finest material, thus allowing the sedimentation to take place.
The diatoms and the algae partly maintain the individual grains,
partly cover and maintain the whole surface; sea meadow grass
(*Glyceria maritima*) and, when in a dense vegetation, glasswort too
(*Salicornia herbacea*) create a certain lee, while *the mollusks* of
different sorts give passage to the material which is so fine that
precipitation is impossible and expel this material in the shape of
small pellets ready for sedimentation. In order to illustrate to which
extent the mollusks are able to bind the material, it may be mentioned, according to an experiment executed by *L. F. Kamps* (1950)
that in a fortnight 80 big mussels produced 4,5 kg. of dry silt from
the water.

The Rømø Dam.

During the years 1939—48 the isle Rømø in the Danish Wadden
Sea was connected with Jutland by the Rømø Dam, which has a
length of 9.170 m. The purpose of the dam was partly to create
a road-connection between Rømø and Jutland, partly to accelerate
the sedimentation and, thereby, the formation of salt-marsh in this
region of the Wadden Sea.

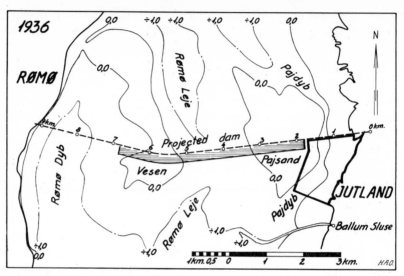

Fig. 1. Part of the Wadden Sea between Jutland and the isle of Rømø 1936 with the projected dam. Only the contours 0,0 m. and — 1,0 m. DNN (Danish Ordnance Datum) are shown. The two framed regions to the south of the dam indicate the areas in which the development of the sedimentation has been examined.

Fig. 1. Del af Vadehavet mellem Jylland og Rømø 1936 med den projekterede dæmningslinie indtegnet. Af hensyn til overskueligheden er kun medtaget kurverne 0,0 m og ÷ 1,0 m DNN (Dansk Normal Nul). De to indrammede områder syd for dæmningen angiver de arealer, hvis sedimentationsudvikling behandles.

The basic material of the researches.

For the examination of the sedimentation along the southern side of the dam a map executed in 1936 by the Committee "Vadehavsudvalget af 1936" has been compared with a series of contouring in the south-western corner between the Rømø Dam and Jutland in the period 1941—59 and with a contouring along the southern side of the dam from the point 1,8 km. to the point 6,8 km. in 1956—57. All these maps and levellings have been executed by the Department of Hydraulic Engineering (Vandbygningsvæsenet), which has kindly placed at my disposal this material as well as a high-water statistics from the tide-gauge at the Højer Sluice.

The natural conditions in the region of the Rømø Dam.

In fig. 1 is shown the section of the Wadden Sea between Rømø and Jutland in which the Rømø Dam has been built. The tides are going to and from the region partly through Lister Dyb to the south and partly through Juvre Dyb to the north of the isle of Rømø.

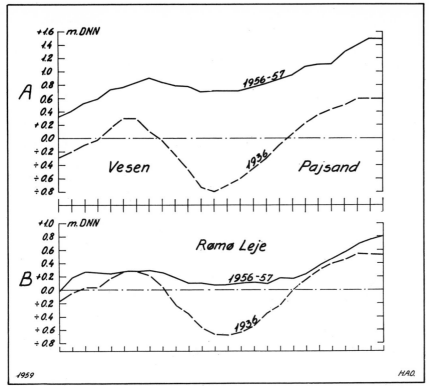

Fig. 2. A shows a profile through the tidal flat 200 m. to the south of the Rømø
Dam and parallel to this between the points 1,8 km. and 6,8 km. B is a profile
through the tidal flat at the southern base of the dam on the same stretch as A.
The two profiles show the levels in 1936 and in 1956-57.

*Fig. 2. A er et profil gennem vaden 200 m syd for og parallel med Rømødæmnin-
gens fod mellem dæmningens 1,8 og 6,8 km, og B er et profil gennem vaden ved
dæmningens sydlige fod på samme strækning som A. De to profiler viser vade-
niveauerne i 1936 og i 1956-57.*

Owing to the fact that the tide decreases from south to north, and
that high water occurs later in Juvre Dyb than in Lister Dyb, an
equalization of the water levels at high tide between the two tidal
regions mentioned took place before the construction of the dam.
This produced a north-going current creating the three channels,
mentioned from east to west: Pajdyb, Rømø Leje and Rømø Dyb.
Observations of the water levels in 1955 in Rømø Dyb to the south
and to the north of the dam on quiet days proved that the high-
water level was 2—4 cm. higher to the south of the dam than to
the north. As already mentioned, this difference of water level was
further increased, because the tide arrived later at Juvre Dyb than

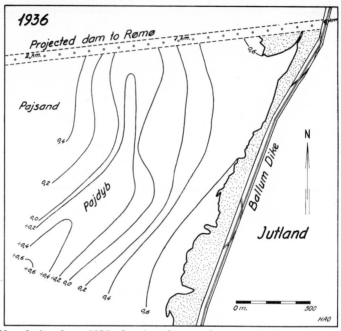

Fig. 3. Map dating from 1936, showing the area between the Rømø Dam and Jutland which in fig. 1 is framed by a thick line. The contours with an interval of 0,2 m. show the levels in Pajdyb and those of the tidal flats before the construction of the Rømø Dam.

Fig. 3. Kort af 1936 over det i fig. 1 med kraftig indramning markerede område mellem Rømødæmningen og Jylland. Kurverne, ækvidistance 0,2 m, viser niveauforholdene i Pajdyb og tilstødende vader før Rømødæmningens bygning.

at Lister Dyb, the water from the south thus being the first to reach the water-shed. The low tide arrives earlier at Lister Dyb than at Juvre Dyb, a fact which formerly should produce a south-going current; however, at low tide the height of the water-shed prevented the creation of such a current; therefore, the resulting current became a one-way, north-going stream. This happened under quiet weather conditions and with wind directions south to west; in cases of north-western and northern winds it can easily be imagined that a south-going current has been predominant. As however, wind-directions WSW are prevailing it will be seen that the wind too has contributed to the north-going direction of the current.

Though the eastern 6 km. of the Rømø Dam have been built at the water-shed between the tidal regions of Juvre Dyb and Lister Dyb it is evident that even this stretch has influenced considerably the equilibrium of the barred channel beds.

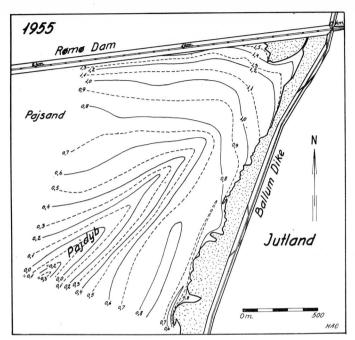

Fig. 4. Map dating from 1955 of the same area as in fig. 3, showing the levels 15 years after the construction of the Rømø Dam. A comparison clearly shows that the contours in the vicinity of the dam have completely changed. The effect of the coast, the bay-effect and the cutting off effect are clearly recognized.

Fig. 4. Kort af 1955 over samme område som fig. 3 og visende niveauforholdene 15 år efter Rømødæmningens bygning. Ved sammenligning med fig. 3 ses tydeligt, hvorledes niveau-kurvernes forløb i dæmningens nærhed er blevet fuldstændig ændret, således at kyst-, bugt- og kuperingsvirkning tydeligt træder frem.

The effects of the Rømø Dam on the sedimentation.

In fig. 1 is framed an area marked by horizontal hatching, of a width of 200 m. and of a length of 5 km. along the southern side of the dam from the point 1,8 km. to 6,8 km. An examination of the variations of the sedimentation in this area makes it possible to point out various geographical effects caused by the presence of the dam in combination with the topography of the tidal flats. The examination has been executed by comparing the maps of 1936 with the maps of 1956—57. By means of these two maps the profiles in fig. 2 have been carried out. A. is a profile through the tidal flat at the base of the dam; the levels of 1936 and of 1956—57 are marked by a dotted line and a full line, respectively. B. is a profile through the tidal flat at a distance of 2200 m. to the south of the dam and parallel to this, the levels of 1936 and of 1956—57 being marked in the same manner as in profile A.

When comparing the two profiles A. and B., a bigger sedimentation on A. will be noticed. This must be due to the presence of the dam, i.e. the effect of forces becoming active in this case when the new-formed, artificial shore line tends to establish a normal beach. This effect on the sedimentation is called *beach-effect*. By a comparison between A. and B. it can be established whether the beach-effect reaches as far as profile B. It appears from profile A. that on Vesen, between the points 5,6 km. and 5,8 km., a sedimentation has taken place since 1936 of a size of about 0,5 m., while in profile B. no sedimentation has taken place; this means that the beach-effect does not reach as far as to distance of 200 m. from the dam. Consequently, the sedimentation which has taken place in profile B. must be due to other effects. It is possible to separate further two geographically conditioned factors, which can be named: the *barring effect* and the *bay-effect*.

The barring effect clearly stands out in fig. 2 in profile A. as well as in profile B. in the barred channel bed of Rømø Leje.

In profile B. is seen a sedimentation on Pajsand which can neither be ascribed to the beach-effect nor to the barring effect; therefore, this sedimentation must be attributed to the bay-effect, which, of course, also reaches as far as the dam. As will be noticed from profile B., none of the three effects appear on Vesen; however, it is probable that a bay-effect exists in Rømø Leje, as this channel is situated between the two high sands Vesen and Pajsand. The bay-effect on Pajsand is probably influenced by the deep bay has situated between the Rømø Dam and Jutland.

From the above it appears that the sedimentation caused by the existence of the dam is dependent on the topographical conditions, the effects of which on the sedimentation along the southern side of the dam can be divided into beach-effect, barring effect and bay-effect. The beach-effect is only of importance in the proximity of the dam and the barring effect in the channels, while the bay-effect has a field of action of a greater extent.

From fig. 2 it will be seen that Rømø Leje is now situated only 20 cm. below the level of Vesen; consequently, the barring effect is coming to a stand-still, and the sedimentation is strongly decreasing. It is true that the beach-effect will move further out simultaneously with the raising of the level along the base of the dam and with the formation of a salt-marsh. By the construction of sedimentation basins (Danish: slikgårde) the coastline is artificially pushed forward, and the outward movement of the land (beach-effect) is accelerated. An extended construction of sedimentation basins on the two protruding high sands Pajsand and Vesen will add to the improvement of the bay-effect.

The sedimentation to the south of the Rømø Dam between the foreland and the point 1,8 km.

In fig. 1 a thick framing marks the region of the Wadden Sea in which the development of the sedimentation during the period 1936—59 is examined. As far as the possibilities of sedimentation are concerned, the geographical conditions correspond to those existing in Rømø Leje; however, the bay-effect is more pronounced, as the bay between the foreland and the high-lying tidal flat Pajsand is fiord-shaped. At a comparison between fig. 3 and fig. 4, the beach-effect, the bay-effect and the barring effect clearly stand out.

Fig. 3 and fig. 4 show the contours of the region in question in 1936 and in 1955, respectively; it is evident that in this period an extremely strong sedimentation has taken place, which is biggest at the base of the dam and smallest at the southern frontier of the area. The extent of this is 200 ha., and the sedimented quantity of material in the period 1936—55 amounts to 1 million cub.m.

The original surface consisted of ordinary tidal flat sand, well-sorted, with a mean grain size of 90 μ and a content of clay ($< 4 \mu$) of less than 10 % (*Kaj Hansen*, 1951). The material which has been sedimented after the construction of the dam is silt, not too well sorted, with a mean grain size of 6—17 μ and a content of clay of up to 36 % (*Kaj Hansen*, 1956).

It has been examined how the intensity of the sedimentation has been distributed over the area. To this purpose have been used the contourings, executed in 1936 and in August 1955, comprising the whole area, and the contourings carried out in August 1941, March 1943, June 1944, October 1945, October 1947 and February 1959, comprising a zone of a width of 320 m. along the base of the dam.

In the period before the construction of the dam started, the area in question can be considered — within a small number of years — as being in equilibrium; this allows to presume that in 1936 the situation was identical with the one which existed immediately before the construction of the dam started on the tidal flats in August 1940.

On the basis of these eight contourings 6 profiles have been drawn through the tidal flat parallel to the dam and with the following positions: along the base of the dam and at a distance from

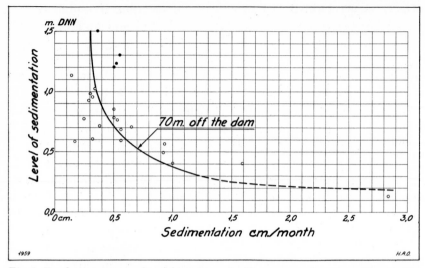

Fig. 5. To show an example of how to make the curves of mean sedimentation the curve for the profile 70 m. to the south and parallel to the dam is drawn here. The individual points represent the sedimentation (cm./month) and the mean level (m. DNN). Table I. The black points to the right of the curve indicate that the sedimentation in these cases has taken place in a *Glyceria* vegetation.

Fig. 5. Eksempel på fremstilling af middel-sedimentationskurven for det profil, der ligger parallelt med og 70 m syd for dæmningsfoden. De enkelte punkter afsættes ved hjælp af tallene i tabel I for sedimentation (cm/måned) og middel-niveau (m DNN). De sorte punkter til højre for kurven angiver, at sedimentationen har fundet sted i Glyceria vegetation.

this — to the south — of 70 m., 170 m., 320 m., 1.200 m. and 2.100 m. In each profile have been chosen 4 verticals at intervals of about 400 m. In each vertical the sedimentation (in cm.) within the respective time intervals has been measured, and the size of the sedimentation in cm./month has been calculated. This is considered as the intensity of the sedimentation in the mean level, i.e. the mean datum between two levelling planes in the vertical.

As an example is given in table I the method of calculation of the 4 verticals in the profile situated at a distance of 70 m. from the base of the dam.

In a system of co-ordinates with the mean datum as ordinate and the sedimentation per month as abscissa are marked out the values of sedimentation and mean level deduced from the 4 verticals in each profile, and a mean curve is drawn. Fig. 5 is given as an example of the profile 70 m. south of the base of the dam and parallel to this.

In table I four of the mean levels have been marked with an x,

Table I.
Tabel I.

Point *Punkt*	Period *Tidsrum*	Number of months. *Antal måneder*	Sedimentation cm. cm./mth. *Sedimentation*		Levelinterval Datum m Datum m *Niveauinterval kote m kote m*		Meanlevel Datum m *Middelniveau kote m*	
			cm	*cm/md.*				
int 1,6 km.	aug. 40—aug. 41	12	19	1,59	+ 0,30 — + 0,49		+ 0,40	
m. south	aug. 41—june 44	34	19	0,56	+ 0,49 — + 0,68		+ 0,59	
dam base	june 44—oct. 45	16	6	0,38	+ 0,68 — + 0,74		+ 0,71	
1,6 km	oct. 45—oct. 47	24	6	0,25	+ 0,74 — + 0,80		+ 0,77	
m syd for	oct. 47—aug. 55	94	30	0,32	+ 0,80 — + 1,10		+ 0,95	
emningsfod	aug. 55—feb. 59	42	6	0,14	+ 1,10 — + 1,16		+ 1,13	
int 1,2 km.	aug. 40—aug. 41	12	34	2,84	− 0,04 — + 0,30		+ 0,13	
m. south	aug. 41—march 43	19	19	1,00	+ 0,30 — + 0,49		+ 0,40	
dam base	march 43—june 44	15	14	0,93	+ 0,49 — + 0,63		+ 0,56	
1,2 km	june 44—oct. 45	16	9	0,56	+ 0,63 — + 0,72		+ 0,68	
m syd for	oct. 45—oct. 47	24	12	0,50	+ 0,72 — + 0,84		+ 0,78	
emningsfod	oct. 47—aug. 55	94	28	0,30	+ 0,84 — + 1,12		+ 0,98	
	aug. 55—feb. 59	42	22	0,52	+ 1,12 — + 1,34		+ 1,23	x
int 0,8 km.	aug. 40—aug. 41	12	11	0,92	+ 0,43 — + 0,54		+ 0,49	
m. south	aug. 41—june 44	34	11	0,32	+ 0,54 — + 0,65		+ 0,60	
dam base	june 44—oct. 47	40	21	0,53	+ 0,65 — + 0,86		+ 0,76	
0,8 km	oct. 47—aug. 55	94	32	0,34	+ 0,86 — + 1,18		+ 1,02	
m syd for *emningsfod*	aug. 55—feb. 59	42	23	0,55	+ 1,18 — + 1,41		+ 1,30	
oint 0,5 km.	aug. 40—aug. 41	12	2	0,17	+ 0,57 — + 0,59		+ 0,58	
m. south	aug. 41—june 44	34	22	0,65	+ 0,59 — + 0,81		+ 0,70	
dam base	june 44—oct. 45	16	8	0,50	+ 0,81 — + 0,89		+ 0,85	
0,5 km	oct. 45—oct. 47	24	7	0,29	+ 0,89 — + 0,96		+ 0,92	
m syd for	oct. 47—aug. 55	94	47	0,50	+ 0,96 — + 1,43		+ 1,20	x
emningsfod	aug. 55—feb. 59	42	15	0,36	+ 1,43 — + 1,58		+ 1,50	x

which means that within the period indicated in the second column to the left of the table a dense *Glyceria* vegetation has immigrated. In fig. 5 these four points have been filled up in black, and it will be seen that in reality the curve ought to have had an angle in the vicinity of the level + 1,1 — + 1,2 m. on account of the new factor: dense vegetation, which highly affects the sedimentation.

The curve in fig. 5 and the five other mean curves, executed in the same manner, are shown in fig. 6. They all indicate the inten-

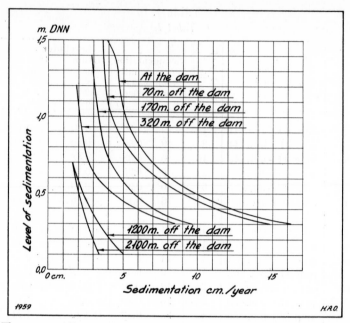

Fig. 6. The mean sedimentation per year in proportion to the level and the distance of the latter from the dam. The curves have been drawn as in fig. 5 and show the sedimentation at the base of the dam and at a distance from this of 70 m., 170 m., 320 m., 1200 m. and 2100 m., respectively.

Fig. 6. Kurver for middel-sedimentationen pr. år i forhold til niveauet og dettes afstand fra dæmningen. Kurverne er fremstillet på samme måde som eksemplet, der er vist i fig. 5, og viser sedimentationen ved dæmningsfoden, samt i en afstand fra denne af henholdsvis 70 m, 170 m, 320 m, 1200 m og 2100 m.

sity of the sedimentation in proportion to the level and to the distance from the dam. In fig. 6 the scale of the abscissa has been altered from cm. per month to cm. per year.

From fig. 6 it appears that at all levels the sedimentation decreases with the distance from the dam, for the first 320 m. at a considerable degree, then gradually lesser. The individual curves show a big sedimentation at the low levels; at rising level the sedimentation is gradually decreasing and, at high-water level ends to become almost even, though feebly decreasing.

When comparing the curves in fig. 6 with the yearly accumulated water-cover at the respective levels we arrive at an expression for the content of deposited material in the water, giving new information about the circumstances of the sedimentation.

A statistics of the changing water levels for 15 years, worked out for the tide-gauge outside the Højer Sluice has been used. This

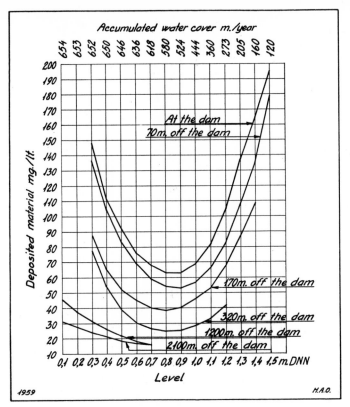

Fig. 7. The quantities of deposited material per year (mg./lt.) in proportion to the level at the base of the dam and at the distances from the dam of 70 m., 170 m., 320 m., 1200 m. and 2100 m. respectively. Each curve represents the quantity of deposited material per litre of the accumulated water cover per year at the different levels. The mean sedimentation in fig. 6 has been compared with the accumulated water cover per year. The specific gravity of the dry wadden-sediment (0,6) has been introduced in order to express the amount of sediment in unites of weight.

Fig. 7. Kurver for årligt sedimenteret materiale (mg/l) i forhold til niveauet gældende for dæmningsfoden og for 70 m, 170 m, 320 m, 1200 m og 2100 m fra dæmningsfoden. Hver kurve udtrykker, hvor stor den sedimenterede materiale-mængde har været i hver liter af den årlige vanddækning på de forskellige ni-veauer. Kurverne fremkommer ved at sammenholde middel-sedimentationskur-verne på fig. 6 med den årlige vanddækning. For at kunne udtrykke sedimentet i vægtenheder er vægtfylden af det udtørrede vadesediment (0,6) indført.

tide-gauge is situated within the same tidal region and has the same mean high-water level as the area in question.

In table II is indicated the yearly accumulated water-cover in m. above + 0,1 m. to + 1,5 m. DNN and in percentage of the yearly accumulated water-cover at + 0,1 m., calculated as the average of the 15-year period 1941—1955.

Table II.
Tabel II.

Level m. DNN. *Niveau m DNN.*	Accumulated water-cover per year m. *Vanddækning pr. år m*	%
0,1	654	100,0
0,2	653	99,9
0,3	652	99,7
0,4	650	99,4
0,5	646	98.2
0,6	636	97,2
0,7	618	94,5
0,8	580	88,7
0,9	524	80,1
1,0	444	67,9
1,1	360	55,0
1,2	273	41,7
1,3	205	31,3
1,4	160	24,5
1,5	120	18,3

As all the previous measurements of suspended material have been expressed in mg./lt. it is desirable, for reasons of comparison, to express the proportion: quantity of sediments/accumulated water-cower in mg/lt. To this purpose has been taken a sample in nature of the topmost 20 cm. of the moist wadden sediment. The water content was found to be 55 %, which corresponds excellently to the value found by *Kaj Hansen* (1956), and the specific gravity of the desiccated material was determined to be 0,6.

The relation between the level and the intensity of sedimentation is shown in fig. 7 for the six curves in fig. 6. The abscissa indicates the level of sedimentation and the yearly accumulated water-cover corresponding to the respective levels; the ordinate indicates the relation between the quantity of deposits and the total yearly water-cover expressed in mg./lt. From fig. 7 appears the result of the following procedure: The sedimentation in dm. at a certain level is taken from fig. 6, then divided by the yearly accumulated water-cover in dm., multiplied by the specific gravity in dry condition

Table III.
Tabel III.

Waterlevel m. DNN *Vandstand m DNN*	Hour rising water falling water *Kl.* *stigende vand faldende vand*		Time difference rising water falling water min. min. *Tidsdifferens* *stigende vand faldende vand* *min. min.*		Rising water + falling water min. *Stigende + faldende vand min.*	$^0/_0$
0,0	10,27	18,17				
			17	10	27	6
0,1	10,44	18,07				
			18	15	33	7
0,2	11,02	17,52				
			18	15	33	7
0,3	11,20	17,37				
			19	17	36	8
0,4	11,39	17,20				
			24	20	44	9
0,5	12,03	17,00				
			24	20	44	9
0,6	12,27	16,40				
			25	25	50	11
0,7	12,52	16,15				
			31	30	61	13
0,8	13,23	15,45				
			72	70	142	30
0,9	14,35	14,35				
					470	100

0,6 and by 10^6. The quantity of deposits in mg./lt. at the level in question is found and the point marked out in fig. 7.

The results of this method all show the same tendency: the sedimentation is biggest at a low level, decreases at rising level till + 0,8 — + 0,9 m. DNN (a little below the mean high-water level) and increases again at rising level. This means that *the sedimentation is less at the high-water level than at any higher or lower level,* when leaving out of consideration the variation of the water-cover; in other words, at high-water level the sedimentation is smaller in proportion to the water-cover than at any other level. This phenomenon occurs everywhere in the Wadden Sea; it manifests itself distinctly when an analysis is made of an over-dimensioned sedimentation, like the one in question; however, it may often be difficult to observe.

The causes of this are to be sought in the astronomical and the meteorological forces. Into table III have been introduced the water level and the hour for rising water and for falling water within the period during which the water rises from and again falls to 0,0 m. DNN. The figures have been taken from a random water level curve for the Rømø Leje on a calm day. The time difference, i.e. the time required for the water to rise and to fall 0,1 m., is calculated, and the time differences for rising water and for falling water are added up. In the last column has been calculated for how long a period, in percentage, of the total time of 470 minutes the water remains at the different 0,1 m. level intervals.

It is evident from table III that the water remains much longer within the topmost 0,1 m. than within any other level interval; for instance, it remains 5 times longer between + 0,8 m. and + 0,9 m. than between 0,0 m. and + 0,1 m.

The small waves which are formed by an even rather feeble wind in water of a depth of but few centimetres are inclined to erode in the surface of the tidal flats and to suspend material which has already been deposited. This material is carried away again at ebb-tide. The longer the small waves are allowed to ripple, the more powerful is the erosion; this means that the closer you come to the high-water line the stronger is the erosion. This is just expressed by the left part of the curves in fig. 7, as the sedimentation is constantly decreasing towards high-water level.

The normal water level situations and weather situations, which occur for long periods in the summer, signify consequently a certain loss of material for the tidal flats; this has been confirmed by numerous observations.

It appears from the above that the sedimentation must take place at a time where the water-cover is of such an extent that the wave-action is unable to reach the bottom.

However, the right half of the curves in fig. 7 shows and increasing sedimentation at rising level. The sedimentation which takes place at a level above mean high water must necessarily depend on extraordinary weather conditions, i.e. when gales create extraordinary high-tides by accumulation. Western gales in the Wadden Sea give rise to considerable accumulations of water in which the tides are moving. Measurements carried out under western gales have proved that under such conditions the tide is considerably smaller than normally; the result of this is reduced currents, which are further weakened because the increased depth of water augments the cross section of the flow. The surges create a violent erosion at the bottom on exposed places; consequently, the suspended quantity of material is 50—100 times bigger than normally. Therefore, on favourably situated localities an extraordinarily big sedimentation will take place under western gales; as it appears from the right half of the curves in fig. 7, the sedimentation increases with the level, i.e. stronger wind, higher water level, bigger sedimentation.

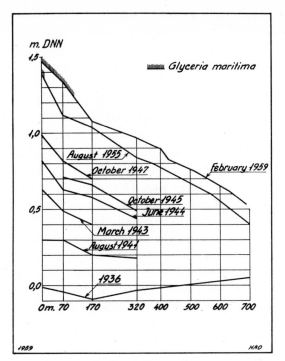

Fig. 8. Profile through the tidal flat to the south of point 1,2 km. of the Rømø Dam. All the measurements executed in the years 1936-59 are marked out. The extent of the *Glyceria* vegetation in this period is shown.

Fig. 8. Profil gennem vaden syd for Rømødæmningens st. 1,2 km med samtlige udførte målinger i tiden 1936-59 indtegnet. Glyceria vegetationen er vist i den udstrækning, den er fremkommet.

As mentioned in fig. 5, the *Glyceria* vegetation is also a factor of considerable importance to the sedimentation at the high-water level and above this, because it is able to retain not only the sand-fraction and the silt-fraction, but the clay-fraction too; thus, this vegetation is of decisive importance to the salt-marsh formation.

The erosion at the high-water level.

The erosion at the high-water level is probably the essential cause of the fact that often it is difficult for the vegetation to start on a high-lying tidal flat, though the necessary height for immigration of vegetation ought to be optimal. It has also been observed that even a rather dense *Salicornia* vegetation on a high-lying tidal flat is destroyed by erosion. Contrary to this: once a *Glyceria* vegetation has immigrated it is only with difficulty destroyed, because *Glyceria* catches and retains the material which has been whirled up and, thereby, consolidates its own position; however, on the wind-exposed sides this vegetation will become the subject of border-erosion, which can only be counteracted by artificial means, for instance by fascines.

A more visible form of erosion on sandy tidal flats is the "puddle" form described by *B. Jakobsen* and *K. M. Jensen* (1956), which often occurs at levels at little below the limit of vegetation. At similar levels on silty tidal flats the surface has a crackled aspect with small, water-filled shallow channels with steep walls situated between silt-islands of varying size. This altered aspect in relation to the sandy tidal flat is due to the work carried out by the diatoms to maintain the already deposited material.

Finally is given an example of the development of the surface south of the dam. Fig. 8 shows a cut through the tidal flat at a right angle to the point 1,2 km. of the dam. This cut comprises the surfaces which have been contoured during the period 1936—1959. Until 1955 the tidal flat was practically without vegetation apart from small hummocks of *Spartina Townsendi,* a little *Salicornia* and a narrow stripe of *Glyceria,* 5—10 m. broad, along the base of the dam.

It is characteristic of the whole of this tidal region that the vegetation does not immigrate until a rather advanced stage of development, i.e. at a relatively high level, because the sedimentation has taken place very rapidly. This resulted in a soft and water-filled bottom, which lacks draining and, therefore, offers unfavourable conditions for the vegetation. Contrary to the greater part of the other regions with initial growth in the Danish Wadden Sea, the vegetation here has hitherto had but small importance to the sedimentation.

During the period 1955—1959 a dense *Glyceria* vegetation has immigrated, stretching until a distance of 110 m. from the base of the dam; this is the reason why the level 70 m. from the base of the dam has risen comparatively more than the points: the base of the dam and 170 m. from this.

In 1958 a ditching has been executed at a distance of 400 m. from the base of the dam. The good draining caused by the ditching has immediately had a favourable influence on the vegetation, especially the *Salicornia;* as a consequence of this the limit of dense *Salicornia* vegetation in the autumn 1958 was situated at a distance of 300 m. from the base of the dam.

However, the ditching has had another favourable effect; by dry-
ing-up the raw surface of the tidal flat, this has been rendered more
resistable against wave-action; which clearly appears from fig. 8 in
the 400 m. point; just at this point the curve of February 1959 gets
an angle downwards at the place where the limit of the ditching
is situated.

Conclusion:

The investigation of sedimentation south of the Rømø Dam for
a period of 20 years has proved the existence of three geographically
conditioned effects of great importance: *the beach-effect, the barring
effect* and *the bay-effect,* factors which it is necessary to consider
at the preparation of projects for land-reclamation.

A further result is the demonstration of the considerable *erosion
at the high-water level caused by wave-action.* It is necessary to
protect this zone by fascines, by ditching and by new-established
Glyceria vegetation, partly man-made and man-protected.

LITERATURE

(1938): Betænkning angående Dæmning mellem Rømø og Fastlandet og
Landvindingsarbejder i Vadehavet inden for Rømø. København.

Hansen, Kaj (1951): Preliminary Report on the Sediments of the Danish
Wadden Sea. Medd. fra Geol. Foren. 12: 1, København. (Medd. fra
Skall.-Lab. XIII, København).

–   (1956): The Sedimentation along the Rømø-dam. Medd. fra Geol.
Foren. 13: 2, København. (Medd. fra Skall.-Lab. XV, København).

Jakobsen, B. (1954, a): The Tidal Area in South-Western Jutland and
the Process of the Salt Marsh Formation. Geogr. Tidsskr. 53, København. (Medd. fra Skall.-Lab. XV, København).

–   (1954, b): Det sydvestjyske vadehavsområde og den nye opfattelse
af marskens dannelse. Dansk Hjemstavn 16. (Medd. fra Skall.-Lab.
XV, København).

Jakobsen, B, og Jensen, Kr. M. (1956): Undersøgelser vedrørende landvindingsmetoder i Det Danske Vadehav. Geogr. Tidsskr. 55, København. (Medd. fra Skall.-Lab. XV, København).

Jakobsen, B., Jensen, Kr. M., og Nielsen, Niels (1956): Forslag til landvindingsarbejder langs den sønderjyske Vadehavskyst. Geogr. Tidsskr. 55, København. (Medd. fra Skall.-Lab. XV, København).

Kamps, L. F. (1950): Enige gegevens over de sedimentatie in het Wad-
dengebied ten Noorden van de provincie Groningen. Tijdschr. v. h.
Kon. Ned. Aardrijksk. Genootschap LXVII: 3, Amsterdam.

Møller, Jens Tyge (1956): Kort over Juvre Dybs tidevandsområde samt
nogle topografiske og hydrografiske problemer. Geogr. Tidsskr. 55,
København. (Medd. fra Skall.-Lab. XV, København).

Schou, Axel (1945): Det marine Forland. Folia Geogr. Danica IV, København. (Medd. fra Skall.-Lab. IX, København).

Wohlenberg, E. (1954): Sinkstoff, Sediment und Anwachs am Hinden-
burgdamm. Die Küste 2: 2.

Types of sedimentation in a drowned delta region
Examples from the salt-marsh area at Tønder

By N. Kingo Jacobsen

Abstract

Four longitudinal sections are given through the post-glacial deposits of the Tønder salt-marshes. They are all departing from about the same point of the geest border. By means of these lines the differentiation in sediment covers and facies types is given in relation to the relative rise of the sea level in this area throughout the Holocene.

Studies related to the post-glacial genesis along the southern part of the North Sea coast i.e. the Wadden Sea and the salt-marsh areas have been going on for more than a generation. Among Danish works should be mentioned those by *Axel Jessen* (1916, 1925) and *V. Nordmann* (1935, 1943) and the researches carried out by the *Skalling-Laboratoriet* and by *De Danske Vade- og Marskundersøgelser, Niels Nielsen* (1960). These three series of investigations cover as many epochs with their totally different basic points of view: *Axel Jessen* worked at a hypothesis of a maximum subsidence in the Bronze Age, *V. Nordmann* at tectonic block movements; at present the conclusions are based on the presumption of a continuous rise of the sea level *(N. Kingo Jacobsen, 1956)* and further on examinations of the sedimentation in the area to-day and the totally new perspectives which they open up *(Børge Jakobsen, 1954, 1956)*. The borings in the North Sea salt-marsh conclude in the typical profile already given by *Wildvang* (1938). Above the pleistocene landscape (the geest) is found a basis peat superposed by old marine facies. On top of these layers a younger peat follows and, uppermost, the young marine deposits. Without discussing the factors involved and their interchanges the result is a relative rise of the sea level during the last 10.000 years of about 20 m. An outline on the factors influencing this retreat of the shoreline has previously been given (1956). The object of this article is to state the results of to-day in the

Tønder area; further to describe the multiple variations in the topography of the present surface inclusive of the latest sediments as a
result of variations of the geest surface and, consequently, of the
holocene deposits too, i.e. to determine the type of the salt-marsh.
This is demonstrated by means of four longitudinal sections, all
departing from about the same point of the geest border and orientated towards: S, SW, W and NW. From pl. II it appears how easy
it is to arrive at very different conclusions about the genesis of the
Tønder salt-marsh drawn from single profiles, not to speak of single
borings. What further complicates the judgment is that even roughly
datings of old facies are difficult; so is the determination of exact
levels, at least at the time of sedimentation; this deplorable draw-
back has made it extremely hard to give a reasonable valuation and
interpretation of existing material. As a final contributing factor
should be mentioned the activity of man, which in the course of the
last thousand years has exercised an influence of vital importance
on the processes just mentioned. By the endikements a damming of
the sea-waters has taken place especially in rough weather. In the
course of time these dikes have been strengthened (both from a point
of view of profile and of height). In case of dike-bursts strong erosive
effects have appeared locally and consequently wide-spread layers of
sand and silt have been deposited further inland. Besides the activity
of man, such as ditching, construction of sluices and other drainage
measures, has conditioned a rather considerable shrinkage in loose,
watery deposits and in sediments of an organic character.

The Tønder salt-marsh is situated just south of the Fenno-Scandian rising block, the outer limit of which stretches from the Esbjerg
region through Ærø and the Fehmarn Belt. Epirogenetic subsidence
in the southern part of the North Sea has been estimated by W.
Dechend (1954) at about 2-3 cm. per century; this small size excludes such forces from being of greater importance in this relation.
What remains to be considered are the eustatic movements which,
on the whole, must be regarded as the principal causes of the above-
mentioned relative subsidence of about 17 m. since the beginning of
Atlanticum, i.e. for the last 7.500 years. Of course, this relative rise
of the sea level has been subjected to fluctuations caused by climatical changes and changes of the local meteorological and hydrographical conditions.

The course of the sedimentation along the west coast of Jutland
has been extremely varying in the different regions, depending,
among other factors, on the topography of the pleistocene landscape.

This appears in details within the Tønder area, as previously described (1959). Considering the evolution in outline, the distribution of outwash plains and older moraines, ranges of terminal moraines and tertiary knots has been decisive in combination with the configuration of the coastal profile. The Danish Wadden Sea in its existing structure is thus conditioned by the presence of two knots: Blåvandshuk and Sild, on which the holocene sedimentation is fixed. Within this line is found a large bay which is being filled with sediments, protected against the North Sea by a festoon of beach deposits: peninsulas, isles, high-sands and sand-bars with interjacent deeps and channels through which the tide spreads across the extensive tidal flats and vast salt-marsh areas of different character on the lee-side of the islands and along the mainland. The original gradient of the coastal profile in this region down to the contours — 10 m. DNN and — 20 m. DNN, (Danish Ordnance Datum) has been decisive too for the result: a Wadden Sea area.

The Tønder salt-marsh and the Wadden Sea immediately to the west are to be considered as a delta region for the Vidå (å = river) with its tributaries, which have been drowned through the above-mentioned rise of the sea level. However, the latter has taken place slowly enough to be balanced by the sedimentation through the formation of the island arc, the Wadden Sea and a fringe of marine foreland along the mainland. Owing to this, belts of salt-marshes are mainly found in the estuaries of the rivers, separated by knots of older moraines which are facing the Wadden Sea with steep erosion cliffs. Højer (pl. III) is situated on a small, isolated knot, and immediately to the north is found the older moraine Hjerpsted with an erosion cliff towards west, 11 km. long.

The following text deals with the stratification and the levels in the four longitudinal profiles mentioned and, further, with the nature and approximate age of the sedimentation covers. Next this location will in outline be placed in the general problems; before doing so, however, it is urgent once more to stress the necessity of exact datings (by pollen analysis, C_{14} determinations and by archaeological excavations of mounds) and determinations of levels. Further it is important to map the layers in order to put them in relation to the factors influencing the sedimentation, cf. the four totally different profiles in pl. II.

The location of the four longitudinal profiles appears from pl. III. Line A may be considered as a typical section starting at the geest border direct facing the rising sea level. *The geest surface* comprises three morphological types: a) the western half forms part of the outwash plain gently sloping towards west; formerly it was intersected in the middle by a channel (the former Vidå), which is filled now with marine sand. In this area the gradient of the outwash plain is ¾ m. per km., and the mean levels are ranging from about — 5 m. DNN to — 8 m. DNN; b) to the east of this area is found a higher lying terrace characterized by dune topography. The mean level of this undulating surface is — 1 m. DNN. It stands with a cliff facing the outwash plain to the west and with a big blow-out to the east towards c) the older moraine of Møgeltønder, where the salt-marsh area ends with an escarpment. *The morphology of the present surface.* To the west we find the tidal flat with a gully, which, to northwest, leads direct into the Lister Dyb (dyb = deep) between the isles Sild and Rømø. In this region the tidal range is about 1.80 m. The two levels: mean low tide (Lv - L, pl. II) ab. — 0.85 m. DNN and the mean high tide (Hv - L, pl. II) ab. + 0.95 m. DNN have been lead through the whole profile together with DNN (pl.II) in order to give an impression of the surface level in the different polders in relation to these important water levels. At the mean high tide is found a small erosion cliff: the foreland border, which sharply marks the transition from sea to land. To the east of this erosion cliff the foreland is seen and the two westernmost polders: Ny Frederikskog, endiked 1861, and Gl. Frederikskog, endiked 1692. The process of salt-marsh formation to-day (foreland-type) acts through immigrated vegetation on sand-bars moving from west. On the seaward side of the new marsh-isles the wave-action forms an erosional cliff and a new gully (landpriel) (*B. Jakobsen*, 1954): this is clearly demonstrated in the profile pl.II. Two such systems are found on the foreland, two in Ny Frederikskog and three in Gl. Frederikskog. The dikes and the two mounds in Gl. Frederikskog have all been built on the western, highest lying part of such »cliffs«. The eastern part of Gl. Frederikskog is situated at a lower level and is gently sloping towards the Vidå. The decline continues into the middle of Rudbøl Kog (endiked 1715), where a previous branch of the Vidå has been running. To the east of this locality, situated above the western border of the previously mentioned terrace of the geest, is found a high projecting salt-marsh area, a »hallig« (undiked salt-marsh island). At the western side of this hallig the oldest sea-dike of the region has been built (1556). Further, in this region we find a number of big farms on mounds; in total there are three big hallig-islands in this area and about ten big farms and several villages, the

most important of which is Rudbøl. The hallig is intersected by a
small creek and a big creek (Danish: lo). To the east the surface is
sloping towards the parish boundary separating: Rudbøl-Gaden and
Møgeltønder Kog; this boundary is identical with the upper reaches
of the above-mentioned big creek, which in the period immediately
before the building of the sea-dike in 1556 acted as a tidal creek for
the eastern basin situated close to the geest border. To the west of
this basin, still in Møgeltønder Kog, is found a higher part of the
salt-marsh, an »isle«, which ows its existence to a corresponding
dune-top in the sub-surface of the geest. Such localities have been
utilized for building of mounds. As far as the levels are concerned,
the various polders show great differences. The foreland, Ny Frederikskog and the western part of Gl. Frederikskog, up to and including
the easternmost mound, are situated above mean high tide, parts of
Ny Frederikskog even above + 2 m. DNN. To the east of this area
are found low-lying regions with the exception of the hallig-area
which together with the salt-marsh deposited on the west side of
the dunes in the sub-surface reach levels considerably higher than
the mean high tide. Apart from this the eastern region is situated
below mean high tide, parts of Rudbøl Kog below DNN. The easternmost basin too is situated at a very low level; especially the region in
the western part of Møgeltønder Kog, where large areas are situated
only a few centimetres above DNN.

After this outline on the topography of the geest and the present
surface a view on *the stratification of the alluvial layers* and their
variations will be given, passing from the tidal flat, where the formations have a thickness of at least 8 m., via the outer polders with
a sedimentation cover of 5-6 m., till the inner polders, which present
great variations until the point where the two surfaces unite, i.e.
where only the geest is projecting. This inner, eastern borderline of
the transgression is varying a lot as far as the levels are concerned.
This is quite reasonable as local conditions regarding the geest topography and the exposition to sea and wind have been decisive; in the
present case the borderline is found at about + 1 m. DNN.

The sedimentation discussed presupposes the above-mentioned
transgression spread via Lister Dyb and the Vidå valley and flooding
the outwash plain which is slightly declining towards west. The
Tønder region must have had its coastline at about — 7 m. DNN (corresponding to the western part of the profile, pl.II) at about 3.500
years B.C. (1956). In the greater part of the profile the geest is covered by a peat-layer (basis peat). This is found at varying levels and

must be considered as the land-facies which corresponds to the sedimentation in the sea existing at that time at corresponding or somewhat lower levels to the west; the lower the position of the peat-layers,
the greater their age: at any rate, this must be the consequence of the
hypothesis just put forward: only a single transgression even if it
is constantly decreasing. *J. Bennema* (1954) and *J. P. Bakker* (1954)
have suggested flooding periods with a certain periodicity. Owing to
variations in the rate of transgression assisted by the formation of
sand-bars etc. an alternation of the following two systems takes
place: 1): Quiet periods with a state of equilibrium, during which
the individual facies were formed and gradually passed into each
other. 2): Powerful and short interventions of extraordinarily high
storm-surges creating new conditions to which, however, the whole
system rapidly adapted itself.

If the layers deposited immediately on top of the basis peat are
considered, irrespective of their age and their level, this corresponds
to following the borderline throughout the ages between the sediments of the land (deposited in fresh water or in slightly brackish
water), and the marine sediments (deposited in salt water or typically brackish); thus it is possible on the profile pl.II,A, to make
a distinction between two types:

1. The western, exposed marine region, where the basis peat is
   superposed by a layer of gytja about 1 m. thick. This stratification comes to an end on top of the geest terrace. The depth of
   the basis peat is varying depending on the relief of the geest surface. The depth of gytja is almost the same all over this area
   (½ — 1 m.), apart from the eastern, highest lying part, where
   they have been heavily eroded, cf. the corresponding effects in
   the profiles C and D demonstrating the conditions in more exposed
   areas to the north. The gytja-layers represent the brackwater
   facies of each level. To the west of it we find marine sand-facies
   and silt-facies and, to the east extensive land-facies: peat bogs in
   all low-lying parts of the geest. The regular picture indicates quiet
   conditions, i.e. the retreat of the shoreline has developed gradually, at any rate up to the level ab. — 2 m. DNN.

2. In the protected, eastern basins the transgression has not taken
   place until very late standing out as a clear-cut from peat to fat
   basin clay. This corresponds to a catastrophe resulting in a change
   of facies. However, further examinations of the peat show minor

forerunners as marine ingressions in the peat. Thus, we find immediately on top of the geest a reddish-brown fresh-water peat, dominated by *Alnus* with *Menyanthes* seeds and *Phragmites;* a clay-layer, 1 mm. thick (level ab. — ¾ m. DNN.), separates this peat from a superior, brown *Phragmites* peat with roots of *Alnus* and *Betula.* By a thin clay-layer (level ab. — ½ to — ¼ m. DNN), this peat is separated from a topmost grey to black *Phragmites* peat, superposed by the fat, marine clay. In the latter may be found a single strip of sand originating from a storm-surge; in the northern region too we often find superior layers deposited during storm-surges and dike-bursts.

The marine facies in the western region consist of sand of a uniform, rather fine grain size (50— 80μ) which is, as stated in certain localities replaced by more fine-grained material: fine-sand (20 — 50 μ) or silt 2 — 20 μ). These layers are often rather waterfilled. The westernmost boring in Ny Frederikskog is rather illustrative of the conditions in this region: On top of the outwash plain (— 6.60 m. DNN) is found a layer of gytja, depth 85 cm. (— 5.75 m. DNN). This layer has been superposed by marine, fine-grained, loose sediments, silt and fine-grained sand, constantly alternating. No shells are found, which seems to indicate a sedimentation even enough for the fauna to follow upwards; therefore, no catastrophe is supposed to have taken place. The fine-grained and loose sediments point to the fact that the sedimentation has taken place behind minor offshore-bars. This state of things continues with variations, until the level ab. — 2.80 m. DNN where a shell-layer of common mussels *(Mytilus edulis)* is found, superposed by loose layers of fine sediments and, next, by more compact layers of somewhat coarser sand up to ab. + 60 cm. DNN, where the salt-marsh, foreland type, starts.

The rise of the sea level shows itself in the drifting towards east of the above-mentioned sand-bars; this drifting meets its first real obstacle at the western slope of the geest terrace mentioned above. Undoubtedly offshore-bars have been formed at the places of the flooded outwash plain exposed to surf; however, all indications known locate all such bars to the west of this region corresponding to the rather fine-grained size of the marine sand found within the area. The easternmost drifting of marine sand as bars: an extent to the east of the tidal-flat area and consequently, of exposed, marine sedimentation, are found below Rudbøl Kog at the level — 2 m. DNN.

No doubt, this is a turning point of great importance. It is true that up to this point and to this level a sedimentation has taken place caused by the transgression; however, until then the rise of the sea level has been dominating. Consequently, during this period unceasing losses of land have taken place. Later the situation changes. The sedimentation has now the predominance over the subsidence, and the conditions are present for the displacement towards west of the frontier line between sea and land. However, the subsequent period is still marked by the relative rise of the sea level, and the influence of the sea extends to even larger areas towards east, cf. the above-mentioned profile from the eastern basins close to the geest border. The heavier sedimentation« is consequently reflected in an extension of the marine foreland. This is reasonable as it is necessary to take the effects of the storm-surges and the range of the tide into account too. At the same time, this development conditions the formation of halliger (salt-marsh islands), beach ridges (offshore-bars), and behind these lower areas are found to the east which, as lagoons, are filled with fine-grained sediments, fat basin clay with up to 85 % of material below 2μ. Parallel to the establishment of a broader marine foreland the conditions are prevalent for a far richer differentiation of all the facies, a differentiation which is continued until man's intervention by the construction of dikes. It is perhaps the most important result of man's cultivation measures: exclusion of the formation of lagoons and of the special types of sedimentation which are found in such regions. The sedimentation to-day in the Wadden Sea almost exclusively comprises tidal flat sand and salt-marshes of the foreland type.

Most probably, the bed of the Vidå has been forced eastward by the intruding sand-masses, i.e. the wide-spread tidal flats. The hallig-area must be regarded as levee formations on the eastern bank of the Vidå, characteristically situated a little to the west of the geest terrace, comparable to a damming effect. The same effect is seen in the mound-carrying salt-marsh »island« in the westernmost part of Møgeltønder Kog. The whole interjacent region (Rudbøl-Gaden) is dominated by erosion and sedimentation of a different nature; a general feature is that the fat basin clay is superposed by facies deposited under more exposed conditions; however, they must all be ascribed to the effect of high flooding during rough weather; it is not likely to think of »cliff«-systems of the same nature as those found in the outer polders. Finally, the attention is drawn to the damming effect at the sedimentation of the basin clay in the easternmost basin, which is clearly seen in the levels of the transition from peat to basin clay in this area.

A closer examination of the genesis of the topmost layers (above — 2 m. DNN) is far beyond the scope of this article, as the stratification is rather complicated; however, the erosion channels and the formations of basin clay which are clearly outstanding in all the profiles seem to indicate alternations of the two sedimentation cycles mentioned in page 83 accompanied by alternations in the balance between »subsidence« and sedimentation.

As a conclusion of this description of the profile the attention must be drawn to the configuration of the present surface of the tidal flat, stretching from its easternmost limit below the dike between Rudbøl Kog and Gl. Frederikskog, farther out below the two outer polders and the foreland to the mean low-tide level to the west. Looking so a big sand-bar demonstrates itself; a bar which has drifted inwards with small sand-bars as ripples on the surface. These small bars are the basis of salt-marsh formation of the foreland type, mentioned as the »cliff«-system (*Børge Jakobsen*, 1954). To-day the level of the former tidal flat to the east is at 0 m. DNN and that of the tidal flat to-day at the foreland border at + 0.95 m. DNN. As indicated, this level is identical with the mean high-tide level at the time being. No doubt the size is demonstrated of the relative rise of the sea level within this period, i.e. in the course of about 300 years. On the eastern side of the cliff-systems we normally meet old gullies situated at a lower level; therefore, the rise of the sea level during the last 300 years must be estimated at a total of 50 cm. As it has been possible for man within the same period by means of construction of dikes to press the shoreline 3 to 4 km. to the west it is evident that the present is a period where the sedimentation is predominant to the relative subsidence. Further, the damming-effect of the dikes is demonstrated as the low-lying, eastern areas, if not protected by dikes, would be overflooded every time the high tide rises above + 2 m. DNN which normally occurs a few times a year. At such occasions sedimentation would have taken place of rather coarse deposits as well as some erosive effects caused by the activity of the tides.

The other three profiles only serve to show the rich variation of sediment covers of the easternmost part of the salt-marsh between the river Vidå and the geest border. The profile to the south (B) shows the conditions in the protected part of the salt-marsh where basin clay and fluvial marsh of a rather brackish type are met with.

In the previous trunk stream of the Vidå, now abandoned, borings
have been carried out to ab. — 10 m. DNN without reaching the geest
(B. Valeur Larsen). The present bed of the Vidå is seen to the south.
Profile C shows the stratification found towards west. As a new
element the hollow in the middle of the Højer Kog (the Søgaard
basin) is of particular interest. This hollow is circular, ab. 1 m. deep
and, no doubt, formed as a lake by bar closure of the beach-ridge
system situated to the west, departing from the Højer knot. Beach-
ridge formations at this level (0 - $+$ 2 m. DNN) have already been
described by *Axel Jessen* (1916) from the Ribe salt-marsh. They
must be interpreted as a period of stagnation either in the »subsidence« or, in the influence of the tide. At any rate, in this period a
strong, south-going beach-drift has taken place, resulting, in Højer
Kog, in the formation of three beach-ridge systems with corresponding bar closures and lagoon lakes, cf. fig. 1. Shrinkage as an explanation is out of the question; this is evident from the substratae which
differ in the eastern part and in the western part of the lake. In the
latter area is seen a big creek, which has cut through the peat-layers
from — 3 m. DNN to — ½ m. DNN. The north-western profile D
situated close to Højer presents a very heterogeneous picture with a
protruding knot of the geest to the west close to the dike of 1556.
Just east of this knot is found a deep channel which has served the
Sejersbæk Kog, situated to the north and east of the previously
mentioned older moraine of Hjerpsted. To the east of this channel
is seen another old channel which has probably functioned in late-
glacial time as a trunk stream for the Lindskov Møllestrøm (from
the older moraine of Møgeltønder). The transgression in the eastern
basins has been less abrupt in this rather exposed area than in the
better protected lagoons to the south-east. This is seen in the presence of a gytja-layer between the basis peat and the basin clay.
Further, this area has almost reached a state of stagnation after the
building of the dikes in 1556 owing to ample supplies of fresh water
from the geest. This has resulted in the formation of peat-layers on
top of the basin clay. During dike-bursts a supply of sea water has
taken place; this is why peat-layers alternate with gytja-like formations.

The available facts, as described above and demonstrated by the
four longitudinal sections, point to a detailed mapping of soil types
and a determination of exact spot heights with accompanying datings as indispensable for providing a valid picture of the genesis in
this region in post-glacial time. Results based on a single profile

would be rather questionable as the point is a pattern of sedimentation types which at each level, i.e. layers from different periods, are built up of a highly differentiated organism of alternating facies. These are varying partly in conformity with the simultaneously existing geest borders of varied topographical configuration, partly in accordance with the rivers and tidal creeks in function. The first type of facies variations might be called the circular variation type, the latter (in relation to the channels) the radial variation type. Adding to this that the balance between »subsidence« and sedimentation during the different periods (different levels) is subjected to systematical fluctuations, impeding the creation of an equilibrium between the hydrographical and sedimentological factors, it is reasonable that these problems still are in question. During the last 50 years where these problems have been discussed neither efforts nor ability have been lacking; however, the complexity of the problems has been overwhelming as to the collected facts. Two-dimensional representations, which can be obtained by single borings or longitudinal sections, are not quite adequate; nor do three-dimensional representations through mapping of soil types suffice as exact datings are necessary too. It is imperative to produce four-dimensional representations of the post-glacial genesis along several localities of the west coast of Jutland to the north and to the south of the outer limit for the Fenno-Scandian rising block before we know any further about the development during this epoch. However, to procure exact levellings and datings supposes hard work. It is therefore necessary to propose the following as a working programme. Through mapping of soil types within a given area (cf. 1956) to get a broad idea about the pattern of facies types at different levels. According to this each epoch and each facies can be investigated just at the place, where it is typically developed, and only in such places it is worth while to go through with detailed and specialized examinations.

LITERATURE

Bakker, J. P. (1954): Relative sea-level changes in Northwest Friesland (Netherlands) since prehistoric times. Geol. en Mijnbouw, N.S.16, pp.232-246.

Bennema, J. (1954): Bodem- en Zeespiegelbewegingen in het Nederlandse Kustgebied. Boor en Spade VII, pp.1-96. Utrecht.

Dechend, W. (1954): Eustatische und tektonische Probleme des Quartärs im südlichen Nordseeraum. Geol. en Mijnbouw, N.S.16, pp.195-200.

Dinemann, W. & Scharf, W. (1932): Zur Frage der neuzeitlichen »Küstensenkung« an der deutschen Nordseeküste. Jahrb. d.Preuss.Geol.Landesanst. 1931:52, pp.317-390. Berlin.

Dittmer, E. (1952): Die nacheiszeitliche Entwicklung der schleswig-holsteinischen Westküste. Meyniana 1. Neumünster.

Jacobsen, N. Kingo (1953): Mandø. En klit-marskø i Vadehavet. Geogr. Tidsskr.52, pp.134-146. Medd.f.Skall.-Lab.XIV. København.

Jacobsen, N. Kingo (1956): Jordbundsundersøgelser i Tøndermarsken. Geogr. Tidsskr. 55, pp.106-146. Medd.f.Skall.-Lab.XV. København.

Jacobsen, N. Kingo (1959): Geest-topografi under Tøndermarsken. Geestoverfladens morfologi i Møgeltønder Kog, beskrivelse og forsøgsvis tolkning. Geogr. Tidsskr. 58, pp. 141–181. København.

Jakobsen, B. (1954): The Tidal Area in South-Western Jutland and the Process of the Salt Marsh Formation. Geogr.Tidsskr.53. Medd.f.Skall.-Lab. XV. København.

Jakobsen, B. & Jensen, Kr. M. (1956): Undersøgelser vedrørende landvindingsmetoder i Det danske Vadehav. Geogr. Tidsskr. 55. Medd. f. Skall.-Lab. XV. København.

Jessen, A. (1916): Marsken ved Ribe. Danm. Geol. Unders. II:27. København.

Jessen, A. (1925): Kortbladet Blaavandshuk. Danm.Geol.Unders. I:16. København.

Nielsen, Niels (1935): Eine Methode zur exakten Sedimentationsmessung. Kgl.Danske Vidensk.Selsk.Biol.Medd. XII. Medd.f.Skall.-Lab. I. København.

Nielsen, Niels (1938): Nogle Bemærkninger om Marskdannelsen i det danske Vadehav. Geogr.Tidsskr. 41, pp.123-138. Medd.f.Skall.-Lab.VI. København.

Nielsen, Niels (1960): The organization of scientifical research work in South–West Jutland. Geogr. Tidsskr. 59. København.

Nordmann, V. (1935): Arkæologisk-geologiske Undersøgelser ved Misthusum i Skærbæk Sogn. Et Bidrag til Marskens Historie. Aarb.f.Nord. Oldk. og Hist. 1935. København.

Nordmann, V. (1943): Tønder-Egnens Geologi. »Tønder gennem Tiderne«. Hist.Samf.f.Sønderjylland.

Rasmussen, Kjeld (1956): Investigations on Marsh Soils and Wadden Sea Sediments in the Tønder Region. Geogr.Tidsskr. 55, pp.147-170. Medd. f.Skall.-Lab. XV. København.

Rewentlow, Arthur, Greve (1863): Om Marskdannelsen paa Vestkysten. København.

Schütte, H. (1939): Sinkendes Land an der Nordsee? Schr.d.Deutschen Naturkundevereins. N.F.9. Öhringen.

Wildvang, D. (1938): Die Geologie Ostfrieslands. Abh.d.Preuss.Geol. Landesamt. N.F. 181. Berlin.

Topography of the late-glacial sub-surface in the salt-marsh area at Tønder.

By N. Kingo Jacobsen.

As part of an investigation of the landscape genesis along the south-western coast of Jutland after the last glaciation, *De Danske Vade- og Marskundersøgelser* have carried out detailed mapping of soil types, levellings and topographical mapping in the western part of the Tønder area, Møgeltønder Kog (polder). The salt-marsh investigated covers about 1.600 ha. The programme comprises a net of borings to a depth of 1.25 m. at intervals of 50 m. and a system of borings in lines going down to the late-glacial sub-surface. These borings were placed at intervals of 50 m. in lines situated at a distance from each other of 2—300 m. The spot height of the borings has been determined by a detailed contouring of the whole area, with points at each 25 m. in a net with a density of four times the borings. The accuracy of the levelling is found within 1 cm. The spot heights are carried forward to the boring points with an estimated uncertainty of up to 5 cm. In a previous article *(N. Kingo Jacobsen, 1956)* this programme has been outlined, and a single profile has been published. In great parts of the area it has been possible, already with the surface drill, to reach the geest, i.e. the old surface of the outwash plains from the Würm Glaciation and the old morainic isles from the Riss.

The contour-map of the geest-surface, description and topography.

On the basis of about 7.000 borings in all, the accompanying contour-map has been drawn of the geest surface in Møgeltønder Kog (Pl. I). In this article is given partly a topographical description, partly an attempt of an interpretation based on profiles (fig. 2)

and on 6 borings to a depth of about 30 m. below the surface (fig. 1).
These borings have been executed by *Dr. Sigurd Hansen, Danmarks
Geologiske Undersøgelse* (D.G.U.). Studies of corresponding phenomena observed in Germany and Holland will be referred to and,
finally, the results will be summed up in a morphological description of the terrain in question.

In view of the distribution of heights, screens have been introduced
between the contours according to a sevenpartite scale (i.e. with
contour intervals of 1 m.), trying to produce an almost 3-dimensional
picture with the highest lying parts dark toned. The fully drawn
contours have an interval of 0.5 m., and taking the intervening dot-
and-dash contuors into account the contour interval is 0.25 m. In the
areas where the geest is situated at such a level that it can be reached
by the small drill (1.25 m. below surface) a very detailed picture of the geest surface has been established. Broadly speaking, the
contours down to − ¾ to − 1 m. D.N.N. (Danish Ordnance Datum)
have been established with this accuracy, considering that in this
area the surface of the salt-marsh is situated at the level + 0.20 to
+ 0.50 m. D.N.N. Certain parts are situated at a higher level; however, they coincide with the areas where the geest too reaches a
high level. An exception from this is only the region in the most
south-western part of the map, where the morphology of the salt-
marsh is of a quite different type. The deeper lying parts (below
− 1 m. D.N.N.) have, as mentioned, been mapped on a rougher scale
than the rest; however, the variations of the spot heights in these
areas have had a pronounced tendency indicating the basins in
question. As an example can be mentioned the spot heights on a
line N/S through the north-western basin (figures in m. — D.N.N.):
0.40, 1.04, 1.20, 1.25, 1.32, 1.42, 2.09, 2.85, 2.91, 2.80, 2.88, 2.85, 2.90,
2.50, 2.13, 2.10, 1.56, 1.72, 1.50, 1.55, 1.52, 1.36, 0.68. As mentioned,
the distance between the points is about 50 m.

The topographical description of the map pl. I is preceded by a
classification which in broad outline results in three types of
terrain situated at different levels:

1: *The high-lying geest,* old morainic island, Riss Glaciation.

This type is found to the north from Bønderby to Møgeltønder
with a lowermost level at about + 1 m. D.N.N., which almost corresponds to the upper shore-line of the Post-Glacial time. The
western part (about 1½ km.) shows but little of this type of geest,
which at this place is steeply descending to the basin situated to the

south. In the eastern half (also about 1½ km.) is partly seen the older moraine cliff facing the Vidå valley (levels above + 2 m. D.N.N.)
and partly, to the south of this, a landscape, undulating on a small
scale with dome-shaped hills and serrated contour lines with the first
signs of funnel-shaped estuaries, which are further accentuated at
the lower levels.

2: *The terrace surface.*

To the south of the high-lying geest is found a geest surface situated at the level + 1 m. to − 1 m. D.N.N. It comprises a border-
zone of a width of 2—500 m. connected with an area of about 3 sq.
km. to the west of Sødam Gård. At the level 0 to − 1 m. D.N.N. it
must be considered as a sort of terrace surface for the whole mapped area to the south of the old moraine island from the Riss
Glaciation (Møgeltønder bakkeø) and to the north of the fluvio-
glacial valley from the Würm Glaciation, which forms the bed of the
Vidå. In its eastern border-zone towards the high-lying geest this
surface is characterized by the above mentioned estuaries in the direction N—NE; in the middle is a ridge, NW/SE oriented. To the
west it is intersected by a channel in the direction N/S and terminates abruptly to south-east at the southern deepest part of the
easternmost basin. On this ridge and on the plain to the west of
Sødam Gård is seen a working-out of the terrace surface with long
ridges WNW/ESE, which have a striking resemblance to dune topography.

The basins.

Almost half of the map comprises levels below — 1 m. D. N. N.
They group mainly around three basins or bays with adjoining
channels.

a): Towards north-west is found a basin of an extent of about 2
sq.km., which has a symmetrical shape with the longitudinal
axis in the direction WNW/ESE (refer the above-mentioned
levels from a cut N/S through the basin). The depth is about
− 3 m. D. N. N.

b): To the east is found a bay-looking basin of an asymmetrical
shape; the greatest depth is about − 3 m. D.N.N. in the southernmost part. The border consists of funnel-shaped tongues towards WNW, NW, NE and N. In the central border of the
basin, at Kærgård (fig. 1) is seen the northernmost of the
meanders of the Vidå (depth about − 4,5 m. D.N.N.)

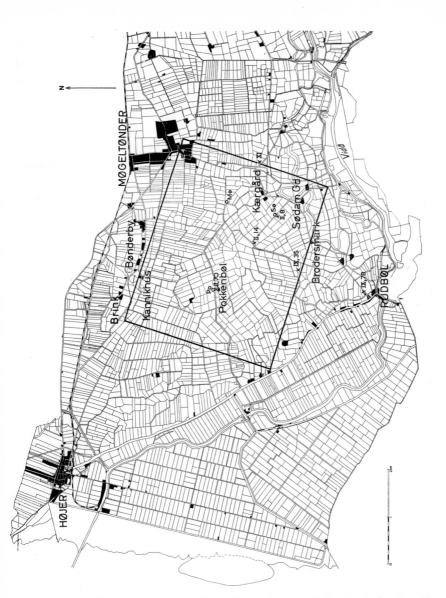

Fig. 1. Map of the western part of the salt-marsh area of Tønder indicating 1)
the position of the described area (framed) corresponding to pl. I, 2) the borings
of D.G.U., and 3) the position of the samples analyzed and described by H.
Kuhlman, cfr. p. 108.

c): Towards south-west is found a deeper lying area of an irregular shape; in the westernmost part this area reaches a depth of about – 3 m. D.N.N. With smaller depths from – 1 m. to – 2 m. D.N.N. it covers an area of about 2 sq.km. and is connected by a channel N/S oriented with the north-western basin (a).

Geology.

At the end of the Tertiary the south-western part of Denmark was a plateau high above the sea and with deep cut valleys. At the end of the Pliocene the deterioration of climate sets in, and the ice masses extend from north to east. At the beginning of the Quaternary a general subsidence took place, the result of which was that the old tertiary land surface was lowered so as to be again below sea level. This subsidence in combination with the forces set in motion by the climatic fluctutations in the Quaternary have supremely determined the landscapes in the southern part of Jutland. The supposition of later block movements advanced by *H. L. Heck* (1936) has been refuted by *E. Dittmer* (1941), who has proved that no such movements have taken place in North Friesland in Younger Pleistocene.

It should here be mentioned that the sea level has been exposed to enormous fluctuations in the course of the changing glacial and inter-glacial times. For instance, during the Würm Glaciation, the sea level was about 100 m. lower than now; at the beginning of the Post-Glacial time the lowering of the sea level was about 55—60 m., in the transition time to Boreal about 40 m., to Atlanticum about 17 m., to Subboreal about 4 m., and at the beginning of Subatlanticum the level of the sea was only about 2 m. lower than now. There is every reason to suppose that in Late-Glacial time the sea level has been subjected to a considerable rise, a process which has taken place in stages corresponding to the retirement of the inland ice. It is supposed that in Post-Glacial time a progressing, though declining rise of the sea level has taken place, perhaps interrupted by periods with a stagnation *(N. Kingo Jacobsen,* 1956). In this connection it is the conditions of the Late-Glacial time which offer a particular interest.

Superposed on the tertiary layers we find deposits from the three glaciations with intervening inter-glaciations. A brief summary of the results of the boring at Brodersmark gives a rather good impression of this even if the possibility exists, that the tertiary in question is a glacial flake, as mentioned by *L. Banke Rasmussen* (1958):

m. D. N. N.	Description D. G. U.	Interpretation
+ 0.94 to + 0.76	humus	salt-marsh deposits
+ 0.76 − + 0.29	clay of the foreland type	
+ 0.29 − + 0.04	heavy, dark clay	
+ 0.04 − − 0.06	peat	basis-peat, post-glacial
− 0.06 − − 0.21	coarse sand mixed with peat	
− 0.21 − − 3.06	sand, fine-grained varied grain-size yellow-brown	blown sand, Late Dryas time
− 3.06 − − 4.06	sand, very fine-grained uniform grain-size, yellow-brown	niveo-eolian and niveo-fluviatile sand from the time before the Allerød period
− 4.06 − − 4.56	sand, very fine-grained, light	
− 4.56 − − 5.06	do. do. with small, dark grains	
− 5.06 − − 6.36	do. do. with mica content	
− 6.36 − − 9.36	sand, very fine-grained uniform grain-size	fluvio-glacial deposits, Würm Glaciation
− 9.36 − −12.61	sand, medium size with a few pebbles, light grey	
−12.61 − −13.31	sand, stony	
−13.31 − −13.56	do. do. with a few clay lumps	
−13.56 − −14.46	boulder clay, grey, of a sandy character, with a few shell fragments in the uppermost part. Fluvio-glacial erosion, Eemian deposits on secondary locality	boulder clay, Riss Glaciation at the latest
−14.46 − −17.06	boulder clay, grey sandy, rather stony	
−17.06 − −21.46	boulder clay, crey, at − 21.31 m. D.N.N. with numerous pebbles	
−21.46 − −25.41	mica clay, brown, with a few shell fragments, among others Nucula sp.	tertiary mica clay
−25.41 − −32.06	mica clay, dark, greasy. At − 30.36 m. and − 31.16 m. D.N.N. with light, yellow-brown concretions	

Examinations of the Urstromtal of the Elbe and of the lower Ems valley have proved that these valleys, which are cut into the tertiary surface without regard to the ancient relief, have kept their appearance unchanged through all three glaciations, apart from unimportant shifts *(W. Dechend,* 1956). A similar development seems to have been the case of the Vidå valley.

At the end of the Riss Glaciation the melt-water rivers of the western Slesvig were assembled in one big Eider Urstromtal with outlet through the present Lister Dyb. Farther to the west it was a tributary to the Elbe Urstromtal. During the Second Inter-Glacial time the climate became again rather mild (temperate), and the sea level was but a few metres below the existing. A big, bifurcated inlet (the Eemian Sea) at that time stretched through the abovementioned Urstromtal from Lister Dyb, partly to the east into the Vidå valley, partly to the south to Husum between the old landgroup Sild — Føhr — Amrum and the present geest-border *(P. Woldstedt,* 1954). At that time the Eider valley was situated to the south of the land-group transgressed by the sea. The Eemian deposits start with sandy layers corresponding to the transgression phase and end with clay deposits in the regressive phase. The layers are grey-green and are characterized by a fauna from a somewhat warmer climate than the present. As reference horizon these deposits are of great value; however, in the greater part of the Vidå valley, the fluvio-glacial rivers from the Würm Glaciation have eroded into the underlying layers. According to *Dittmer* (1954) the orginal surface of the Eemian deposits is supposed to have been situated at a level of about − 5 m. D.N.N. As already mentioned, the erosion in the Vidå valley has been heavy, and Eemian deposits on primary locality are often totally lacking. The results of five borings immediately to the south of Tønder show that the Eemian deposits are found at a level of − 12 m. to − 16 m. D.N.N., at Dyrhus (2 km. east of Kærgård) − 7 m. D.N.N., at Rudbøl − 22 m. D.N.N.; three borings at Gl. Frederikskog show − 16 m., − 18 m. and − 23 m. D.N.N., *Sigurd Hansen* (1955). Thus, we have got a rather good impression of the powerful erosion which has taken place, and which in the central parts of the Vidå valley has been at least 20 m.

At the transition to Late-Glacial time the coastal line was situated at the Dogger Bank and the Jutland Bank. The changing sea level has caused new states of equilibrium for the rivers; however, in Pleni-Glacial time the sea has been situated at a distance of at least 100 km., and in this region the fall of the river terraces has been comparatively great, coinciding with a big discharge in summer.

The morphology of the late-glacial sub-surface (geest) in the Møgeltønder Kog (polder).

The following is an attempt to describe the morphology of the geest surface below Møgeltønder Kog. In support of this is given a schematical review of climatic conditions, soil conditions, dynamic forces (fluvio-glacial and eolian), the result of these forces (erosion and sedimentation) and an approximate indication of the changing sea level. Further is given an account of the effect of the different forces at various times. Finally, an attempt has been made of uniting these results into a total impression.

The effect of the Eemian Sea.

The most impressive feature in the terrain to the west of Møgeltønder is the rather high, marked geest cliff to the south of Bønderby; it has previously been ascribed to the sea in the Bronze Age. However, this cannot be the case, as at that time the level of the sea was situated about 3 m. below the existing. Nor can it be a question of a coastal cliff from the Late Middle Ages, considering that the upper shore line is situated at about + 1 m. D.N.N. and that the region of the whole Subatlanticum was an inner protected basin. It is more probable that the cliff has been formed by the Eemian Sea, which, it is true, did not reach higher levels than those of the Bronze Age sea. At this age, however, deposits existed from the Würm Glaciation and from Late-Glacial time which were not found at the time of the Eemian Sea. Therefore, it is probable that the cliff has continued below the present surface. However, Eemian deposits may hardly be found because of the fluvio-glacial erosion from the Würm which took place at these levels. In accordance with this, fluvio-glacial erosion may also have been contributary to the formation of the cliff mentioned. Especially in the melting phase of the Würm Glaciation, when the ice sheet retreated from the east coast of Jutland. Referring to the boring pag. 95 it is nevertheless probable that this effect is inferior to that of the Eemian Sea.

The effect of the solifluction.

In the terrain description the attention has been drawn to the extreme difference of the topography to the west and to the east

A-horizon

0,38 cm. b. s. →

B-horizon

0,61 cm. b. s. →

B-horizon

0,81 cm. b. s. →

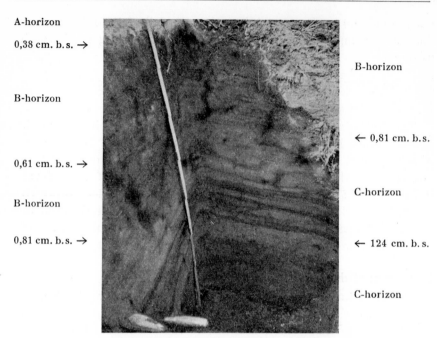

B-horizon

← 0,81 cm. b.s.

C-horizon

← 124 cm. b. s.

C-horizon

Fig. 2. Geest ridge of blown sand (Sødam II,8) podzolized and superposed by clay, cfr. description p. 101.

along the geest cliff, a difference which is mainly due to soli-fluction during the Late Dryas time. Also during Pleniglacial A a strong solifluction took place. However, the effects of this have no doubt been washed away by the melt-water during the high water levels in summer-time. The fact that the solifluction has especially taken place along the eastern half of the geest border is partly due to the materials of which the old morainic island is composed, partly to its terrain forms. To the west the Bønderby peninsula consists of marl and boulder clay, and at the same time the water-divide is placed directly above the geest cliff. It means that the area is mainly drained to the north, a direction which has been followed by the solifluction. The eastern part of the morainic isle, immediately to the west of Møgeltønder, is composed of gravel and sand, and the water-divide is situated somewhat farther to the north of the cliff. Both these factors have greatly favoured a con-siderable solifluction to the south. Consequently, an area of about 4 sq.km. with slided material is seen at this place. The contours offer a characteristic serrated picture, and the landscapes are flat-tened and dome-shaped. Apparently, the slidings have filled up the

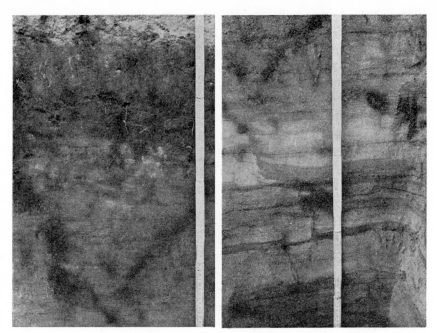

Fig. 3 A. Close-up of the B-horizon (Sødam II,8) 40 — 90 cm. below surface.
Fig. 3 B. Close-up of the C-horizon (Sødam II,8) 80 — 140 cm.
below surface.

terrain down to the level – 1 m. D.N.N. The greatest landslide has
taken place from Møgeltønder towards south-west, where it reaches
the previously mentioned central ridge, which is NW/SE oriented.
In the westernmost border of the map is seen a corresponding
sliding, which originates from a branch valley between Kannikhus
and the farm Brink; this farm is situated on a separate, small,
dome-shaped, morainic isle.

The effect of eolian action.

As appears from table II, a strong eolian action has been prevailing
during three periods: Pleniglacial B — Earliest Dryas, Early Dryas
and Late Dryas — Preboreal. However, it is necessary to treat the
first two mentioned jointly, as it has been impossible to indicate
any effect of the Bølling Interstage. There is an older period before
Allerød with prevailing wind direction NW and a younger period
after Allerød with prevailing wind direction WNW; the effect of
the eolian action is partly blow-outs, partly formation of dunes.
The grain size increases from the oldest to the youngest eolian
deposits: simultaneously, the wind-blown sand from the oldest pe-

riod and from the Arctic part of Late Dryas has no doubt been deposited together with sublimated snow evaporated later on (niveo-eolian deposits), *Edelman & Zandstra* (1956) and *Edelman & Maarleveld* (1958). Thereby, the older forms have been more levelled, as the sand, after the evaporation of the snow, is deposited in thin layers.

Older blown sand.

Considering the topography with blow-outs and ridges, longitudinal or irregular, in the direction NW/SE, and leaving out of account the solifluction from Late Dryas, just described, the existence appears partly of a big blow-out, partly of a characteristic ridge. The blow-out has been situated along the total border of the morainic isle and has a width of about 1½ km. The bottom of the blow-out must have been situated at the level about – 3,50 m. D.N.N. In this big U-shaped valley there has no doubt occasionally existed a dune topography in minor scale, which, however, for the above-mentioned reasons, has later on been smoothed out. To the south of the described blow-out is seen the above-mentioned ridge (the central ridge, direction NW/SE). It can be followed beyond the map up to and including the mound Husum at a distance of 2 km. south-east of Højer. Here it consists of comparatively coarse sand. It is therefore possible that the ridge has been formed in the latter part of the first eolian period (Older Dryas), in which the sand became coarser and the tendency to formation of ridges more pronounced. Only the boring at Pokkenbøl: II,70 is situated on this ridge. It should further be mentioned that the Pokkenbøl boring is one of the few places where the ground moraine from the Riss Glaciation has been met with (– 9,05 m. to – 14,30 m. D.N.N.)

Younger blown sand.

In Late Dryas and Preboreal another period arrives with big sand-drift, blow-out and formation of dunes. The wind-direction is WNW; the material is coarser and of varied grain size; often we find thin layers of fine, small-grained gravel *(Edelman & Maarleveld,* 1958). In the upper part are found distinct cryoturbations, refer fig. 2 and fig. 3 and the following description of the profile at Sødam: II, 8. Surface level: + 1.23 m. D.N.N. (p. 101).

The whole of this profile must be taken as younger blown sand; according to the profile p. 156, the Allerød horizon is found at – 1,07 m. D.N.N., below which we meet the older blown sand.

m. below surface	Description
0.00 to 0.23	clay
0.23 – 0.25	A_0, dark-grey humus layer
0.25 – 0.38	A_1, bleached sand
0.38 – 0.81	B-horizon, partly stratified, cryoturbations. Dark »chimneys« 1 to 3 cm. thick, a single one is 20 cm. broad, filled with black illuvation of humus.
0.61	A stripe ½ cm. broad with small-grained gravel. It is characteristic of the whole upper part of the profile to 0.81 m. below surface that small-grained gravel of a size of about 1 mm. are found in big quantities.
0.81 – 1.24	Purer sand, fine to medium-grained, light yellow-brown with horizontal deposits of coarser grained sand. In two horizons: 1.10 m. and 1.23 m. to 1.24 m. below surface were found dark-brown ferrugineous illuvation layers.
1.24 – 1.60	Grey-green sand, medium-grained with a few horizontal layers, for instance in 1.33 m. below surface.

The younger blown sand has completely dominated the working-out of the landscape in details on the central ridge and on the plateau to the south of this. The result is a smalldomed terrain, which on the plateau forms a small parabolic dune with a height of about 1,5 m. Further, the wind has caused blow-outs in the remainders of the big blow-out before Allerød along the geest-border, remainders which had not been filled up by solifluction in Late Dryas. This has led to the formation of the north-western symmetrical basin and the south-eastern basin asymmetrically shaped by the solifluction. The central part of the latter and the tongue towards WNW must be of eolian origin in the same period.

Post-Glacial erosion.

In Subboreal the western part of the area was transgressed by the sea (the Cardium transgression about 2.000 B.C.); at that time the sea level was about − 3.50 D.N.N. The N/S oriented gully to the north-western basin may have its origin in that time. At the transition to Sutatlanticum about 700 B.C. the sea level has risen to about − 2,25 m. D.N.N.; consequently, the gullies and creeks created by the sea in connection with the tidal streams in the south-western basin were then active and drained off the north-western basin. However, this basin has been well protected by the central ridge (NW/SE) and is mainly filled up with peat formations. When the sea covered the area in the Middle Ages, before the diking took place in 1556, the peat has been superposed by a clay layer of 20—50 cm. The south-eastern basin has been in connection with the sea through the northern meandering channel of the Vidå, seen on the map, and which has functioned as tidal stream at the end of Post-Glacial time. Therefore, in this basin exclusively fine-grained sand has been deposited, starting with fine-sand at the bottom and ending with fat basin clay apart from the ridge (fine-grained sand) which closes the basin and which is at the same time a sort of levee from the Vidå channel.

Genesis of the region.

As a result of these examinations, the following landscape genesis can be summarized: Already in the Riss Glaciation the Vidå valley acted as a fluvio-glacial valley. In the higher lying parts is sporadically found ground moraine from the same glaciation with under-lying fluvio-glacial deposits, perhaps Tertiary. During the subsequent inter-glacial time the Vidå valley is exposed to a transgression by the Eemian Sea, which has extended far to the east and to the south, and which has originally formed the characteristic geest cliffs along the morainic isles. These cliffs have further been exposed to fluvio-glacial erosion at the melting phase of the land-ice from East Jutland. The gradient of the cliffs depends on the solifluction, especially during the Late-Glacial time (Late Dryas). During the Würm Glaciation the Vidå valley has functioned as a fluvio-glacial valley for big parts of the outwash-plain of Tinglev. At Tønder there has been a narrows; the discharge has been big, and at the same time the fall of the fluviatile terraces has been comparatively great, as at that time the sea level was 100 m. lower than now. Consequently, the fluvio-glacial river has cut down to a great depth (at least 20 m.), which appears from borings to Eemian deposits on primary locality. During the first part of the Würm Glaciation (Pleniglacial A) the climate has been cold and oceanic with violent snow-storms prevailing; during the second part (Pleniglacial B) somewhat more continental, cold and dry with prevailing eolian action and wind-direction from NW. The fluvio-glacial rivers have formed a braided system with sand and gravel deposits, which in the dry winter-time have supplied material to

the sand-drift. At the beginning of the Late-Glacial time the conditions are unchanged; however, at the transition to the warmer
Allerød period the character of the landscape changes. Permafrost
and solifluction disappear, which means greater regularity of flow
in the Vidå; simultaneously, the supply of the material is lesser
and more fine-grained. At first, the Vidå formed a meandering
pattern, main channel with high levees, as a transitional stage to
the cutting-down of a trunk-stream, where the rest of the former
system is left back empty. This development was caused by the
fact, among others, that the river adapted itself to a new state
of equilibrium and, therefore, was cutting down into the former
fluviatile terrace. This was partly due to a reduced distance to
the sea caused by the considerable retreat of the inland-ice. The
previous system was completely put out of action, and the abandoned
channels were filled with peat. At the same time the vegetation has
spread, and the forest has immigrated (birch and pine). At that
time a big, U-shaped blow-out valley with a longitudinal ridge
was situated to the south of the Bønderby peninsula; the ridge
was running almost parallel to the cliff of the morainic isle. The
existence of this ridge is proved by the presence of podsolic profiles at the level – 1 m. to – 2,9 m. D.N.N., refer table II. Besides,
it makes itself distinctly known in the central ridge (NW/SE).

The terrace surface, mentioned in the topographical description,
has been formed by fluvio-glacial deposits superposed by niveo-
eolian sand along the rivers of the braided system in Pleniglacial B.
However, the presence of the terrace surface was predetermined
by high-lying morainic deposits from the Riss Glaciation, which had
the effect that this part of the fluvio-glacial valley only has functioned at extraordinarily high water levels in the Vidå. In addition,
the surface has been further raised and worked out by eolian action
in Earliest, Early and Late Dryas time and by solifluction especially
in Late Dryas time.

From the boring at Rudbøl it appears that the melt-water has
eroded as far down as to at least the level – 22 m. D.N.N.; to the
south of Møgeltønder the erosion has reached the level – 13 m. to
– 17 m. D.N.N. and to the south of Tønder – 12 m. to – 16 m. D.N.N.
Against erosion at these levels the terrace surface, as just mentioned, has been protected by deposits from the Riss Glaciation,
the surface levels of which are as follows: Pokkenbøl: – 8,50 m.
D.N.N.; Herredsvejen: – 9,81 m. D.N.N. and Brodersmark: – 13,56 m.
D.N.N. The levels of the uppermost layers of the fluvio-glacial, fine-

grained deposits in the valley to the south of the terrace surface are, to the south of Møgeltønder: – 8,72 m.; at Sødam: – 9,27 m. and at Brodersmark & Rudbøl: – 9,36 m. D.N.N. On the terrace the uppermost fluvio-glacial fine-grained deposits are situated at about level – 5 m. to – 6 m. D.N.N. Consequently, the fluvio-glacial deposits from the Würm Glaciation have here only a thickness of 2½ to 4 m., and they are found at a higher level than those situated along the southern border of the terrace. The fluvio-glacial deposits here must have their origin in the melting-phase of the land-ice in eastern Jutland, where the water level in the Vidå must have been highest. In evidence of this but one clay layer of fluvio-glacial origin is met with on the terrace, whereas two layers are found in some places along the southern border of the terrace. Borings in the abandoned meandering channels show that the borders of these are very steep, and that the bottom is situated at about – 7 m. to – 7½ m. D.N.N. These channels are filled with peat up to a level of about – 3,75 m. D.N.N.; on top of this are found fine-grained sediments. It is probable that these channels have been meandering main channels in the latter part of Early Dryas, abandoned in the Allerød time and filled with about 3½ m. of peat. The trunk-stream from this time has at Ny Frederikskog cut at least down to – 13 m. D.N.N., which appears from the above-mentioned boring-line published in 1956. The establishment of these sparse facts leads to the conclusion that in Early Dryas the Vidå valley was in this region situated at the level – 9 m. D.N.N. On account of the ground-moraine, which at Brodersmark was deposited on a high, protruding knot of tertiary mica clay, a terrace surface was situated to the north of this. To a level of about – 5 m. D.N.N. fluvio-glacial deposits from the end of the Würm Glaciation were found superposed by (niveo-fluviatile and) niveo-eolian deposits with a feebly domed relief, dominated by the central ridge and by a big blow-out valley along the cliff of the geest. The levels of this surface have ranged from – 3,75 m. (the topmost part of the peat from Allerød in the abandoned channels) to –1.07 m. D.N.N. (the lowermost podsoled horizon, Sødam, II,8). In Late Dryas the big slidings from the morainic isle to the west of Møgeltønder first took place, followed by the blow-out, described above, of the north-western basin and the south-eastern basin as well as the formation of the dune topography on the terrace surface to the south of the central ridge and upon this ridge, i. e. the final working-out of the surface which on account of vegetation is rather stable until the formation of the Post-Glacial basis-peat. The erosion of the south-western part of the terrace surface during the Post-Glacial transgression has already been described in outline.

LITERATURE *A further list for additional studies is given in the article of H. Kuhlman (p. 119).*

Dechend, W. (1954) : Eustatische und tektonische Probleme des Quartärs im südlichen Nordseeraum. Geol. en Mijnbouw, N. S. 16, 195–200.

Dechend, W. & Sindowski, K.-H. (1956): Die Gliederung des Quartärs im Raum Krummhörn-Dollart (Ostfriesland) und die geologische Entwicklung der Unteren Ems. Geol. Jahrb. 71, 461–490. Hannover.

Dittmer, E. (1954): Interstadiale Torfe in würmeiszeitlichen Schmelzwassersanden Nordfrieslands. Eiszeitalter und Gegenwart 4/5, 172–175. Öhringen.

Edelman, C. H. & Maarleveld, G. C. (1949): De Asymmetrische Dalen van de Veluwe. Tijdschr. Kon. Ned. Aardr. Gen. 2. Ser. LXVI, 2. Leiden.

Edelman, C. H. & Maarleveld, G. C. (1958): Pleistozän-geologische Ergebnisse der Bodenkartierung in den Niederlanden. Geol. Jahrb. 73, 639–684. Hannover.

Edelman, C. H. & Zandstra, K. J. (1956): Niveo-äolische Sande im Saargebiet. Kon. Nederl. Akad. v. Wetenschappen. Proc. B. Phys. Sci. 59, 253–258.

Fisk, H. N. (1944): Geological Investigation of the Alluvial Valley of the Lower Mississippi River. War Dept. Corps of Engineers U. S. Army.

Gross, Hugo (1954): Das Alleröd-Interstadial als Leithorizont der letzten Vereisung in Europa und Amerika. Eiszeitalter und Gegenwart 4/5, 189–209. Öhringen.

Hansen, Sigurd: Foreløbig rapport over geologiske, hydrologiske og grundvandskemiske undersøgelser i Tøndermarsken. Maj–juni 1955. (Upubl.).

Heck, H.-L. (1937): Die nordfriesische neuzeitliche Küstensenkung als Folge diluvialer Senkung. Jahrb. d. Preuss. Geol. Landesanst. 1936: 57, 48–84. Berlin.

Iversen, Johs. (1947): Plantevækst, Dyreliv og Klima i det senglaciale Danmark. Geol. Fören. Förhandl. 69:1, 67–68. Stockholm.

Jacobsen, N. Kingo (1956): Jordbundsundersøgelser i Tøndermarsken. En metodisk redegørelse med relation til den postglaciale udvikling. Geogr. Tidsskr. 55, 106–146. Medd. fra Skal.-Lab. XV. København.

Kuhlman, H. (1957 a): Sandflugt og klitdannelse. Geogr. Tidsskr. 56, 1–19. Medd. fra Skal.-Lab. XVI København.

Kuhlman, H. (1957 b): Kornstørrelser i klit- og strandsand. Geogr. Tidsskr. 56, 20–56. Medd. fra Skal.-Lab. XVI. København.

Kuhlman, H.: (1958): Quantitative measurements of aeolian sand transport. Geogr. Tidsskr. 57. 51–74. Medd. fra Skal.-Lab. XVI. København.

Maarleveld, G. C. (1949): Over de erosiedalen van de Veluwe. Tijdschr. Kon. Ned. Aardr. Gen. 2. Ser. LXVI, 2. Leiden.

Pons, L. J. (1957): De Geologie, de Bodenvorming en de waterstaatkundige Ontwikkeling van het Land van Maas en Waal en, een Gedulte van het Rijk. van Nijmegen.'S-Gravenhage.

Rasmussen, Leif Banke (1958): Det maritime ungtertiær ved Sæd. Medd. fra Dansk Geol. Foren. 14:1, pp. 1–28. København.

Veenenbos, J. S. (1954): Het Landschap van zuidoostelijk Friesland en zijn ontstaan. Boor en Spade VII, 117–122. Wageningen.

Woldstedt, P. (1954): Saaleeiszeit, Warthestadium und Weichseleiszeit in Norddeutschland. Eiszeithalter u. Gegenwart 4/5, 34–38. Öhringen.

Table II.

| | Würm Glaciation | | Late-Glacial time | | | | | Post-Glacial time continued → | |
| | Pleniglacial A. | Pleniglacial B. | Old Dryas time | | | Allerød time | Late Dryas time | Preboreal | Boreal |
			Earliest Dryas time	Bölling time	Early Dryas time				
Temperature ° C.	<0	<0	−3	+2	−1	+5	+1	+4	+6
Precipitation	+	−	−	(−)	−	+	+	−	+
Permafrost	+	+	+	+	+	−	+	−	−
Solifluction	+	(+)	(+)	(+)	(+)	−	+	−	−
Fluvio-glacial erosion	F	LE	(LE)	(F)		F	LE	(LE)	F
Fluvio-glacial deposits	Gravel + niveo-fluviatile sed.	Sand and gravel + niveo-fluviatile sed.	Sand	Fine-grained sand	sand→clay	Peat and fine-grained sediments	Gravel	Fine-grained sand→clay	Fine-grained sediments
Eolian erosion		B	B		B		B	B (local)	
Eolian deposits		Blown sand and loess, niveo-eolian sed.	O		O		Y	Y	
River phases	1	1	2	3	3	4	1−2	3	4
Sea-level ab.	−100 m						−55 m. to ab. −60 m.	−40 m.	−17 m.

F = Formation of erosion valleys.
LE = Cutting-in of the rivers, lateral erosion.
B = Blow-out depressions.
O = Older blown sand.
Y = Younger blown sand.

1 = Braided river system.
2 = Braided river system with various kinds of channels in a fixed system.
3 = Strongly meandering main channel with high levees.
4 = Cutting-down of a trunk stream; the rest of the former system is left back empty.

Compiled after
P. Woldstedt, L. J. Pons, J. Iversen,
C. H. Edelman and G. C. Maarleveld.

On Identification of Blown Sand.

An example from the salt-marsh area at Tønder.

By Hans Kuhlman.

In 1958 six representative samples of sand were collected from 2 profiles in the soil surface of the salt-marsh at Tønder; further one sample of sandy moraine material was drawn to be used like a "scale material". The sampling was done at the request of Niels Kingo Jacobsen, cf. Geografisk Tidsskrift volumes 58 p. 143 and 55 p. 106—146. The purpose of the collecting was by means of analysis of the sand texture to contribute to the solution of problems concerning identification of deposition environment of the sand, cf. *Jacobsen, N. K.* (1956) p. 119 and 130. Three of the sand samples were collected in a ditch immediately north of Pokkenbøl Gård (west of Møgeltønder), and three samples derive from the ditch at a field road which passes in the direction north west from Ved Åen, and which is situated north of the farm Sødam Gd. The moraine material was taken from a shallow boring in a field 800 m. due north of Nr. Sødam. The three localities mentioned are indicated in fig. 1 in this periodical, p. 93 *(Jacobsen, N. K.)*; in the following they are called Pokkenbøl, Sødam, and Møgeltønder S. respectively.

Profile description.

At the locality Sødam a profile of a depth of about 1.5 m. was dug in the roadside ditch; at this place the surface was situated at a level of 102 cm. above DNN (Danish Ordnance Datum). The topmost 23 cm. below the vegetation were composed of basin-clay; underneath was found a layer of bleached sand of a thickness of 10 cm. with an underlying layer of an undisturbed podsol-horizon. From the uniform bleached sand was collected the sample: SøA,ca at the level 74 cm. (DNN). The precipitation zone below the bleached sand consisted of homogeneous, brown-coloured sand without pebbles and with no distinct traces of stratification and of lamellation. The precipitation was modest, only consisting in a colouring of the sand; however, this colouring appeared with varying strength, the cut showing light circles and finger-shaped designs, which can admirably be represented by fig. 8, *Dücker & Maarleveld*, 1958, p. 229; their figure shows a cut in a blown-sand cover. In the hard-pan-like zone, at a depth of 68 cm. was collected a sample which has been named SøB. The raw sand without any precipitation began at a depth of 118 cm.; to all appearance, it was structure-less and without pebbles, with a yellowish colour. At a depth of 143 cm. (—41 cm. DNN) the sample: SøC was collected.

In 1955 Danmarks Geologiske Undersøgelse has executed, in the vicinity of the trial locality Sødam, a boring which proved the existence of an order of the strata in the surface homologous to the stratification described above. This boring was continued to a greater depth and proved that at a depth of 230 cm. (—107 cm. DNN) the C-horizon was replaced by a new podsol-horizon, which at a depth of 240 cm. passed into sand with a few pebbles. The two orders of stratification from Sødam show that below the clay is found a sand-layer of a thickness of a few metres; this sand-layer is uniform and almost without structures, with the exception of two distinct podsol-zones. One is tempted to draw an immediate conclusion of analogy to the descriptions of blown-sand covers which have been published by *Dücker & Maarleveld*, 1958.

At Pokkenbøl too was dug a profile in the surface of a depth of 1.5 m. The visual general impression was identical with the one which we had got at Sødam. Below a layer of 60 cm. of clay were 10 cm. of bleached sand, somewhat discoloured by clay which had been washed down. From the bleached sand, the A-layer, was collected the sample PoA at a depth of 65 cm. (level +12 cm. DNN). The precipitation zone, the B-layer, had a thickness of 65 cm. and consisted of brown sand, structure-less and without pebbles. The sample PoB was collected from this sand at —21 cm. DNN. The raw sand, the C-layer, resembled the corresponding material from Sødam; the sample PoC originates from a depth of 145 cm. of this material.

For comparison with the above-mentioned samples a sample was taken from the geest material from Møgeltønder S. at a depth of 92 cm. (—32 cm. DNN) below a clay-layer of 80 cm. The sample was rather dirty owing to infiltration from a peat-layer at a depth of 80—82 cm. At a few metres to the north of the locality the geest reaches the surface and makes its appearance at this place as well as in our small boring as a stony moraine. It will be seen that within the short distance between the localities Sødam and Møgeltønder S. the material and the level are considerably altered.

Procedure of analyses.

The laboratory work on the sand samples was concentrated on the determination of their distributions of grain sizes, whereas the other textural qualities: shape, surface texture, etc. only were subjected to an inexact examination. Therefore, in the following pages the attention is concentrated on the sizes of the particles.

After a stay in a solution of 30 % hydrogen peroxide, the samples collected were given a parboiling, the plant residues were skimmed off, whereafter a suitable quantity of sediments was thoroughly rinsed in a sieve with a size of meshes of 60 mu. The material which was washed through the sieve was collected, and its weight was determined without further analysis. The retained sand was, in a dry state, passed through sieves with the following sizes of meshes: 2000 μ (— 1.00 φ), 1000 μ (0.00 φ), 750 μ (0.415 φ), 500 μ (1.00 φ), 400 μ (1.32 φ), 300 μ (1.74 φ), 250 μ (2.00 φ), 200 μ (2.32 φ), 150 μ (2.74 φ), 120 μ (3.06 φ), 100 μ (3.32 φ) and 60 μ (4.06 φ).

The weight quantities which had been fractioned out by means of these sieves were distributed in cumulative frequencies, "bigger than". Each sieve-fraction was microscoped, during which procedure the shape, the roundness and the polish of the grains were examined. We have previously given an account of the classification, the scale and the statistics which we usually employ. We refer to the prescriptions given by *Krumbein & Pettijohn* and by *Bagnold.* In order to facilitate the comprehension of the following text, some comments are given here on the applied statistics. The results of the wet sieving and of the dry sieving are represented in three different sorts of diagrams. The abscissa of the first diagram-type (fig. 1) was logarithmically divided, its ordinate was linear; the abscissa indicated the grain-size, the ordinate the cumulative frequency. The other type (fig. 2) was normal probability paper with a linear abscissa, which was divided into *Krumbein*'s units. The last diagram-type (fig. 3) was the one described by *Bagnold;* here the ordinate was log. N., where N. is the weight percentage, retained between two sieves, divided by the logarithm to the proportion between the size of meshes of the two sieves. The abscissa indicated the grain-sizes in the logarithm scale.

From the two types of cumulative distribution curves the following parameters were read: the three quartiles Q_1, Md, Q_3 and the deciles P_{10} and P_{90}. Md, the median value, represents the average of the distribution. The statistical deviation $\dfrac{Q_{3\varphi}-Q_{1\varphi}}{2}$ and $\dfrac{Q_{3\varphi}-Q_{1\varphi}}{2(P_{90\varphi}-P_{10\varphi})}$ were chosen as the expression of the sedimentological sorting, the parameters being expressed in φ units; refer *Kuhlman* 1957 b.

In order to make it possible to determine the parameters, the distribution curve sketched in *Bagnold*'s diagram must form a figure of a definite nature, comparable with a pair of compasses. To the right and to the left of the modal grain-class, characterized by the concept Pd, the other grain-frequencies must decrease at two constant rates of speed, which differ from each other, in the fine and in the coarse addition of material. The decrease of the coarse grains is represented by the coefficient:c, that of the fine grains by the coefficient:s.

The aeolian separation-processes.

By the term of separation is understood the dispersion of the elements of the sediment which takes place during the transport; if this has gone on for a long time or over big distances it can be said that the "separation-route and the separation-time" have been long, the sediment thereby having obtained "a mature sorting", whict reflects the homogenizing effect of the separation. It is open to question whether the separation is specific to a given kind of transport. Therefore, it is unknown whether one can always determine the physical environment which was reigning during the deposition of the sediment, if only the texture and the composition of the mass is known. In some cases the determination of the environment is easy, for instance for moraine material; in other cases it is apparently impossible, cf. *Udden* 1914, *Pettijohn* 1957 and *Sindowski* 1958.

As far back as the time of *Udden* a great importance has been attached to the distribution of the grain sizes of sand as a contribution to the determination of its sedimentary environment, because the grain sizes gave a picture of the forces which had been active there. However, it looks as if different environments may produce identical grain distributions, cf. *Sindowski*'s outline from 1958. Such a convergence is especially known for dune-sand and beach-sand, cf. *Pettijohn* 1957 p. 590—592, *Kuhlman* 1957 b, *Mason & Folk* 1958.

The problem of diagnosis is rendered further difficult thereby that the terminology concerning the sedimentary environment is unprecise and illogical from a geo-dynamic point of view. The environments are nearly always designated according to the general geo-morphological usage. This may give rise to a certain confusion; for instance: "beach sand" stands both for aquatic and aeolian sorting; consequently, the resemblance to "dune sand" is natural enough.

Let us try to consider "blown sand" — "dune sand" from a geo-dynamic point of view; below we are speaking, for the sake of convenience, of almost ball-shaped quartz grains. In the aeolian environment it is possible to distinguish between the following kinds of transport: suspension, saltation, creeping and landslides (for instance in the case of lee dune-slopes). Each of the three first mentioned kinds of transport is, at a given velocity interval, inseparably bound up with definite grain dimensions, *Inman* 1949, *Bagnold* 1954 and *Sundborg* 1955 and 1956. For winds below gale force, grains smaller than 0.10 mm. are transported suspended in the air and are not deposited until the terminal velocity of fall exceeds the buoyancy, Stoke's law. Grains bigger than 0.10 mm. most often saltate or "creep" (pushed by the saltating grains). The saltation and the creeping is bound to the surface. Saltation grains are able to move creeping material having six times its own diameter; however, in return the creeping is much slower.

The diameter of a saltating grain is directly proportional to the square of the smallest wind-force required for keeping alive the movement, cf. *Kuhlman* 1958, p. 54. This means that a small decrease of the wind-force will cause the exclusion of many grainsizes from the saltation material. Under aeolian transport the grains about 0.10—0.20 mm. are almost always in a jumping movement, whereas grains of a size of about 1 mm. but rarely reach beyond the "crawling stade". A pronounced separation of the material is liable to take place owing to the different kinds of transport.

Bagnold has experimentally examined the grain separation in the course of the aeolian transport. In his diagram the grain distribution of the saltation material is represented by the above-mentioned "compasses"; it is possible to describe the creeping material too by this characteristic figure.

The aeolian material subjected to long-time influences shows a coarseness coefficient which is very close to —9. This drop of coarser elements during the action of the wind has been demonstrated in nature in recent processes, cf. *Harris* 1957 and 1958, *Kuhlman* 1957 and *Mason & Folk* 1958.

It is near at hand to ask whether aquatic transport may not give the same grain distributions as those proved in blown sand by *Bagnold,* whose results can be summarized as follows: In aeolian sand extra-modal, coarse material only seldom appears. In stream-ing water grains between 0.15 mm. and 0.50 mm. require almost the same stream-force in order just to be transported, cf. *Å. Sund-borg* 1956 p. 169—201. This means that in the grain-interval men-tioned a separation only with difficulty takes place in a water-stream, whereas in a current of air it is easily realized. However, oscillating water-streams seem to be able to produce as fine separa-tions as those created by the wind, cf. *Sindowski* 1958.

The natural sorting by the wind often interferes with other pro-cesses, the theoretical scheme thereby being distorted. During the wanderings of dunes, landslides, on a large as well as on a small scale, often happen, partly at lee-slopes, partly at erosion-walls. As a result of the landslides, coarse grains are concentrated at the foot of slopes; high-lying sand-material is further homogenized, cf. *Bagnold* 1954 p. 140 and *Kuhlman* 1957 p. 38—39. In humid regions the humidity of the sand causes an alteration of the move-ment thresholds; the fine sand will be hardly as mobile, cf. *Sund-borg* 1956 p. 179 and *Kuhlman* 1957 p. 45—50.

The material of the aeolian environment can be dynamically classified as follows; suspension- (dust and loess), saltation-, creep-ing-, residual- (aeolian pavement-) and landslides-material. Each of the five groups may have either an arid or a humid character. It will be seen that the terms "blown sand" and "dune material" are ambiguous notions.

Description of the sand samples.

In table 1. are shown selected, characteristic grain-size para-meters, read from the normally drawn distribution curves, fig. 1. In table 2 are indicated the same parameters; however, they have been determined by means of fig. 2, which shows the grain distri-butions of the seven samples marked out on probability paper. Homologous values in the two tables deviate at highest 0,03 units from each other.

From fig. 2 it appears that none of the samples was evidently bi-modal or poly-modal. With the exception of the sample from Møgeltønder S. they have a pronounced tendency towards a Gauss

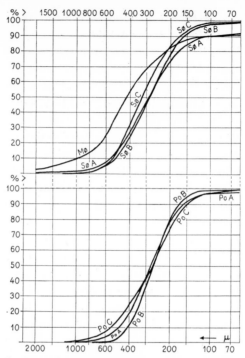

Fig. 1. The destributions of grain sizes in the seven samples of sediment from the salt-marsh area at Tønder. The abscissa is the log. grain diameter in mu, the ordinate shows cumulative weight percentage. The marking of the curves is explained in the text.

distribution in relation to the φ scale in the interval $0\varphi - 3\varphi$; the diverging distribution among the fine grains is due to secondary material infiltrated with water. With the applied sieves the sand showed a monomodal grain distribution, which seems to be in equilibrium with the ancient sedimentological forces.

The variation range offers a certain interest by virtue of the extreme values by which it is marked. In the present case the maximum grain diameter has importance as an aid at the determination of the nature of the sand, whereas the minimum grain size, which it is almost impossible to determine, does not offer any interest. The sand from Pokkenbøl and from Sødam did not contain grains larger than 2 mm., whereas it was accidental that the moraine material did not contain cobbles. The absolute lack of granules and pebbles may be interpreted to the effect that the wind has been active. The content in the sand of particles <0.06 mm. is, as far as the layers below the bleached sand are concerned, less than 1 %.

Table 1.

Sample	Md		Q_1		Q_3		P_{10}		P_{90}	
	μ	φ	μ	φ	μ	φ	μ	φ	μ	φ
Mø	422	1.25	600	0.74	255	1.97	1000	0.00	110	3.19
SøA	282	1.83	405	1.30	192	2.38	550	0.86	109	3.20
SøB	284	1.82	395	1.34	208	2.27	505	0.99	157	2.67
SøC	320	1.64	433	1.21	230	2.12	530	0.92	168	2.57
PoA	276	1.86	370	1.43	206	2.28	475	1.07	159	2.65
PoB	264	1.92	338	1.57	209	2.26	412	1.28	171	2.55
PoC	270	1.89	395	1.34	199	2.33	562	0.83	150	2.74

Table 3 shows the sorting ($QD\varphi$ and $Kq\varphi$) and the symmetry ($Skq\varphi$) of the samples, calculated on the basis of the parameters noted. $Kq\varphi$, kurtosis may be called the sorting of second degree; it indicates the proportion between the quartile-sorting, $QD\varphi$, and the range between 1st and 9th decile; its normal value is 0.26.

As could be expected, the moraine material has a moderate sorting (0.6 and 0.2) obliquely distributed around an "average grain size" of about 0.4 mm.

The three sand samples from Sødam have almost the same mean value 0.3 mm., and their quartile sorting is about 0.5 with a symmetry, or almost. The central grain size of the sand from Pokkenbøl is close to 0.27 mm. in the three samples. The quartile sorting varies from 0.35 to 0.50, the B-horizon being the best sorted. Of all the six sand samples only SøA is distinctly anormal. The "average grain sizes" and the parameters which have been found must be characterized as exceptional for monomodal sand, cf. *Sindowski* 1958, p. 236.

Figure 3 and table 4 show grain distributions described by means of *Bagnold*'s method. It is remarkable that his parameters only with difficulty can be determined, because the distribution curve has absolutely not the expected form, cf. also *Kuhlman* 1957b. The divergence from the hypothetical corresponds to the approximate Gauss distribution which has been observed, and which is seen in fig. 2, cf. fig. 34, *Bagnold* 1954 p. 117. However, from fig. 3 clearly appears the poor sorting in modal grain classes.

The microscopy of the sand showed the following conditions: in the samples from Pokkenbøl and Sødam the greater part of the grains bigger than 0.30 mm. were well rounded and half-mat, whereas smaller grains were shiny and edged. The uncorroded grain structure was predominant in all sieve-fractions from the

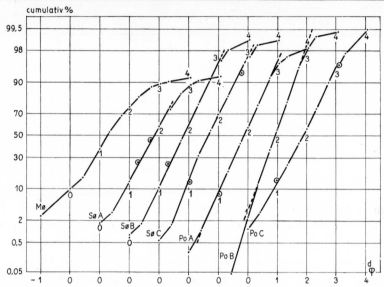

Fig. 2. Size compositions of the sediments that were pictured in fig. 1, the cumutative weight percentage is plotted on logarithmic probability paper, abscissa shows grain sizes in Krumbein phi-scale. For each curve the abscissa is moved in accordance with figures given.

Table 2.

Sample	Md φ	Q_1 φ	Q_3 φ	P_{10} φ	P_{90} φ
Mø	1.25	0.70	1.98	0.01	3.20
SøA	1.83	1.32	2.38	0.86	3.23
SøB	1.82	1.37	2.26	0.97	2.67
SøC	1.65	1.23	2.13	0.89	2.56
PoA	1.88	1.45	2.29	1.07	2.67
PoB	1.92	1.58	2.26	1.29	2.56
PoC	1.88	1.34	2.34	0.86	2.75

geest material; further, it was striking to see that the sand from the C-horizons in the finest sieves contained considerable quantities of light mica flakes.

Discussion of the measuring results.

The unidentified sand was surely not mature aeolian saltation-material and creeping-material; however, there is no observation which excludes the diagnosis: wind-sediment. If it is here a question of aeolian material the separation-time must have been short, and it must be classified as creeping material with a residual character. Unfortunately, we have still but a poor knowledge of

Table 3.

Sample	QD$_\varphi$	Skq$_\varphi$	Kq$_\varphi$
Mø	0.62	+ 0.11	0.19
SøA	0.54	+ 0.02	0.23
SøB	0.46	− 0.01	0.27
SøC	0.46	+ 0.02	0.28
PoA	0.42	0.00	0.27
PoB	0.35	− 0.01	0.27
PoC	0.50	− 0.05	0.26

dune material having glacial deposits as mother material; nor do we know enough about the aeolian separation processes in connection with landslides and humidity cohesion.

The sand cannot be marine or lacustric, because, cf. *Kingo Jacobsen* 1956, the transgression did not reach the examined localities until after the beginning of the Bronze Age; this means, if marine, that afterwards there could not be sufficient time for creating two undisturbed podsol-horizons. Nor can the sand have been deposited by the river Vidåen, as the depth-researches carried out by *Kingo Jacobsen* in these localities show that no fossil ravines are found in the geest below the alluvium. This leaves two possible diagnosis: either it is a question of glacio-fluviatile sand from the Ice Age, or it is niveo-aeolian from late-glacial time, cf. *Edelman & Maarleveld* 1958 p. 665—668. The distribution of the grain sizes speaks in favour of fluviatile sand, because it is monomodal, approximate Gauss-normal and because the modal grain classes between 0.15 mm. and 0.50 mm. are equal; there is here a moderate quartile sorting of 0.4, and kurtosis is almost normal. The even sorting about 0.3 mm. is typical of streaming water, because the critical stream-force varies but little for the above-mentioned modal grain sizes, cf. *Sundborg* 1956 p. 197. If it is a question of aeolian deposits it is strange that *Bagnold*'s diagram dit not allow a reliable determination of the parameters applied by him. The statistical probability of encountering a distribution deviating from *Bagnold*'s distribution is unknown; however, studies in literature seem to indicate that it is but small.

Conclusion:

On the basis of the knowledge which we now possess we are able to give the following exposé of the facts speaking in favour

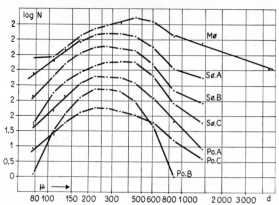

Fig. 3. The seven samples of sandy sediments demonstrated by means of Bag-nold-diagram for size analysis. The abscissa is the log. grain diameter in mu, the ordinate shows logarithmic weight percentage per unit in the abscissa scale. For each curve the ordinate is shifted in accordance with the figures given.

of and those speaking against the supposition that the sand collected at Pokkenbøl and at Sødam had been deposited by the wind. In favour of this supposition speak the following facts:

1) The unevenly hilly morphology of the geest surface below the alluvium in the region in question.

2) Probably the region has not been exposed to a marine trans-gression in the period between Older Dryas and the Bronze Age.

3) The cut structure almost free of stratification which appeared at the digging of the surface profiles.

4) The presence of undisturbed podsol-horizons, the precipitation layers of which showed patterns of finger-shaped and circle-shaped spots, cf. *Dücker & Maarleveld* 1958.

5) The sand was free of granules and pebbles.

The following circumstances speak against the above mentioned supposition:

a) The grain-size distribution of the sand.

b) The presence of mica flakes in the fine sieve-fractions.

The reason why we have given here the result of this "torso"-like examination is to expose a problem which offers the possibilities of unprejudiced considerations on an interesting "sedimentological paternity case".

Table 4.

Sample	$\dfrac{Pd}{\mu}$	s	—c
Mø	?	?	ca 1.5
SøA	282	3.5	3
SøB	260	5	4
SøC	?	?	ca 4.5
PoA	300	4	4.5
PoB	?	?	ca 8.5
PoC	276	3.5	3

RELEVANT LITERATURE

The following list contains more literary works than those used for the elaboration of this paper, because we consider it useful to give a guidance on the essential sources for additional studies of aeolian sediments. Abbreviations:

D.G.U.   Danmarks Geologiske Undersøgelse, København.
G.A.   Geografiska Annaler, Stockholm.
G.J.   Geologischen Jahrbuch. Geologischen Landesanstalten der Bundes-republik Deutschland, Hannover.
G.T.   Geografisk Tidsskrift, København.
J.S.P.   Journal of Sedimentary Petrology, (Tulsa, Oklahoma), Menasha, Wisconsin.
P.R.S.L.a   Proceedings of the Royal Society of London. Series A. London.

Bagnold, R. A. (1937): The size-grading of sand by wind. P.R.S.L.a 163 p. 250–264.
  – (1938): The measurement of sand storms. P.R.S.L.a 167 p. 282–291.
  – (1951): The movement of a cohesionless granular bed by fluid over it. British Journal of Applied Physics. 2 p. 29–34. London.
  – (1954): The physics of blown sand and desert dunes. (1. ed.: 1941) London.
Bradley, J. S. (1957): Differentiation of marine and subaerial sedimentary environments by volume precentage of heavy minerals, Mustang Island, Texas. J.S.P. 27:2 p. 116–125.
Cailleux, A. (1942): Les actions éoliennes périglaciaires en Europe. Mém. Soc. Geol. France 46. Paris.
Chepil, W. S. (1946): Dynamics of wind erosion. 6. Sorting of soil material by the wind. Soil Science. 61:4 p. 331–340. Baltimore.
  – (1957): Sedimentary characteristics of dust storms. 1. Sorting of wind-eroded soil material. American Journal of Science. 255 p. 12–22. New Haven, Connecticut.
Doeglas, D. J. (1946): Interpretation of the results of mechanical analyses. J.S.P. 16 p. 19–40.
  – (1949): Loess, an eolian product. J.S.P. 19:3 p. 112–117.

Dücker, A. & Maarleveld, G. C. (1958): Hoch- und spätglaziale äolische Sande in Nordwestdeutschland und in den Niederlanden. G.J. 73 p. 215–234.

Edelman, von C. H. & Maarleveld, G. C. (1958): Pleistozän-geologische Ergebnisse der Bodenkartierung in den Niederlanden. G.J. 73 p. 639–684.

Folk, R. L. & Ward, W. C. (1957): Brazo river bar: A study in the significance of grain size parameters. J.S.P. 27:1 p. 3–26.

– (1958): See Mason & Folk (1958).

Harris, S. A. (1957): Mechanical constitution of certain present-day egyptian dune sands. J.S.P. 27:4 p. 421–434.

– (1958a): Probality curves and the recognition of adjustment to depositional environment. J.S.P. 28:2 p. 151–163.

– (1958b): Differentiation of various egyptian aeolian microenvironments by mechanical composition. J.S.P. 28:2 p. 164–174.

Inman, D. L. (1949): Sorting of sediments in the light of fluid mechanics. J.S.P. 19 p. 51–70.

– (1952): Measures for describing the size distribution of sediments. J.S.P. 22 p. 125–145.

Jacobsen, N. Kingo (1956): Summary: Soil investigations in the salt-marsh area at Tønder. Method and interpretation. G.T. 55 p. 106–146.

Jakobsen, B. & Jensen, K. M. & Nielsen, Niels (1956): Forslag til landvindingsarbejder langs den sønderjyske Vadehavskyst. (English summary). G.T. 55 p. 62–87.

Jessen, A. (1922): Kortbladet Varde. D.G.U. 1:14.

Jonassen, H. (1954): Dating of sand-drift east of Ulfborg. Botanisk Tidsskrift 51. København.

– (1957): Bidrag til Filsøegnens naturhistorie. (English abstract). Meddelelser fra Dansk Geologisk Forening 13:4 p. 192–205. Kbhvn.

Krumbein, W. C. & Pettijohn, F. J. (1938): Manual of sedimentary petrography. New York.

Kuhlman, H. (1957a): Sandflugt og klitdannelse. (English summary). G.T. 56 p. 1–19.

– (1957b): Kornstørrelser i klit- og strandsand. (English summary). G.T. 56 p. 20–56.

– (1958): Quantitative measurements of aeolian sand transport. G.T. 57 p. 51–74.

Maarleveld, G. C. (1958a): see: Dücker & Maarleveld, 1958.

– (1958 b) see: Edelman & Maarleveld, 1958.

Mason, C. C. & Folk, R. L. (1958): Differentiation of beach, dune and aeolian flat environments by size analysis, Mustang Island, Texas. J.S.P. 28:2 p. 211–226.

Milthers, V. (1925): Kortbladet Bække. D.G.U. 1:15.

– (1939): Kortbladet Brande. D.G.U. 1:28.

Pettijohn, F. J. (1938): see Krumbein & Pettijohn, 1938.

– (1957): Sedimentary rocks. 2.ed. New York.

Rasmussen, Kjeld (1956): Investigations on marsh soils and wadden sea sediments in the Tønder region. G.T. 55 p. 147–170.

Schou, A. (1949): Atlas of Denmark I: The landscapes. København.

Sindowski, K.H. (1956): Korngrössen- und Kornformen-Auslese beim Sandtransport durch Wind. G.J. 71 p. 517–526.

–   (1958): Die synoptische Methode des Kornkurven-Vergleiches zur Ausdeutung fossiler Sedimentationsräume. G.J. 73 p. 235–275.

Sundborg, Å. (1955): Meteorological and climatological conditions for the genesis of aeolian sediments. G.A. 37:1–2 p. 94–111.

–   (1956): The river Klarälven. A study of fluvial processes. G.A. 38:2 p. 127–316.

Tanner, W. F. (1958): The zig-zag nature of type I and type IV curves. J.S.P. 28:3 p. 372–375.

Udden, J. A. (1914): Mechanical composition of clastic sediments. Bulletin of the Geological Society of America. 25 p. 655–744.

The terminology of the geo-aeolian environment
especially in relation to Danish landscapes
By Hans Kuhlman

Abstract

Localities with aeolian materials are classified, tentatively on three independent basic principles: 1) dynamic, 2) sedimental, 3) geometric (morphometric). The nominated terms are arranged in a table (II) in order to suggest a system of aeolian geo-environments.

Introduction

Excellent reviews of the geomorphology of Danish landscapes influenced by the wind have been worked out by *Warming* 1907-1909, *A. Schou* 1945, 1949 and *Niels Nielsen & Schou* 1958. However, an attempt of composing a consistent terminology for the geo-aeolian environments in Denmark makes it desirable to link these works together with the newest studies of sand drifting and dunes (*Bagnold* 1954, *Sindowski* 1956, *Cooper* 1958, *Kuhlman 1958* and *Finkel* 1959). The attempt below does not pretend to be exhaustive; it only tends to outline the fundamental features in a »natural system«.

For a geomorphological classification different points of view may be adopted: 1): dynamic; 2): sedimentological; 3): form-descriptive; 4): evolutionistic. A distinction between these four categories is normally not maintained; however, elements from all of them contribute to the explanatory description of the landscapes. The common descriptions bear the stamp of *W. M. Davis'* ideas of the natural evolution of the landscape; these sometimes imply pseudo-explanations and uncertain hypotheses. Therefore, some modern geomorphologists maintain an attitude of reserve towards *Davis'* evolutionistic points of view, which may involve scientific pitfalls. In Scandinavia *Behrens* has recommended to adopt a clear distinction between morphologic description and genesis; this will make it easier to arrive at scientific explanations, which to-day are further facilitated because exact observations and experiments are gaining foothold in the geomorphological methodology. Especially the studies of dunes and of wind-erosion have profited from the quantitative measurements, without which it is impossible to elaborate a valid systematism. A form description will be systematic, when it is based both on the geometrical figurations and on their »ontogeny« and »phylogeny«. The development of the form-shaping processes may be called the geomorphological ontogeny, the basis of the dynamical classification. The descent of the forms is the morphologic phylogeny. Pure descriptions are rare in the dune topography, and often they have a curious »two-dimensional« character, for instance: »white dune« and »grey dune«.

In the following the landscape influenced by the wind is treated on the basis of the above-mentioned principles.

History

Since the works of *Sokolow* 1884 and *Steenstrup* 1894 appeared many geo-aeolian papers have been published, among which the present text only refers to those which have dominated the treatment of this subject in Denmark and which are the origin of our modern theories. *E. Warming* 1907-1909 in his monography of the vegetation on Danish dunes gave a comprehensive review of dune forms and of their birth; his work authorized the opinion that the most important aeolian sedimentation in a humid climate is the result of an interaction between vegetation and sand drifting; this has also been mentioned by ancient authors: *Viborg* 1788, *Groos* 1847, and *Andresen* 1861; however, Warming brought us the understanding of the biology and of the morphological effect of the dune vegetation. He introduced terms which became classic, for instance »white dune« and »grey dune«, »grønning« (= green dune valley), see *Lemberg, Schou, Kihlström;* these terms referred to the plant communities and not unambiguously to the geomorphology — a fact which at times has been overlooked by the posterity. From Warming a clue leads to *J. W. van Dieren,* whose book from 1934 brought a culmination of the research line of a botanical character, originating in the combating of the anthropogeneous sand drifting in Europe in the sixteenth to the eighteenth centuries; see *Wessely* 1873, *Gerhardt* 1900 and *Braun* 1911. The results cristallized in *v. Dieren's* work had been anticipated by many authors, see *Lemberg* and *Behrmann.* The dunes of North-West Europe and their plant communities have had correlative evolutions. Possessing this knowledge, *v. Dieren* established a systematism, including a latin terminology. The following dune evolution was fundamental: embryonal dunes (tussock dunes) — bank of dune sand with Ammophila — blow-outs — parabolic dune — secondary barchan . According to *v. Dieren* this sequence is due to self-degeneration of the vegetation. Such a pessimistic opinion is open to discussion, see *Cooper* 1958; however, it is not to be doubted that the said development has taken place in Europe and in the United States: *Paul* 1944, *V. Hansen* 1957 and *Hack* 1941, *Hefley & Sidwell* 1945. Van Dieren introduced a clear distinction between »physical« dunes and »organic« dunes (p. 204-207); in the United States »organic« has been replaced by »phytogenic« *(Smith, Cooper)*. More particularly a distinction is made between desert dunes and coastal dunes, see *Schou* 1945, p. 148; this distinction is critizised by *Cooper* 1958, p. 66-68. The present-day standpoint must be that *v. Dieren's* classification is misleading, because gradual transitions are seen between »phytogenic« and »physical« dunes, and because the forms in arid zones and in humid zones may be explained by the same »natural laws« as those formulated by *R. A. Bagnold* 1935-1954.

Bagnold, whose works are epoch-making, introduced the modern aerodynamics in the dune morphology; his results have been confirmed by *Chepil* and *Zingg.* On a number of points *Bagnold's* studies open a new »era«; here are only mentioned the most relevant. He demonstrated that the sand drifting is caused by the saltation of the grains and by the resulting surface-creeping, the so-called »reptation«. The movement which takes place across loose sand creates wind ripples, which mark the most frequent points of impact of the saltation grains. *Bagnold's* explanation of the occurrence of the ephemeral wind ripples (see also *Trikalinos* 1928) has encountered difficulties in chasing wrong interpretations, especially the »Helmholtz theory«, which came to life because *Baschin* considered cirrocumulus to be homologous with wind ripples; other »wave-theories« too have ravaged the dune morphology, see *Exner*. *Bagnold* has given a mathematical expression of the relation between wind, sand and transport quantities. He further demonstrated that it is the wind force in the air layers next to the surface which influences the aeolian deposition and erosion; example: mobile sand sheets in relation to fixed, smooth surfaces are sheltered; i.e. the wind velocity at the same level is reduced. Consequently, a sand spot in a smooth environment will »catch« more sand. This phenomenon has been called by *H. T. U. Smith* 1953: psammogenic dune genesis, which explains the

growth of many dune forms. In a Western European dune environment *Sindowski* and, later, the author have verified some of *Bagnold's* theories; it appeared that the aeolian transport and the dune
genesis here are not essentially different from the conditions in an
arid region; however, certain corrections had to be made of the
formulae, see *Kuhlman* 1958. *W. Walther* has also worked in such
terrains; however, with other theories as a point of departure. The
most astonishing factor in relation to sand drifting in our climate is
the feeble restraining effect exercised by rain and humidity. *Bagnold*
has but a small influence on the recent morphological principal
works, which are important by virtue of the amounts of their observations: *Paul* 1944, *Schou* 1945, *Melton* 1941 (a systematism) and
Cooper 1958, whereas *Landsberg* 1956 and *Finkel* 1959 have probably
initiated a new era of the aeolian geomorphology; their papers contain a lot of quantitative observations and mathematical models; the
pronounced approach to the pure science will be the characteristic
of the future geomorphology, which, otherwise, was bound to stag-
nate.

The status of the dune terminology

The modern dune literature (after 1930) has partly standardized
certain dune types, the terms of which may change, whereas their
identity is unmistakable. Among these, the most common are repeated here and commented on the basis of the most recent ideas.
Barchan (Dunus falcatus, *v. Dieren*) is a bounded accumulation of
blown sand of a well-known aspect: crescent-shaped ground-plan,
triangular cross-section with angles of about 10°-140°-30°, the greatest of which at the dune crest. Less known are the genetic demands
of the barchan: an immobile, even substratum, which by means of
the psammo-genesis transforms into dunes the moderate sand quantities (per area) which blow from an almost constant direction. The
nominal form is known from arid deserts, for instance Peru and
Libya; in humid regions homologous forms are seen, partly ephemeral, small beach-forms, partly stable, atypical macro-forms: secondary barchans; German: Wanderdüne; Danish: mile *(Kuhlman*
1960). *Transverse dunes* (transverse ridges, *Cooper,* some Dunus
anticus, *v. Dieren)* are big sand masses modelled in dense, interfering, barchanoid forms; they constitute a rythmically repeated
pattern of not very inclined windward sides and steep lee sides
(slip-faces). The dune crests may form long, sinoidal lines transverse to the wind. The creation of these sand seas demands enormous quantities of mobile, sorted sand. The big transports arrive from

Fig. 1. A blow-out, a hollow-dune on the west coast of Skallingen, near Esbjerg.
In the centre of the photo a person is seen.

almost the same points of the compass. The repeated »wave-forms«
are not the result of wind vortexes attached to definite localities
(*Cornish, Exner, Matschinski*), but of the self-created shelter and
exposition of the superficially transported sand, because the wind
behind the slip-faces is morphologically inactive *(Cooper)*. *Longitudinal dunes* are high banks of a partly residual character and with
a cross-section whose appearance is changing; this makes the dune-
profile more symmetrical than is the case of the barchanoid forms.
It is probable that the genesis is strongly affected by a seasonal alternation between two diverging transport directions (*Bagnold, Cooper*). The *seif dunes* mentioned by *Bagnold* must be classed with
this group. *Blow-outs* (German: Windkuhlen) are best known from
dunes with vegetation. This term covers the hollows and troughs
shaped by the wind in the dunes, see fig. 1. The inside of the hollow
is corroded and eroded, while the outer side receives the removed
material; the development of an erosion hole is very complicated;
however, the formation of vortexes and the macro-turbulence are not
necessary as a genetic condition, as maintained (*v. Dieren*, see also
Olson 1958). *Parabolic dunes (Steenstrup, Solger, v. Dieren, Hack,*

Schou) — also called *U-shaped dunes (Landsberg)* or *upsiloidal dunes (H. T. U. Smith)* are asserted to be a dune form particular to humid climate zones. It is a question of long, blown-sand banks, resting on a rather plain substratum, and which in a map, thanks to the contour lines, appear as a U-shaped figure. This pattern stands out more clearly in a map than in nature, where it can only with difficulty be distinguished, because the detail forms, the slip-faces and the blow-outs are more conspicuous. The big, Danish parabolic dunes, when regarded in the field, have a big resemblance to seif dunes and secondary barchans; their parabolic axis is said to be dominated by the »wind-resultant«, *Schou, Landsberg, V. Hansen;* see also *Jennings* 1957 and *Finkel* 1959.

A kind of a model

In the following classifications we intend to use a naive model as a condensing agent for notions and explanations. The model fig. 2 represents a bloc of a stylized landscape with the locality A in an environment called O. This primitive figure serves to point out some basic features of the geo-aeolian environment. 1): A dune is an accumulation of blown sand rich in reliefs; the words: »rich in reliefs« show that »dune« is a relative concept; a spot with wind-sedimentation is termed (partly) in accordance with the distribution of heights of the environs; *Schou* 1945, p. 148, remarks that half of the blown-sand covered area of Denmark is avoid of »dune-character«. 2): Suppose that a known dune type, for instance the barchan, is sketched in at A; the block-side of the figure could then represent now 1 m., now 1 km.; still, the constructed situation will correspond to conditions existing in nature, independent of the chosen scale. This goes to show that a certain constancy of forms exists, however, not accompanied by constancy of the terms. 3): If, conversely, the model represents a certain landscape the extent represented by the diagram will contribute to determine »what can be seen« and, consequently, a description and denomination. The normal terms are pronouncedly depending on the »observation height« above the aeolian environment. An example of this peculiarity has already been referred to in the comments on parabolic dunes. 4): A contemplation of fig. 2 may lead to think of the problem known from psychology: What is motive, and what is background, here: $\frac{A}{O}$ or $\frac{O}{A}$? When bearing in mind this association, it is possible to study the landscape in a more untraditional way and to jump at discoveries. During the study of

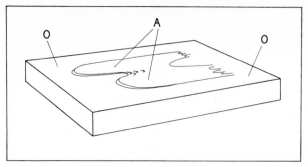

Fig. 2. In general a model of a stylized landscape is shown: an aeolian locality A in the environment O; further information in the text. In particular is demonstrated a schematic outline of a psammogenic shield-dune on a beach.

the development of the blow-outs this manner of treating the problems is useful; for instance, a small deposition of material is discovered in localities where we would immediately have foreseen an erosion. 5): The presentation of this model also is an indication — perhaps not needed — that landscape forms ought to be described in relation to a three-axial co-ordinate system. However, many authors in such descriptions use terms which in reality are surface denominations: White dune and grey dune. For the contemplation of Danish dunes from a solid geometric point of view we refer especially to *A. Schou* 1945 and 1949.

The peculiarities mentioned above make it difficult to compose a »natural« dune terminology.

Dynamical classification

From *Bagnold, Chepil* and others we know that the wind transports material by means of suspension, saltation and reptation. It is possible, in most cases, to identify these transport types each with its delimited grain-size interval: dust (loess), fine-medium sand and coarse-sand/gravel. The dust is suspended in the air-flow, is moved far away and to high altitudes, until the wind dies away. During the movement the sand and the gravel are linked to the surfaces of the terrain; this superficial transport, which is analogous to the hydro-dynamical expression »bed load«, contributes to inducing the morphologists to give »two-dimensional« descriptions. If supposing that the model in fig. 2 represents a locality with active wind it may serve to give an answer to the question: What is the result arrived at in a locality with aeolian activity ? The effect of the wind on the landscape may be temporary or definite; however, at any rate it is useful to classify the result in relation to the transport of material, whether *superficial* or *suspensive*. Both in A and O a net loss of material may take place: *erosion;* or an increase of the sedimentation: *deposition.* If the passage of the sand drifting over the localities does not alter the quantities of material, this is designated by the term: *transit.* Finally, as another possibility should be mentioned that the given localities are not affected by a transport: *neutrality.* It is proposed to reserve the term: »deflation« for a definite kind of aeolian erosion: the removing from non-aeolian sediments and rocks. If the possible combinations of A and O are composed in respect to the four dynamical effects mentioned above we shall be able to make the terminology indicated in table I.

When deposition/erosion occurs in a locality it is because here is found shelter/anti-shelter. Both in common and in scientific usage the term »shelter« indicates a relativity: wind-force reduction in proportion to a »standard force«; therefore, an aeolian terrain-form is created as a natural consequence of a neighbourhood. The shelter/anti-shelter of a locality is ascribable to exterior or interior factors. It may be situated in a wind-shadow from isolated objects sticking out into the air; or it may constitute in itself an obstruction exposed to the wind. The local lee situation may also be conditioned by differences in the structure and contents of neighbouring areas. The

Table I

Aeolian-dynamic terms for a locality (A) in a given environment (O).

O \ A		Dynamical effect in A			
		erosion	deposition	transit	neutrality
Dynamical effect in O	erosion	O>A: erosion-residue A>O: erosion-focus	deposition area	residual transit area	residual neutral area
	deposition	erosion area	O>A: retardative deposition area A>O: deposition focus	transit area	neutral area
	transit	erosion area	deposition area	transit area	refuge area
	neutrality	erosion area	deposition area	(impossible)	(non-aeolian)

different causes of the shelter indicate two types of deposition and erosion: the type conditioned by obstruction and the one conditioned by roughness. The morphologic effect of the obstruction (*obstructogenic*) is due to the influence which a terrain-element of but small extent exercises on the air-current, in which it is a relatively isolated obstruction. Hedges or plant tussocks cast a limited wind-shadow, which may be filled with aeolian material, fig. 3; or, as a result of an isolated elevation of the terrain the stream-lines are situated close to the top of this hill, causing the material of the locality to be exposed to the wind. We would call a deposition caused by a marked wind-shadow *umbratogenic*. The effect of the roughness *(asperitogenic)* is attributable to the frequent difference between the transport capacities of neighbouring areas at a given wind, see *Bagnold* 1954, p. 83, and *Kuhlman* 1958, p. 68. The amount of the transported material in a given surface is determined by the nature, size and distribution of the roughness-elements. Immobile, smooth surfaces have an extremely big, optimal transport capacity, even if the surface is moist. In Denmark the pseudo-hygrophoby of the saltating sand is of fundamental importance. We have learned with astonishment that wet dune surfaces are erosion areas, and that moist material does not inevitably bring the drifting to a standstill. The optimal, equivalent transport is smaller on a dry, loose sand surface than on a smooth, firm surface; this is why the psammogenic dune formation takes place *(H. T. U. Smith; Schou* 1945: Physical dune formation). We have only with difficulty understood the observation according to which sand could be accumulated without a pronounced shelter. The transport conditions of a rough, semi-mobile surface are of a peculiar nature; at gentle winds the equivalent transport is smaller here than on a loose sand surface, whereas it is bigger at strong winds. A mobile sand-spot in a pebbled locality will act as an erosion area at moderate wind forces and as a deposition area a strong winds. The surfaces grown with plants have only a small sand movement or none at all; almost invariably they are deposition areas. The capability of certain plants for regenerating the surface type after the deposition of the sand is well known. The optimal growth of Ammophila arenaria demands sanding-up. Although plants often create stable sediment-sections, and in spite of the fact that dunes characterized by vegetation have a complicated evolution the author does not see the practical in pointing out the shelter of the plants as a specific, odd phenomenon: the organogenic (phytogenic) dune formation; the vegetation functions as shelter in the same manner as do the

Fig. 3. An umbratogenic deposition — a prismatic dune — of soil material in a
road side, Thy. The soil-drift had taken place from right.

inorganic terrain elements, and the aeolian landscape forms which
the vegetation develops have a striking resemblance to »physical«
types.

Grouping of wind-sediments

In Denmark several kinds of wind-sediments occur; it is not intended here, when commenting upon these sediments, to use the traditional groupings according to texture, composition and the like,
whereas we recommend a classification based on the nature and the
effect of the transport. This classification has previously been dealt
with in the present periodical (1957, 1959). We propose the following denominations: suspension-, saltation-, reptation-, slip- and residual sediment and corroded material. Observations in nature have
shown that these terms are closely associated with the textural
terms. *Aeolian suspension material* is rarely found deposited in appreciable quantities in this country, see *S. A. Andersen* 1935 and *S.
Hansen* 1948, whereas every year in numerous plough fields in Jutland a rise takes place of suspensive, aeolian material, whose future
fate is only uncompletely known. The *saltation material*, whose
predominant grain size is 0.15 - 0.40 mm., forms the bulk in the

numerous dunes and blown-sand covers the position of which is given in »Atlas of Denmark« (*Schou* 1949); their total area is said to be about 1.400 sq. km. (*Schou* 1945). The *reptation material* forms an integrating part of the »blown sand« in dunes and covers; however, it may have grain sizes six times as big as those of the local, saltating sand; this leads to the formation of sporadic dune material which is so coarse-grained (10 mm.; commonly: 1-5 mm.) that hurricanes have been considered as necessary for their accumulation; however, this is not the case (see *Kuhlman* 1960, fig. 3). Separated, coarse reptation material is especially found in the dunes in Western Thy, at Grindsted and on Anholt. In our climate wet, steep erosion slopes of aeolian material are not unusual; when slidings happen in these slopes and at slip-faces an *aeolian slip-sediment* is formed, characterized by being situated low in the terrain and by being relatively poorly sorted. The land-slides and slips steered by gravitation make it difficult to identify the aeolian environment sedimentologically. *Residual sediments* consist of pebbles and cobbles, left by the wind in a process of deflation; we meet »pavements« just as in arid deserts — a phenomenon which may be observed at many places along our recent beaches, for instance at Skallingen and Blåvands Huk. At Kandestederne, near the Scaw, are also found planes with pebbles, resulting from a wind-erosion in elevated, marine sediments. Many agrarian fields in Jutland may in spring have the same wind-ravaged aspect. Among the *materials influenced by corrosion* we know from Jutland numerous occurrences of faceted pebbles/ cobbles, which lie in the field-soil on glacial material from the Riss glaciation; the period of their shaping is probably Würm (Tubantian, Weichsel). The best opportunity of studying these polished field pebbles is found in the district between Holstebro and Ringkøbing, and Grindsted-Hejnsvig. In Bornholm have been observed wind-sculptured rock surfaces (*Mattsson* 1957).

It is worth noticing that only the two last-mentioned sediment types may be interpreted stratigraphically as having been caused by wind-erosion. If the other types are embedded in a stratification a later researcher will undoubtedly conclude that a deposition has taken place in an aeolian environment. Much of what we characterize to-day as erosion localities cannot, at a later embedding, be given this name. The plains surrounding the parabolic dunes are termed by some authors as: deflation plains; however, this expression is not too well chosen, because from a stratigraphic-dynamic point of view they are most often underdeveloped deposition areas. This is

Fig. 4. Lense-dunes — cushion dunes — on the western beach of Rømø; the houses of Lakolk are seen in the background. The genesis of dunes, half a metre high, is named asperitogenic.

one of the reasons why the author recommends only to use the term: deflation when the wind removes »foreign« material.

Geometrical grouping

The geometric figuration of a locality in the landscape influenced by the wind may be divided into a few elementary forms. Such a division in constituents is known from other dune topographies; however, our system is perhaps of a greater simplicity and consistency.

The first sort to which we are drawing the attention may seem to be a truism: a locality *non-specific* in relation to the environs; however, it is overlooked that the wind-ravaged spot often forms a vaguely marked element of the landscape. In Denmark it is common that ancient or recent wind-activity cannot be immediately deduced from the shape of the terrain; it is necessary to observe the very transport or to study the soil more closely. In Vendsyssel-Thy and in Himmerland the soil-drifting hits big field-areas every year without leaving any distinct morphological effects; further, cultivation and road-work eliminate most of the small traces. The geological

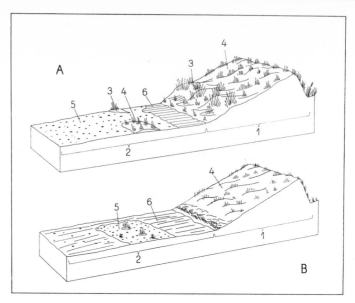

Fig. 5. The transition from beach to coast dunes west of Skomagersletten, Skallingen. Summer: A and winter: B in 1954—1956. 1 = the coast dune, an 8 m. high profile dune. 2 = the beach. 3 = umbratogenic tongue dunes. 4 = lense dunes (cushion dunes). 5 = an aeolian, asperitogenic transit plane. 6 = beach washed by the sea. The block side represents 150 m., and the exaggeration is about 10.

mappings *(Milthers, Jessen)* have shown that moraine hills in Western Jutland and in Central Jutland at places are conformably covered by Late-glacial aeolian sand; this corresponds to the cover-sand from Holland and Germany, of which descriptions have been given (cf.*Kuhlman* 1959).From the aeolian-non-specific localities there are continuous transitions to *planes* with aeolian material. The deflation planes with »pavements« known from arid regions exist, as mentioned, in our country too; however, plains with blown sand are much more common.Initial deposition areas are more easily found than embryonal erosion spots; the umbratogenic deposition has an outstanding initial form: the *tongue dune;* as the name indicates, the material adopts a shape resembling a cleaved cone resting on the cleave plane in the shelter of a wind-obstructing object (compare *Cooper's* »lee projection«). Behind a onesidedly extended shelter tongue dunes may grow together so as to form prismatic drifts: *prismatic dunes.* The commencing asperitogenic deposition forms lenses more or less asymmetric, fig. 4; we suggest the term: *lense dunes.* Usually, they are called embryonal dunes, primary dunes, tussock dunes and other names. When it is a question of isolated

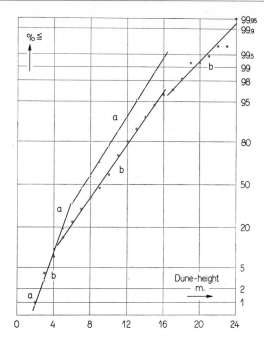

Fig. 6. The frequency distribution of the estimated dune heights in Blåvand — Rømø (a) and Frederikshavn — The Scaw (b) plotted on probability paper.

occurrences this initial form rarely has a thickness of more than a few decimetres, whereas its ground area may be big. At Danish coasts two sub-types are frequent; one of them is seen in planes with no vegetation: *shield dune;* it has a slightly curved shape which, if the material is moist, is provided with a steep micro-slope against the wind (fig. 2). The other sub-type appears in places where there is some vegetation; its shape is expressed in the name: *cushion dune* (fig. 4). Both are embryos of a later stable dune formation; they consist of semi-hygrophobic sand, which becomes the source material of the future drift. It is most probably a question of shield dunes, mentioned by *Schou* 1945, p. 151, and by *Cooper* 1958, p. 46.

Big, asperitogenic accumulations of saltation material acquire by and by the figuration which is usually associated with the term »dune«. The characteristic of these accumulations is the presence of slip-faces, slopes of 25°-30° with loosely packed material, and the opposite orientated slopes of 5°-12°. As a result of this the vertical profile becomes »barchanoid«, i. e. triangular with constant angles. Leaving out of consideration the figuration of such dunes in the horizontal section, we name them all: *profile dunes* (fig. 5): a basic form comprising a series of common names, for instance the beach barchan, the secondary barchan, elements of sand seas, Dunus anticus, and parabolic dunes. The barchan is a well defined sub-type and, perhaps, the real primary form; however, we need more observations for being able to pronounce a judgment. The height of profile dunes is generally said to be 10-30 m., rarely 100 m. In this country no dune is rising more than 25 m. above its bed; however, it may sometimes be difficult to establish the level of the dune basis. In fig. 6 is shown the distribution of the heights of the dune tops (found during studies of map 1:20.000) in two Danish dune areas: The Scaw — Frederikshavn and Blåvand — Rømø. The approximate top constancy, which is dimly seen in the figure, has dynamical causes. The wind force increases with the height above the terrain; at a certain level the force will be equal to the suspension threshold of the local sand (see *Kuhlman* 1960), and if an isolated accumulation of sand grows to such a height that the normal winds of the region have a suspensive effect at this level the »dune-hat« is blown off; a suspensive transport does not create any topography rich in reliefs, only covers. The theoretically maximum dune height is positively correlated with the grain size of the material, but negatively correlated with the degree of isolation of the dune and the usual local wind forces.

Large dunes with vegetation may have a more symmetrical cross-section than is normally the case of profile dunes; when regarded from a certain distance, they have the aspect of banks with a curved, elliptic cross-section. These *bank dunes,* unsatisfactorily defined, are especially seen at progressive coasts with nutritious sand, for instance Rømø and the Scaw. In mobile material the wind may form big erosion areas with bizarre micro-forms; big, steep slopes are shaped, sculptured by corrosion. In North-Western Europe the erosive effect is pronounced because of the frequent weather changes and the resulting big fluctuations of the degree of moisture of the material; moist sand may stand in vertical inclinations, which slide when dried in fine weather. Moist surfaces between dry areas are strongly corroded on account of their great transport capacity, which, in addition, accentuates an adjacent accumulation. In our dunes the erosion areas and the deposition areas stick together, just as the front and the back of the paper, see *v. Dieren* 1934, p. 198. The characteristical initial form in a deflation area is the somewhat oblique *wind-hollow* or *wind-trough;* when old dune-material is eroded, *hollow-dunes* and *trough-dunes* are born (fig. 1).

Table II.

orm-type	Material	Dynamical class	Normal synonymous	Locality example
ormarten	*Materialet*	*Dynamisk klasse*	*Normal synonym*	*Lokalitet eksempel*
eolian on-specific	residual gravel + pebbles	asperitogenic/obstructogenic deflation	fields with wind erosion	North Jutland
olisk specifik	*residual grus + sten*	*asperitogen/obstruktogen deflation*	*jordføgne agre*	*Nordjylland*
	saltation-/reptation-sand+gravel	asperitogenic/obstructogenic deposition	drifts covers	Near Fjerritslev
	saltations-/reptationssand og grus	*asperitogen/obstruktogen deposition*	*dækker driver*	*Omkring Fjerritslev*
eolian plane	layer of residual gravel and pebbles	asperitogenic deflation/transit	pavement sheets with pebbles	Kandestederne at the Scaw
olisk plan	*lag af residual grus og sten*	*asperitogen deflation-transit*	*brolægning stensletter*	*Kandestederne ved Skagen*
	mixed, partly mobile	asperitogenic erosion	deflation plane	Foreshore of the West coast
	blandet, delvis mobilt	*asperitogen erosion*	*deflationsslette*	*Forstranden, Vestkysten*
	saltation-/reptation + vegetation	asperitogenic deposition	blown-sand sheet	At Blåvand Kalsmærsk Heath
	saltations-/reptations + vegetation	*asperitogen deposition*	*flyvesandsslette*	*Ved Blåvand, Kalsmærsk Hede*
ongue-dune	saltation-/reptation	umbratogenic deposition	lee-tongue embryonal dune	Foreshore Skallingen, Fanø
ungeklit	*saltations-/reptations*	*umbratogen deposition*	*lætunge embryonalklit*	*Forstranden Skallingen, Fanø*
rismatic dune	saltation-/reptation	umbratogenic deposition	lee-drifts	Foreshore Skallingen, Fanø
rismeklit	*saltations-/reptations*	*umbratogen deposition*	*lædriver*	*Forstranden Skallingen, Fanø*
mall lensedunes	saltation-/reptation-	asperitogenic deposition		
må linseklitter	*saltations-/reptations*	*asperitogen deposition*		Foreshore Skallingen, Fanø
hield-dune	÷ vegetation		primary dunes	*Forstranden*
kjoldklit	*÷ vegetation*		*urklitter*	*Skallingen, Fanø*
ushion-dune	+ vegetation		tussock dune embryonal dune	Foreshore of Rømø
udeklit	*+ vegetation*		*tueklit embryonalklit*	*Rømøs forstrand*
ig lensedunes	+ vegetation	asperitogenic + umbratogenic deposition	foredune sea-dune Dunus anticus	Skallingen, Fanø Rømø
tore linseklitter	*+ vegetation*	*asperitogen + umbratogen deposition*	*forklit, havklit Dunus anticus*	*Skallingen, Fanø Rømø*
rofile dunes	saltation-/reptation	asperitogenic/obstructogenic deposition		
rofilklitter	*saltations-/reptations*	*asperitogen/obstruktogen deposition*	beach barchan sec. barchan	(Fanø) Råbjerg Mile
	÷ vegetation		strandbarkhan sek. barkhan	(Fanø) Råbjerg Mile
	÷ vegetation		*strandbarkhan sek. barkhan*	*(Fanø) Råbjerg Mile*
	+ vegetation		Dunus anticus	Skallingen
	+ vegetation		*Dunus anticus*	*Skallingen*
			parabolic dune sec. barchan	Jessens Sande Ho
			parabelklit sek. barkhan	*Jessens Sande Ho*
hollow-dune	mobile sand + vegetation	asperitogenic/obstructogenic erosion + deposition	blow-out	SW-Fanø
rugklit	*mobilt sand + vegetation*	*asperitogen/obstruktogen erosion + dep.*	*vindkuler*	*SW-Fanø*
rough-dune	mobile sand + vegetation	asperitogenic/obstructogenic erosion + deposition	deflation furrows	NW-Thy
rugklit	*mobilt sand + vegetation*	*asperitogen/obstruktogen erosion + dep.*	*deflationsfurer*	*NW-Thy*
wind-hollow	mixed, mostly mobile	asperitogenic/obstructogenic erosion		
vindgryde	*blandet, mest mobilt*	*asperitogen/obstruktogen erosion*		
wind-trough				
vindtrug				

This review does not contain a precise and detailed description of the elementary forms, and it is no doubt possible to suggest an additional number of initial forms; however, the author hopes to have accomplished the object of this passage: to draw the attention to the pure form-types, which, at any rate, have a high »rank«.

An outlined system and a summary

An exhaustive systematics in Danish aeolian landscapes cannot be established until more quantitative observations are available; however, it is possible to give a summary of the terms mentioned in the preceding paragraphs, ranged according to an outlined system; this has been done in table II.

LITERATURE

Andersen, S. A. 1935: En Forekomst af løsslignende Finsand ved Hornborg Vest for Horsens. Medd.f.Dan.Geol.For. 8 p. 477–479. København.

Andresen, C. C. 1861: Om Klitformationen og Klittens Behandling og Bestyrelse. København.

Bagnold, R. A. 1935: The movement of desert sand. Geogr.Jour. 85 p.342-369. London.

Bagnold, R. A. 1954: The physics of blown sand and desert dunes. London.

Baschin, O. 1899: Die Entstehung wellenähnlicher Oberflächenformen. Zeit. Ges. für Erdkunde 34 p. 408–424. Berlin.

Baschin, O. 1903: Dünenstudien. Zeit. Ges. für Erdkunde 38 p. 422-430. Berlin.

Behrens, S. E. 1953: Morfometriska, morfogenetiska och tektoniska studier av de nordvästskånska urbergsåsarna, särskilt Kullaberg. Lund.

Behrmann, W. 1933: in Klute, F.: Handbuch der geographischen Wissenschaft. Allgemeine Geographie I. p.485-501. Potsdam.

Braun, G. 1911: Entwicklungsgeschichtliche Studien an europäischen Flachlandsküsten und ihren Dünen. Veröff.Inst.f.Meereskunde 15. Berlin.

Chepil, W. S. 1945 and 1946: Dynamics of wind erosion. Soil Science 60-61. Baltimore.

Cooper, W. S. 1958: Coastal sand dunes of Oregon and Washington. Geol. Soc. of Amer. Memoir 72. New York.

Cornish, V. 1897: On the formation of sand-dunes. Geogr.Jour. 9 p.278-309. London.

Dieren, J. W. van 1934: Organogene Dünenbildung. Haag.

Exner, F. M. 1927: Über Dünen und Sandwellen. Geogr.Annaler 9 p.81-99. Stockholm.

Finkel, H. J. 1959: The barchans of southern Peru. Jour.Geol. 67 p.614-647. Chicago.

Gerhardt, P. 1900: Handbuch des deutschen Dünenbaues. Berlin.

Grooss, N. C. 1847: Vejledning ved Behandling af Sandflugtsstrækninger i Jylland. København.

Hack, J. T. 1941: Dunes of the western Navajo Country. Geogr.Rev. 31 p.240-263. New York.

Hansen, S. 1948: En Løssaflejring i NV-Jylland. Medd.f.Dan.Geol.For. 11 p.391-393. København.

Hansen, V. 1957: Sandflugten i Thy og dens indflydelse på kulturlandskabet. (English summary). Geogr.Tidsskrift 56 p.69-92. København.

Hefley, H. M. & Sidwell, R. 1945: Geological and ecological observations of some High Plains dunes. Amer.Jour.Sci. 243 p.361. New Haven.

Högbom, J. 1923: Ancient inland dunes of North and Middle Europa. Geogr.Annaler 5 p.113-243. Stockholm.

Jennings, J. N. 1957: On the orientation of parabolic or U-dunes. Geogr. Jour. 123 p.474-480. London.

Jessen, A. 1897: Kortbladene Læsø og Anholt. Dan.Geol.Und. I:4. København.

Jessen, A. 1922: Kortbladet Varde. Dan.Geol.Und. I:14. København.

Jessen, A. 1925: Kortbladet Blaavandshuk. Dan.Geol.Und. I:16. København.

Kihlström, J. E. 1957: Dynfältet på Sandskär i Haparanda skärgård. Geographica 31 p.148-165. Uppsala.

Kuhlman, H. 1957a: Sandflugt og klitdannelse. Geogr. Tidsskrift 56 p.1-19. København.

Kuhlman, H. 1957b: Kornstørrelser i klit og strandsand. Geogr. Tidsskrift 56 p.20-56. København.

Kuhlman, H. 1958: Quantitative measurements of aeolian sand transport. Geogr. Tidsskrift 57 p.51-74. København.

Kuhlman, H. 1959: On identification of blown sand. Geogr. Tidsskrift 58 p.182-195. København.

Kuhlman, H. 1960: Microenvironments in a Danish dune area, Raabjerg Mile. Medd.f.Dan.Geol.For. 14 p.253-8. København.

Landsberg, S. Y. 1956: The orientation of dunes in Britain and Denmark in relation to wind. Geogr.Jour. 122 p.176-189. London.

Lemberg, B. 1933, 1934 and 1935: Über die Vegetation der Flugsandgebiete an den Küsten Finnlands I-II-III. Acta Bot.Fennica 12-13-14. Helsingfors.

Matschinski, M. 1955: La formation des dunes dans les déserts. La Nature 83 p.169-175. Paris.

Mattsson, A. 1957: Windgeschliffenes Gestein im südlichsten Schweden und auf Bornholm. Svensk Geogr.Årsbok 1957 p.49-68. Lund.

Melton, F. A. 1940: A tentative classification of sand dunes. Jour.Geol. 48 p.113-145. Chicago.

Milthers, V. 1925: Kortbladet Bække. Dan.Geol.Und. I:15. København.

Milthers, V. 1939: Kortbladet Brande. Dan.Geol.Und. I:18. København.

Nielsen, N. & Schou, A. 1958: in Trap: Danmark I:1, 5 edit. p.9-17 and 32-90. København.

Ohlson, B. 1957: Om flygsandfälten på Hietatievat i östra Enontekiö. Terra 69 p.129-137. Helsinki.

Olson, J. S. 1958: Lake Michigan dune development 1-2-3. Jour.Geol. 66 p.254-263, p.345-351 and p.473-483. Chicago.

Paul, K. H. 1944 and 1953: Morphologie und Vegetation der Kurischen Nehrung I (and) II. Nova Acta Leop.N.F.13:96 – 16:113. Halle-Leipzig.

Schelling, J. 1957: Herkunft, Aufbau und Bewertung der Flugsande im Binnenlande. Erdkunde 11 p.129-135. Bonn.

Schou, A. 1945: Det marine forland. Folia Geogr. Danica IV. København.

Schou, A. 1949: Atlas of Denmark I, The landscapes. København.

Sindowski, K. H. 1956: Korngrössen- und Kornform-Auslese beim Sandtransport durch Wind. Geol.Jahrbuch 71 p.517-526. Hannover.

Smith, H. T. U. 1953: Classification of sand dunes. Abstract in Capot-Rey: Congrès géologique international Alger 1952, Comptes rendus 19. session.

Smith, H. T. U. & Messinger, C. 1959: Sand dunes shore-line history in the Provincetown area Cape Cod, Massachusetts. Abstract in Geol.Soc. Amer. Program 1959 Annual Meetings p.119A. Pittsburgh.

Sokolow, N. A. (1884) 1894: Die Dünen, Bildung, Entwicklung und innerer Bau. Berlin.

Solger, F. 1908: Parabeldünen. Zeit.Deut.Geol.Ges. 60 Monatsberichte 3 p.54. Berlin.

Steenstrup, K. J. V. 1894: Om Klitternes Vandring. Medd.f.Dan.Geol.For. 1 p.1-14. København.

Trikalinos, J. 1928: Windrippeln. Petermanns Mitt. 74 p.266-271. Gotha.

Walter, W. 1951: Neue morphologisch-physikalische Erkenntnisse über Flugsand und Dünen. Rhein-Main.Forsch. 31. Frankfurt/M.

Warming, E. 1907-1909: Dansk Plantevækst 2. Klitterne. København.

Wessely, J. 1873: Der europäische Flugsand und seine Kultur. Wien.

Viborg, E. 1788: Efterretning om Sandvexterne og deres Anvendelse til at dæmpe Sandflugten på Vestkanten af Jylland. København.

Zingg, A. W. 1953: Wind-tunnel studies of the movement of sedimentary material. State Univ.Iowa, Stud. in Eng. Bull 34 p.111-135. Iowa City.

GLACIOLOGY

Recent investigations of the Greenland Ice Cap.

By Børge Fristrup.

In 1954 *Albert Bauer* published the results of a planimetric investigation of the American World Aeronautical Chart 1: 1.000.000, and according to him the total area of Greenland is 2.186.000 sq.km., of which the area of the Ice Cap covers 1.726.400 sq.km., and smaller glaciers outside the Ice Cap have a total area of 76.000 sq.km. Consequently, the radio between the glacierised area and the ice-free area in Greenland is 5/6, and Greenland is the largest and most important glacier region outside the Antarctic. Therefore, glaciological studies are naturally very important for most geographical work in Greenland. The modern technical facilities and instruments have changed the character of the Arctic expeditions. During the last few years many expeditions have worked on the Greenland Ice Cap and have acquired much new knowledge about the nature and the physical conditions for the large ice sheets in Greenland.

The object of the present paper is to give a summary of the work which has been carried out, especially in the 1950'ies.

I. Expeditions.

The modern geographical exploration of the Greenland Ice Cap started with the German *Alfred Wegener Expedition* 1929—31; during this expedition the first wintering on the interior of the Ice Cap was organized with the establishment of the station »Eismitte« at 70° 54'N., 40° 42'W. in the central part; further, the first attempts to determine, by seismic soundings, the thickness of the ice were carried out. The results were published by *Kurt Wegener* (1933—40). Almost at the same time the *University of Michigan Greenland Expeditions* under *William Herbert Hobbs* 1926—31 and

R. L. Belknap 1932—33 investigated the marginal zone especially around SøndreStrømfjord, and from Camp Scott in UpernavikFjord. Studies on the Ice Cap itself with wintering farther south than that of the Wegener Expedition were conducted by the *British Arctic Airroute Expedition* 1930—31 under *Gino Watkins* (1932), where *Courtauld* from 8th September — 26th April carried through the wintering alone on the Ice Cap at an altitude of 2.500 m. at 67° 03'N., 41° 49'W. Results were also obtained by the *British Oxford University Expedition* 1938 under *J. G. S. Sugden* and *P. G. Mott* from the Sukkertoppen Ice Cap, where *E. Etienne* (1940) made some studies of the snowstratification in pits and also studied the mass balance of the Ice Cap.

During the second world war airbases were established in Greenland; however, no scientifical activities took place on the Ice Cap proper. Of special importance for the work on the Ice Cap are now the bases: The Thule Air Base (established in 1951), and Søndre Strømfjord (BW 1) and Narssarssuaq (BW 8), of lesser importance are the East Greenland air-strips at Mesters Vig and Íkáteq, from 1958 also on Kulusuk, near Angmagssalik. The war brought many new inventions for the technique of Arctic exploration and travelling, among other things especially the weasels, the snocats and the tractors. The mechanical transportations in co-operation with airplanes and helicopters have now made scientifical investigations on the Ice Cap possible on a much larger scale than in the past.

The geographical explorations in Greenland after the war started with the *Danish Pearyland Expedition* 1947—50 under the leadership of *Count Eigil Knuth;* the main object of the expedition was an investigation of the northernmost part of Greenland: Peary Land. A reconnaissance expedition 1947 brought knowledge of the ice-conditions, and the site for the wintering-station was found in the icefree Jørgen Brønlund Fjord, 82° 10'N. and 30° 30'W. In 1948 the station was established, and from 1948 to 1950 scientists worked in Peary Land with the station as a base for long sledge journeys. Geographical and some glaciological investigations were carried out by *B. Fristrup* (1951) in the region around Academy Gletscher and Navy Cliff at the head of Independence Fjord and on the smaller ice cap Chr. Erichsens Iskappe on Heilprin Land.

In 1948 *Expéditions Polaires Françaises, Missions Paul-Emile Victor,* started their work in Greenland. This organization was established the 27th of February 1947 by *Paul-Emile Victor,* as he »recevais du Conseil des Ministres la mission d'organiser, réaliser

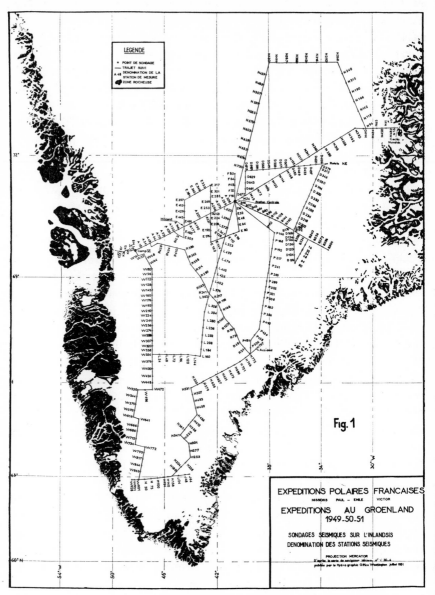

Fig. 1. Seismic surveyings of the Expèditions Polaires Françaises 1949-51.
(Holtzscherer 1954).

et diriger des expéditions de recherche scientifique dans l'Arctique au Groenland et dans l'Antarctique en Terre Adélie«. (Rapports d'Activités p. 5). In 1948 the first campaign started with reconnaissance of the access route to the Ice Cap from de Quervains Havn a Eqip sermia. In order to get the weasels to the Ice Cap it was necessary to construct a road 11 km. long from the coast and to prolong it by a 700 m. long cable-way. In 1949 the wintering station »Station Centrale« was constructed in the central part of the Ice Cap at 70° 55'N. and 40° 38'W. in the vicinity of the old Eismitte Station, which in the meantime had been completely covered by snow and could not be found. The altitude of the Station Centrale was 2.994 m.; the supplies to the station were partly effected by weasels transport, and partly and mainly by airdrop — especially by free drop without parachute. 8 men spent the winter 1949— 50 on glaciological studies and meteorological surface observations as well as aerological investigations. In 1950 a summer-expedition relieved the winter-group, and a new team of 9 men continued the work. Different summergroups worked on the Ice Cap with geodetic, gravimetric and seismic surveyings; several traverses of the Ice Cap from Disko Bugt to Cecilia Nunatak and back were accomplished. The glaciological investigations were carried out by measuring accumulation and ablation along ablation markers and registration of snow profiles etc.; further, deep drillings with core sampling were taken at Camp VI (69° 42'N. and 48° 16'W., altitude 1.598 m.); here a depth of 126 m. was reached, and at Station Centrale to a depth of 151 m. At this place a hole was excavated by means of a special one-ton plunger down to 30,5 m. It had a diameter of 80 cm., which allowed a man to be lowered down and study the stratigraphy. *J. C. Heuberger* (1954) was in charge of the drilling operations. The seismic work this summer was very intensified in order to construct a map of the substratum of the Greenland Ice Cap. In 1951 a fourth expedition relieved the group from Station Centrale, whereafter the station was closed in August 1951. The seismic group worked this year on long trails on the Ice Cap, and the ice thickness was measured from 74° N. down to J. A. D. Jensens Nunutakker at 63°N. and from the western border of the Ice Cap to the Cecilia Nunatak at the east coast. In 1952 different geodetic and glaciological observations were continued, and a new, though small, expedition worked on the Ice Cap to bring the equipment back to the coast, from where it was shipped back to France. These observations were continued in 1953.

In co-operation with the Danish Pearyland Expedition Commander

C. J. W. Simpson in 1950 started a reconnaissance of the Dronning Louise Land from the air with a view to establishing a *British Expedition to North Greenland*. In 1951 a British reconaissance expedition landed at Sælsøen in Dronning Louise Land, and in 1952 the proper expedition started; a base was established at Britannia Sø, 77° 09' N., 23° 36' W., and another base, Northice, was constructed on the Ice Cap at 78° 04' N., 38° 21' W., at an altitude of 2.343 m. In spring 1953 the glaciological work was commenced on the outlet glaciers from the Ice Cap, while seismic and gravity teams worked between Northice and Britannia Sø. During the second wintering 1953/54 the observations were continued, and in 1954 a traverse from Northice to Thule was accomplished. It had been planned to measure the thickness of the ice sheet by seismic soundings, but no reflections from the ice-bedrock interface were recorded at any point between Dronning Louise Land and Northice and east of a separating line running approximately 330° through 77° N., 45° W. Markers were erected on the inland ice, and their positions were determined, thereby making it possible by a resurveying to obtain information about the movement of the ice sheet and the net accumulation of snow *(W. S. B. Paterson,* 1858). A pit at Northice down to 14 m. allowed the determination of the annual accumulation back to the year 1878. Snow studies on the Ice Cap were carried out by *C. Bull* (1958). The regime of the outlet glaciers was studied as well as the heat balance of the glacier surface. Reports on the expedition and the scientifical results have been published by *C. J. W. Simpson* (1955, 1957) and *R. A. Hamilton* (1958).

After having established the Arctic bases in Alaska, Canada and Greenland, the Canadian and US military organisations have been interested in the Arctic problems, especially the climatology, glaciology and periglaciology. In 1946 the *Arctic Institute of North America* was founded, and in 1949 the chief of engineers US Army created a special *Snow, Ice and Permafrost Research Establishment.* The studies of snow classification and basic research of mechanics of snow compaction acquired in a rather short time so great an importance that the Research Establishment erected its own laboratories at Wilmette, where a great organization with numerous scientists, both Americans and foreigners, has worked for SIPRE. The scientifical investigations in the field have for the greater part been carried out in Greenland and especially in the vicinity of Thule Air Base. Members of the SIPRE group have been working in Alaska and in co-operation with the Canadian Defense Board on the projects of Arctic shelf ice, at T 3 and in the Antarctic; however, they have especially organized expeditions to the Greenland Ice Cap and to the marginal areas of the ice sheet. Many expeditions have worked on the Greenland Ice Cap, some of them only with military problems; but many of them have accomplished very important scientifical investigations, of which only the most important will be cited below:

In 1952 a small expedition of 9 men with *R. Guillard* and *Victor Layton* as leaders crossed the Ice Cap from Thule to Kap Georg Cohn. Seismic soundings were taken by *Jean Jacques Holtzscherer* (1954) in collaboration with the University of Georgetown (*Victor* 1955). The snow studies were carried out by *Carl S. Benson*.

In 1953 the Americans started the *Operation Icecap* in the Thule region for studies of the physical characteristics of the Greenland Ice Cap and its marginal zones. Four groups of scientists were working in different areas: group 1 called *Ramp* under the leadership of *Richard P. Goldthwait* studied the edge of the Ice Cap on the Nunatarssuaq peninsula at the head of Wolstenholme Fjord; studies were carried out by *Laurence Nobles* (1954) and by *S. E. White* (1956), among others. Group 2 called *Solo* under *Coleman C. Fischer* studied the access route to the Ice Cap near Thule, and seismic soundings and snow studies were made along a route on the Ice Cap to a point 300 miles east of Thule. Group 3, the *Norcut,* under *Robert L. Nichols,* carried through a traverse to Inglefield Land, studying the ice cliffs and the ice-free areas in front of the Ice Cap. Seismic work on the Ice Cap was here carried out by *Holtzscherer* (1954). The fourth group studied the geology of the Thule region, independently of the Ice Cap investigations. A preliminary report of the results was published by *Howard B. Hutchinson* (1953), who was the co-ordinator of the research programme for the Stanford Research Institute.

At the same time another American expedition *Project Mint Julep* worked in Southwest Greenland. In 1947 a military ground operation »Snowman« found a smooth ice area approximately 100 miles southeast of Søndre Strømfjord at 66° 16' N., 47° 46' W. at an altitude of about 1650 m; the whole area was very close to the firn-line*), and it will be possible to use some of the areas for air-strips, necessitating but little care and maintenance; therefore, a research programme was sponsored by the *Arctic Desert Tropical Information Center* together with the *American Geographical Society*. In May

---

*) These hard, smooth areas of glacier ice, free of crevasses, are found at many places along the firn-line.

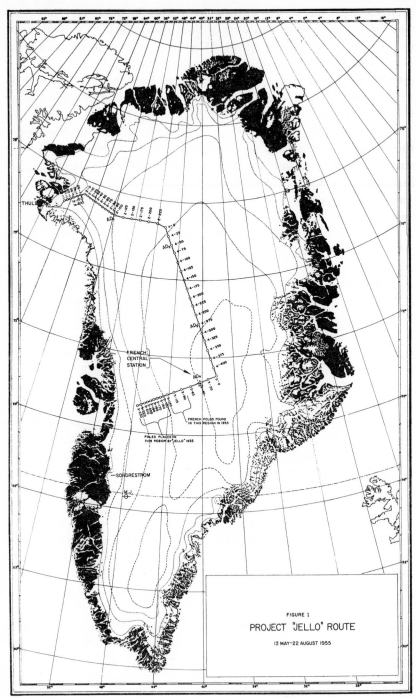

Fig. 2. Snow studies made by Expedition „Jello" 1955.
(C. S. Benson & R. H. Ragle, 1956).

1953 eight Jamesway huts were brought in by planes; a camp site was constructed, and investigations were carried out in the area until August. Snow-stratification was studied by *Robert L. Shuster* (1954), the ablation by *R. L. LaChapelle* (1954), while the sastrugi and the »nieves penetente« especially were studied by *L. R. Wilson* (1954); the hydrology of the meltwater streams was measured by *G. William Holmes* (1954).

In 1954 several projects were started in the Thule region and on the Greenland Ice Cap. *Carl S. Benson* (1955) was the leader of a small mobile scientific expedition *Party Crystal* with weasels working on the Ice Cap eastward of Thule Air Base. The work included measuring of elevation, snow accumulation, summer melting and snow properties. *George P. Rigsby* (1955) carried out the first studies of ice fabrics from a polar glacier, taking samples from the ice fronts at Nunatarssuaq and from the Moltke Gletscher. Extensive studies of the accumulation, the ablation, the glacial meteorology and the superimposed ice were conducted by *Valter Schytt* (1955) on the Thule Ramp of the Ice Cap. In connection with this project *Barry C. Bishop* (1957) started a study of the well developed shear moraines at the edge of the Ice Cap at Thule. Of special importance for the glaciological studies are the investigations carried out under the direction of *Henri Bader* at a test site established 320 km. east of Thule Air Base at an altitude of 2.134 m.; the latitude of the place, which was called Site 2, is very near 78° N. In 1954 a pit was excavated here to a depth of 30 m, and a 18 m core drill hole was sunk by hand drilling from the bottom of the pit to a total depth of 48 m. The stratigraphic study of the snow in the deep pit permits dating of the annual layers back to 1908. Investigations of the density, viscosity and all other physical properties of the snow were conducted at Site 2 and on the basis of samples brought to the cold laboratory at Wilmette (*Bader* 1955). Studies of snow — with a view to examining the traficability of snow and the possibilities of using it for constructions — were carried out by *R. Waterhaus* (1955) and others. The investigations of the Nunatarssuaq were continued under *Laurence Nobles* and a study of the glacier crevasses was started by *R. L. Schuster* and *F. A. Small* in Blue Ice Valley, one of the big tributaries to the Moltke Gletscher at the head of Wolstenholme Fjord. 1954 was a very warm summer, perhaps the warmest in North Greenland for the last 30 years; the melting on the Ice Cap was bigger than normal, a fact which makes the 1954 surface a very distinct feature for snow pit studies in the future.

In 1955 the SIPRE work from the preceding years was continued; studies of the aspects of geometry, mechanics and thermodynamics of processes for the developing of crevasses were this year conducted by *Mark F. Meier* (1957) at Blue Ice Valley, while the studies of the ramp at Tuto were continued by *Thomas M. Griffiths* (1957), and *Laurence Nobles* worked in the Nunatarssuaq region. Of special interest this year was the expedition »*Jello*« under the leadership of *Carl S. Benson* and *R. H. Ragle* (1956). The expedition started from Thule Air Base; one of the objects was snow studies along the route from Thule to a point on the Ice Cap at 77° 06' N., 43° 00' W., from here along the crest of the inland ice down to 71° 28' N., 37° 15' W., and further on to the French Station Centrale and along the French trail to Victor's old camp VI at 69° 45' N., 48° 15' W., where the members of the expedition were evacuated by plane. Another purpose of the expedition was to extend all the markers and to measure the accumulation of the French prominent markers as well as their displacement since 1951. A resurveying of Station Centrale was carried out by *George Wallerstein*, who found the position to be 70° 54' N. and 40° 37' 57" W., and a calculation made by *L. Tschaen* and *A. Bauer* (1958) showed a displacement of 170 m. per year in a southwestern direction, a fact which was rather astonishing.

Another important investigation in 1955 was the studies at Site 2; here the deformation of excavations in the névé was measured by *J. K. Landauer* (1957), glacial meteorological observations were executed by *M. Diamond* and *R. W. Gerdel* (1956), who especially studied the global and net radiation, the conditions for the whiteout and the occurrence of blowing snow on the Ice Cap. At the edge of the Ice Cap, near Tuto, the construction of a tunnel 152 m long and $1,7 \times 2.0$ m wide in the ice was started; in 1956 the tunnel was extended over a distance of 32 m, and a room 18×18 m and 8 m high was excavated. It is the first time that such big rooms have been excavated in the glacier ice. The tunnel was made partly for engineering purpose, partly with a view to scientifical studies, especially for measuring of the shearplanes and as control of the seismic and gravimetric determinations of the thickness of the ice. The tunnel started from a vertical ice cliff, and the excavations were directed by *Donald O. Rausch* (1958). A smaller ice tunnel was excavated on Nunatarssuaq in connection with the studies of the vertical ice cliffs of the North Ice; here *Richard P. Goldthwait* (1956, 1957) carried out comprehensive studies of the conditions for the position and the balance of the vertical ice cliffs.

In 1956 the SIPRE studies continued at the Site 2 and at other places on the Ice Cap, and a special expedition under *Norman Goldstein* made seismic soundings with a new type of instrument in the area where no reflection was recorded by the British Simpson Expedition; this time the investigations were successful, and the thickness of the ice was determined. Another expedition under *Robert Frost* reconnoitred the access routes to the Southern Greenland Ice Cap, especially in the Narssarssuaq and the Ivigtut areas and along Frederikshåb Isblink. In many respects this year was a preparation for the IGY, and an international glaciological course was held in the Thule area under the leadership of *Henry Bader* and *B. Fristrup*. Experiments with deep core drilling were made at Site 2, and a depth of nearly 1.000 feet was reached; the core from this depth represented real glacier ice, the age of which is estimated to go back to 1500. A very careful examination was carried out, and analyses of grain size, density, particulates, rati $0^{16}/0^{18}$, volcanic ash horizons, gas content, deuterium etc. were executed. The HIRAN stations on the Ice Cap were also established in connection with the IGY, and simultaneously with the construction of the sites very detailed snow studies were carried out. A 10 m. high steel-tower of a special SIPRE construction was erected, making it possible to find the stations even after they had been covered by snow; in spring 1959 at least one of the stations has been completely covered, and its presence is only revealed by the steel tower. The positions of the stations are according for the »Manuel d'Operations« of the International glaciological Expedition.

> station 26:   68° 15' N., 36° 30' W.
> »   27:   69° 23' N., 35° 55' W.
> »   28:   70° 37' N., 36° 10' W.
> »   29:   68° 04' N., 42° 20' W.
> »   30:   69° 33' N., 43° 10' W.
> »   31:   70° 55' N., 40° 48' W.

A resurveying of the French Station Centrale showed the position to be 70° 54' 43" N. and 40° 37' 21" W. and, consequently, overthrew the theory of displacement of the Station Centrale as put forward by *Tschaen* and *Bauer* (1958). A new calculation of the position af Station Centrale have been published by L. Tschaen (1959).

In 1957 the SIPRE programme still continued. The deep drilling this year started with a new equipment, and a hole was drilled down to 411 m. The diameter of the core was 10 cm., and a continued core was taken up from a depth of down to 300 m.; from below this depth only some separate cores were brought up; 160 m. of selected half-cores were transported by air in dry ice to the SIPRE Laboratory at Wilmette for further detailed investigations: stratigraphy, pressure in the enclosed air bubbles, shape and size distribution of the bubbles, porosity and permeability, snow structure, metamorphism and ice fabrics, content of particles, isotopic analyses (e. g. $0_{16}/0_{18}$, deuterium, tritium), grain-size distribution and content of bacteria. A preliminary report has been given by *Langway* (1958). The studies at the Thule Ramp under *M. Griffiths* were continued and achieved. At Site 2 the investigations of the snow drift were carried on, and studies of the snow structure were also executed. In South Greenland a surveying with a view to an access route to the Ice Cap was carried out in the region of Narssarssuaq.

In 1958 the studies in the Thule region were continued, and an American reconnaissance expedition named *Operation King Dog* worked in the Søndre Strømfjord region, studying the access to the Ice Cap and the marginal zone; glaciological investigations were carried out.

The Danish glaciological investigations under the IGY were executed under the leadership of *Fristrup* (1958); however, all the stations were local glaciers outside the Ice Cap, and only the measurements at the Hurlburt Gletcher in the Thule district have some relation to Ice Cap studies, especially as a control and reference for the ramp studies at Thule Air Base.

At the International Congress of the Geophysical Union in Rome in 1954 the plans were made public for an *International Glaciological Expedition to the Greenland Ice Cap*, usually called *E.G.I.G.*, under the patronage of the International Association for Scientifical Hydrology, and a co-operation between Denmark, France, Germany, Switzerland and Austria was established with the object of studying the mass balance of the Greenland ice sheet. In April and May 1957 a reconnaissance of the access route was carried out, and an air reconnaissance of the Kangerdlugssuaq region and of some of the outlet glaciers to Umanak and Disko Bugt was made in July the same year. The possibility of using air photogrammetry for determination of the velocity of ice movements in glaciers was discussed on the basis of some air photos taken in July 1957, see *Finsterwalder* (1958), *Baussart* (1958) and *Hofmann* (1958). Preliminary plans for the geodetic work of the expedition were published by *Lichte* (1957) and *Hofmann* (1958). In 1958 a ground reconnaissance was carried out, and a remeasuring of some ablation markers was put into work; *Bauer* found that some of the old markers in the Eqip sermia region from the French work in 1949—53 seem to indicate a lowering of the firn-line, and superimposed ice up to 2 metres was covering some of the markers originally put up. On the basis of observations in 1958 *Bauer* estimates the line of equilibrium to have lowered 200 m. from 1950 (rapport interne d'E.G.I.G. 1958).

In connection with the E.G.I.G. a French expedition under *Dumont* established a base on the Ice Cap at 71° 21' N., 33° 55' W. by parachuting all the equipment and the members of the expedition. Meteorological investigations were carried out, and during the winter time a glaciological pit was excavated down to 42 m. below the surface. At the evacuation of the station in spring 1957 the pit was closed very carefully. A detailed investigation of the stratigraphy and other snow studies will be carried out during the wintering of the E.G.I.G. expeditions at the same place 1959/60. The meteorological results have not been published.

In 1958 The *British West Greenland Expedition* under *O. Henry* and *White* worked on the Lyngbræen descending from the Sukkertoppen Ice Cap; the main object was to study the formation of ogives.

An expedition to the West Greenland waters was organized in 1958 by the Arctic Institute of North America under the leadership of *David Nutt* and *Per F. Scholander;* however, although this expedition did not include the Ice Cap proper it is possible that it will give the answer to the problems of the age of the Ice Cap and also to other problems. The object of the expedition was to investigate the gas content in glacier ice; to this purpose a continuation of investigations was carried out on samples from icebergs from Labrador waters (»Blue Dolphins«, *Labrador Expedition* 1954). Previous investigations had been devoted to studies of the air pressure in the bubbles in glacier ice; from the Ice Cap measurings have been made by *Chester C. Langway* (1958), among others. According to some preliminary results published by *Scholander, Kanwisher* and *Nutt* (1956), *Coachman, Hemmingsen, Scholander, Enns* and *de Vries* (1958) it is possible to determine the age of the gas content by Carbon 14 analyses of the carbon dioxide in the gas bubbles and, thereby, to determine the age of the ice. According to investigations made by *Epstein* (1956), by *Robert P. Sharp* and *Epstein* (1958) and by *Dansgaard* (1954, 1958), the ratio of the common isotopes of oxygen O^{18} to O^{16} in snow is influenced by the temperature at which the precipitation takes place and, therefore, by the altitude of the place where the snow is deposited; consequently, the O^{18} content most likely decreases with increasing distance from the coast. *Epstein* found a decrease in the H_2O^{18} content in the precipitation at increasing altitude. *Dansgaard* is of opinion that on the basis of these preliminary results it will be possible to determine not only the age of the ice in the icebergs produced by the Greenland Ice Cap, but also the region of the Ice Cap from which the ice originates. Only a preliminary report has yet been published.

In spring 1959 the International Glaciological Expedition started the work from Søndre Strømfjord.

II. Scientific Results.

Since the first crossing of the Greenland Ice Cap carried through by *Nansen* in 1888 many geographical problems in this region have been solved; however, many researches still remain to be carried out before we know the age, the origin of the ice sheet, the total regime and the balance of the whole Ice Cap, and at present we know very little about the geophysical conditions of the ice in the interior part of the Ice Cap. During the last years many papers concerning the glaciology of the Greenland Ice Cap have been published, among them some summaries, see *Kayser* (1928), *Milthers* (1953), *Bauer* (1954) and *Sharp* (1956); further, a number of publications from the recent American and British investigations have appeared; therefore, the following summary will be of some interest:

Topography:

The general topography of the Ice Cap is well known from the maps; a picture of the altitudes is given by the following maps:

1. *Grønland 1 : 5.000.000* published by *the Geodetic Institute, Copenhagen;* the latest edition from 1957.

2. *Géographie Glaciaire du Groenland* par *Paul-Emile Victor,* carte révisée au 31er janvier 1955; a) étendue probable de la fonte d'été et b) altitudes.

3. *Altitudinal map of part of North Greenland and North-East Greenland* in Meddelelser om Grønland 143, no. 1, 1950.

4. *World Aeronautical Chart 1 : 1.000.000* published by *Aeronautical Chart Service, U.S. Air Force, Washington.*

As it appears from the maps, the predominant topographic feature is the division of the Greenland Ice Cap in two domes, a smaller southern summit with altitudes up to 2.700—2.800 m. and a larger, very uniform northern dome with altitudes up to 3.200—3.300 m. Between the two domes is a broad depression running approximately from the Disko Bugt to south-west of Angmagssalik. The greater part of the depression has an altitude of 2.200 m. The highest point of the Ice Cap has not been exactly determined; however, it seems to be very near 3.300 m.; the highest part of the ice sheet is situated west of Scoresby Sund, and over a distance of more than 800 km. the Ice Cap has altitudes above 3.000 m. The highest part of the Ice Cap with the crest or the surface ice-divide is much nearer the east coast than the west coast; this makes the Ice Cap very asymmetrical. The reason why and the development of the ice crest have been the subject of much speculation. According to *Wager* (1933) the crest represents the region of the greatest ice thickness, while *Sorge* (1933) supports the view that the ridge is the result of a maximum accumulation, to all probability not from recent time, but from an earlier date, the ridge thus being a relict of a former climatic condition. In 1943 *Demorest* published as his opinion that the crest reflects an elevation in the subglacial topography. The numerous traverses across the Ice Cap have made it clear that the surface is rather uniform over big areas, and a study of the region on both sides of the crest has been published in a preliminary report from *Benson* (1955); according to him the slopes near the crest are very gentle, only 5—50 feet per mile, and the surface of the ice sheet is relatively smooth and featureless; however, more detailed surveying has revealed several relief features with numerous hills, basins and other topographic features; the majority of the slopes averaged 0,3 %, and the steepest slope measured was 1,9 %. Further, a very characteristic undulation of the surface has been reported from many expeditions. The micro-relief is most probably the result of local meteorological conditions and, consequently, is dynamic and liable to change from time to time. Many of the sastrugi patterns have a very close resemblance to the ripple marks in sand dunes at the coasts and in the deserts, while other sastrugi forms are erosion forms and have no related patterns in dune-landscapes; the whole problem of the sastrugi forms and the developing of one from another has not been studied in Greenland; however, such studies would probably explain some of the features of the micro-relief.

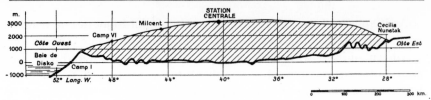

Fig. 3. Cross section through the Ice Cap from Disko Bugt to Cecilia Nunatak
(Exp. Pol. Franc., Rapp. prél. 16, 1953).

The macro-relief with the two domes and the asymmetrical shape of the Ice Cap is very complicated. According to the seismic soundings by *Holtzscherer* (1954) the southern dome overlies a high part of the subglacial substratum; however, this is not the case of the northern dome. Here the substratum is formed as a large saucer, the central part of which is extending below sea level to a maximum depth of —250 m.; a system of subglacial valleys is coming from the Disko Bugt reaching far in below the Ice Cap. No such valleys have been found draining off to the east coast; the bed-rock surface under the ice is higher at the east coast than at the west coast. Consequently, according to *Holtzscherer,* the crest has no direct relation to the subglacial topography; therefore, he advanced the opinion that the ice crest is due to a restraining of the easy outflow eastward caused by the high eastern mountains. As pointed out by many authors, among them also *Victor,* a predominant feature of the ice dynamics of the Greenland Ice Cap is the occurrence of »ice streams«, i.g. the ice streams flowing in a colder and therefore more solid ice. Ice streams are predominant in several regions of Greenland and especially in the region around Disko Bugt and Umanak Fjord; here many glaciers are descending to the sea, many of which are very active with high velocities, up to 25—30 m. a day, and with a big production of icebergs. Such glaciers seem not only to follow subglacial valleys in the bed-rock floor, but also appear as ice streams draining a larger area than the one corresponding to the subglacial bed-rock topography. The depression between the two domes therefore can be explained as a result of the rapid outflow of the ice to the Disko Bugt which lowers the ice surface. The easy glacial outflow to the west as compared with the restrained outflow to the east may be interpreted as follows: the mass of ice moving west is bigger than the mass moving east, and the result of this is that the ice-divide is pressed to the east of the centre-line. In this connection it should be pointed out that in North Greenland the ice-crest is nearer to the centre-line than farther south, and according to the general topography and to the seismic results obtained by *Holtzscherer* there is no great difference in this region between the possibilities of outflow of ice to the east and to the west.

The difference in the accumulation has been studied by *Benson and Ragle* (1956), who found a decrease of accumulation towards higher elevation; the 4-year accumulation established on the basis of the resurveying in 1955 of the French markers indicates an approximate eastward decrease of 5 cm. per 20 miles. The results obtained are only from central Greenland; in North Greenland *Benson* (1955) found that the greater part of the accumulation comes from the Melville Bugt, and the areas to the south and to the east of the expedition routes act as catchment-basins; in addition a considerable portion of the new snow was blown off the ridge, and there was no variation of any importance of the annual accumulation according to the longitude. From the British North Greenland Expedition *Bull* (1958) and *Hamilton* (1958) report as a result of their investigations that the mean annual accumulation was almost constant at the altitudes between 1850 and 2500 m.; along the whole traverse-route where the gravity had been examined and near the coast the accumulation was less, due to a presumably increased ablation. The general direction of the winds above the Ice Cap was found to be south-westerly, and there is a considerable asymmetry in the surface wind-system in North Greenland, as mentioned by *Bull*. In the area above the ridge the south-westerly winds are predominant, whereas farther to the east catabatic winds are ruling; therefore, *Bull* supports, though with a certain reservation, the point of view that the change in accumulation is more associated with the wind-pattern than with the differences of precipitation. *Bull* is of opinion that the results of the Koch und Wegener Expedition (1930), which found the accumulation along the western part of their route to be more than twice the accumulation along the eastern half, the demarcation line coinciding with the north-south ridge, must have their origin in an exceptional year with precipitation very far from the normal conditions. After having compared his investigations with *Benson*'s results, *Bull* has come to the conclusion that in the area north-east of Baffin Bay, bounded by the main north-south ridge and by the ridge of the lobe extending west and south towards the Thule Air Base, the annual accumulation is about 35 g./sq.cm. and greatly exceeds that to the north and to the east, where it has been found to be 15 g./sq.cm.; the difference of accumulation is obviously due to a concentration of the differences of precipitation and of the deflation in the areas situated to both sides of the ridge.

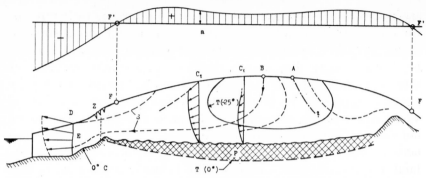

Fig. 4. A rough sketch of the Ice Cap. *Above:* Accumulation and ablation.
Below: Ice streams and temperature conditions (hypothetic). F (snow line)
S (shear lines) C_1, C_2, D (profile of velocity of the glacial drift) E (ice streams)
Z (zone of crevasses) A (hydrographical ice-divide) a (accumulation of snow)
B (cinematical ice-divide) T ($\div$ 25°) (isotherm $\div$ 25° C (Robin)) T (0°)
(isotherm 0° C) P (permafrost). (Haefeli 1957).

The influence of the wind and of the blowing snow has been
emphasized by many authors, see *Ljungner* (1944), and as pointed
out by *Bauer* (1955) the Ice Cap is very sensitive to all accumulation
fluctuations; therefore, it is evident that even if the crest is a result
of differences of meteorological conditions a change of climate may
have the result that at present the crest is not situated at the place
of greatest accumulation; and, according to the above-mentioned
observations, it is most probable that the crest is not in the proximity of the region of greatest accumulation, at least not under the
present conditions, and there is no direct relation between the crest
and the topography of the substratum; however, a certain relation
may be sought in the restraining of the outflow of the ice to the east
exercised by the high mountains at the east coast of Greenland,
culminating in Gunnbjørns Fjeld, 3.700 m.

Another cause of the surface-form of the Greenland Ice Cap must
be brought into discussion: the historical factor, which has not been
much mentioned in literature. As pointed out by previous authors,
the Ice Cap has a very great age. According to *L. R. Wager* (1933)
and *Lauge Koch* (1950) the Greenland Ice Cap has existed since
Miocene time, and ice coming to the surface to-day is possibly many
thousand years old. Consequently, the Ice Cap not only reflects the
existing conditions, but also the conditions which were prevailing many thousand years earlier. We must also take into consideration that
the present Ice Cap has not originally developed as a single, rather
uniform glacier; until a few years ago the normal opinion among
the geologists was that the Ice Cap might have developed as a high-

land glacier and from the central part spread out over the surrounding lower land; however, judging from the knowledge obtained
by the seismic soundings this supposition cannot hold good; it may
be true of the southern dome, whereas the whole northern dome
must have developed not as a single glacier, but by fusion of several
glaciers descending from the coastal mountain range; how fast, at
which plane and at which place the fusion has taken place, we do
not know. When taking into consideration the difference in climate
between the humid West-Greenland and the continental East-Green-
land, there is all probability that the fusion has taken place at a
rather long distance to the east of the centre-line of Greenland. After
the fusion of the glaciers, which most likely were of the type Piedmont glaciers, the building-up of the Ice Cap took place and thus
completely changed the whole system of movement and shearplanes etc. It seems rather natural to think that in the interior part
of the ice still certain features remain which have more relation
to the older rheology of the ice than to the existing and, therefore,
also may influence the present shape of the Ice Cap. In this connection it is of the greatest importance that according to several
glaciologists, cf. *Haefeli* (1957), it ist probable that part of the
deepest ice does not contribute to the general ice movement, and
at present we do not know if the whole Greenland Ice Cap is in
equilibrium or not.

The total area of the Greenland Ice Cap has been calculated by
several authors. Official Danish statistics have been based on a
planimetry of the Danish maps from 1920, according to which the
total area of Greenland is 2.182.000 sq.km. and that of the Ice Cap
1.869.000 sq.km. *Bauer* (1955) found by a planimetry based on the
15 World Aeronautical Chart US AF in the scale 1: 1.000.000 covering Greenland that the area of the Ice Cap was 1.726.400 sq.km.
and that of the other glaciated areas 76.200 sq.km., while the total
area of Greenland was found to be 2.186.000 sq.km. Considering the
greater scale of the map, *Bauer*'s figures are most probably quite
correct. The highest point was found by the French expeditions to
be at 72° N. lat. 37° 30' W. long., and according to a hypsometric
curve calculated by *Bauer* (1954) the mean height was 2.135 m.

The climate of the Ice Cap
has been studied by nearly all the expeditions crossing the ice sheet.
The glacial anticyclone theory advanced by *William Hobbs* in 1910

has been much discussed. The observations from the Wegener Expedition and from the British Arctic Airroute Expedition have shown that the central part of Greenland is not dominated by good weather and high pressure and that calm weather, contrary to the theory, very seldom exists on the Ice Cap; in spite of this, Hobbs and with him many other geographers still have supported the theory of glacial anticyclone. When *Helge Petersen* in 1938 published his volume on the climate of Greenland in Köppens Handbuch der Klimatologie he demonstrated the importance of the cyclonic activities especially in South Greenland; however, his work does not seem to have acquired the expected importance, perhaps because it was written in German and not in English. In 1946 and in 1950 *Matthes* published the results of his study of the anticyclone theory and demonstrated very clearly, based on the observations from the expeditions in the 1930-ies, that there is no glacial anticyclone over the Greenland Ice Cap; his results were confirmed by the observations carried out at Station Centrale by the French expedition. These observations showed that there is a very low catabatic wind draining the slopes of the ice sheet to the coast. This wind is local and is strongest in the marginal zone of the Ice Cap and weak at Station Centrale. Here the mean wind was 7 m./sec. with a maximum speed of 35 m./sec., and real calm weather was seldom; the predominant wind-direction was E.S.E. The mean temperature of the year is –30,3, the mean temperature for January is –47,3 and for July –10,8 (according to *Georgi* 1953/54). The temperature varies very much, and in the course of four days the temperature rose from –62° to –15°, at another occasion from –64,8° to –36° in the course of 24 hours (22–23/2 1950); the minimum temperature for the whole period was –64,8° and the maximum temperature 0,7°. The observations from the Northice have been published by *R. A. Hamilton* and *G. Rollitt* (1957), and they are very similar to those made by Station Centrale; the maximum temperature was found to be –1° and the minimum temperature –66°; the mean wind speed was only 4 m./sec. The observations from Site 2 and from Station Dumont have not yet been published.

Snow studies

and especially studies of the snow stratification were already carried out by *de Quervain* and by *Koch und Wegener;* however, the most important studies were carried out by *Sorge* (1935) at Station

Eismitte; here he found that the grains in the summer layers were slightly larger than those in the winter layers, and that this variation could serve to determine existing boundaries down to 6 m.; below this level it appeared to be difficult to measure the grain size. According to *Sorge* the winter deposits consisted of hard and dense layers, while the softer and less dense firn originates from snowfall during the summer. A study of the snow stratification was made by *Etienne* (1940) on Sukkertoppen Ice Cap, and his conclusion was this: high density identical with summer-layers and low density with winter-layers, which is the opposite of *Sorge*'s conclusions; *Schytt* (1958) is of opinion that this is most probably a misinterpretation of the layers, and *Sorge*'s classification of the layers has been confirmed by the studies carried out by *Schuster* (1954), by the American snow investigations around Site 2 and by *Benson* on the Ice Cap. A comprehensive report on the snow-pit studies is being prepared by *Carl Benson*.

The density variation as a function of depth has been studied by *Heuberger* as a result of the French drilling operation; the results have been much discussed by *Schytt* (1958), who argues that the measurings have been carried out in such a way that the compression of the drilling cores has varied much, thus provoking a wrong calculation of the densities; this is expected to be confirmed or not when the results from the American deep drilling are published.

The temperature in the ice

has been determined at several places. At Site 2 in North Greenland the mean annual temperature was found by *Langway* (1958) to be –25°, and during the deep drilling he found the temperature to decrease with the depth; the temperature gradiant between 250 m. and 400 m. was constantly 0,14° per 100 m., and at 400 m. the temperature was –25,42°. At Northice the temperature was –28° at 15 m. below the snow-surface. At Station Centrale *Heuberger* (1954) found that the mean temperature was –27°, and that the temperature from 90 m. to 100 m. and downwards was constantly –27,78°. At Camp VI the temperature was –12 at a depth of 10 m. decreasing to –16,5 at a depth of 130 m. According to a theory advanced by *Victor* (1956) the Ice Cap should at present have a temperature lower than could be expected from to-day's climatic conditions.

The temperatures at the bottom of the ice and in the substratum have not been measured; however, some informations have been collected from the geophysical investigations, in the first place from the seismic soundings. From the high speed of the seismic waves found by the French seismic investigations *Holtzscherer* (1954) drew the conclusion that the central part of the Ice Cap was cold down to the bottom; the temperature at the bottom he estimated to be –10°, and below the ice he found evidence of a 200 m. thick layer of permafrost. In 1955 *G. de Q. Robin* published a very fascinating calculation of the distribution of temperature in an ice sheet by making simplified assumptions of the heat flow, and he worked out a quantitative method of estimating the temperature distribution near the centre of the Greenland Ice Cap. Based on a thickness of the ice of 3.000 m., an accumulation of 30 cm. per year and a surface temperature of –29°, *Robin* calculated the bottom temperature to be –12°, which is very close to the figure arrived at by *Holtzscherer*. *Haefeli and Brentani* (1956) calculated the bottom temperature on a completely different base, the results of a rheological investigation of an approximately 50 m. thick ice cap at the Jungfraujoch were used for calculating the thermal conditions in the Ice Cap and especially the temperatures at the bottom; from the movement and the viscosity conditions they concluded that the Ice Cap in the central part is frozen hard to the base, where the resultant shear stresses are well below the shear strength; this means that the temperature is below zero and, consequently, we will find permafrost; as pointed out by *Haefeli* (1957), this should be interpreted as follows: the movement near the bedrock is insignificant and, therefore, the erosion is inconsiderable. Also at Camp VI *Holtzscherer* found that the velocity of the seismic waves in the layer below the ice was very near the velocity found in permafrost, and he therefore assumed the existence of permafrost at this place too. In North Greenland investigations and calculations have been carried out by *Bull* (1957), who came to the conclusion that near the centre of the Ice Cap in North Greenland the bottom of the ice sheet must be at the melting point (–1,5°), and he advances as his opinion that the result of the melting is a lubrication between the ice and the underlying substratum; consequently, the movement of the ice here should be possible with a smaller stress than in the region of Station Centrale. Along the eastern part of the British traverse the bottom temperature was most probably at the melting point at all places, while in the western side as well as farther south the temperature was presumably so low that permafrost layers existed. According to present informations it seems that the thermal conditions in the Ice Cap itself are far from uniform, and a distinct picture of the conditions for the greater part of the ice sheet can only be obtained by further investigations.

The regime and the balance of the Ice Cap

have been studied from many sides. It is evident from many observations that under the present climatic conditions most of the outlet glaciers from the Ice Cap are retreating. Retreat of the glaciers descending to Independence Fjord and to Hagen Fjord has been found by *Fristrup* (1950, 1951); the retreat of the glacier to Inglefield Fjord has been described by *Fristrup* (1959) and of the glacier to Wolstenholme Fjord by *Wright* (1939). A study of the frontal variations of Upernaviks Isstrøm and of the inland-ice margina around Upernaviks Isstrøm has been published by *Weidick* (1958); glacier oscillations in the Umanak district have been studied by *Ransley* (1952), and the retreat of Eqip sermia has been described by *Bauer* (1955 b). A study of the oscillations of Jakobshavns Isbræ has been carried out by *Meldgaard* (1958) in connection with the archaeological investigations, and he found that during the last 2.500 years the front has not advanced farther than the position in 1850—70; since there has been a retreat. A study of the border of the Ice Cap and of the outlet glacier published by *Weidick* (1959) contains much information based on studies of old photos, maps and so on. Observations of a retreat of the glacier descending from the Ice Cap to the sea in the Angmagssalik district have been carried out by *Fristrup* (1959); retreat of glaciers in NE Greenland has been described by *Foster Flint* (1948) and others and of glaciers from Dronning Louise Land by *H. Lister* (1956); retreat of several glaciers in NE Greenland was also found by *Fristrup* (1951) during the Danish Pearyland Expedition.

From the above mentioned publications it appears that the border and the outlet glaciers from the Ice Cap have been retreating for a long time and, further, that the retreat started earlier in South Greenland than in North Greenland. The very small number of observations carried out — such as the lowering of the equilibrium line in Eqip sermia described by *Bauer* (1959) — seem to indicate that the retreat is possibly diminishing, and that the ice is even slightly growing in somes places. The well developed trim-lines along the greater part of the Greenland Ice Cap have undoubtedly been noticed by most geographers who have flown across Greenland.

The retreat of the marginal zone is not a proof of a diminishing of the whole Ice Cap, and at several occasions *Bader* has supported the theory that at present a construction of the central part of the Ice Cap is going on, tending to a greater and greater height, and when the culminating point has been reached the ice will suddenly spread out over the surrounding low land (see *Lliboutry* 1957). His theory is based on the calculation of the movement velocity for the discharge of icebergs and for the ablation according to the accumulation going on to-day, and he came to the conclusion that the known ice-movement seems to be very insignificant in proportion to the great amount of precipitation falling over the central Ice Cap. Contrary to this *Bauer* (1955) made a calculation by estimating the total accumulation to be 446 sq.km. of water, the ablation to 315 sq.km. and the production of icebergs to 215 sq.km.; accordingly, the deficit for the whole Ice Cap will be about 100 sq.km. of water or nearly a fourth of the accumulation. Previously, several calculations have been carried out, showing other results; however, as all the estimates have been based on very few observations, the results remain uncertain, and it has very little scientifical value to make a calculation on purely estimated figures. A rather interesting problem which may have some relation to the balance of the Ice Cap has been described by *Saxov* (1958), who found that after a long period of sinking of the West Greenland coast a rising has taken place since 1940, and even at a very high speed, on an average around 14 mm. per year; the most probable explanation of this is a diminishing of the Ice Cap and, consequently, an uplift of the land in accordance with the isostasy. Changes in precipitation during the last 30 years have been studied by Diamond (1956).

Only a very accurate levelling across the Ice Cap combined with determinations of the ice thickness along the whole profile and a resurveying of all measurements 10—12 years later will give the answer, and the main object of the EGIG Expedition 1959—60 is to established the first measuring of the profile from the Disko Bugt to Cecilia Nunatak.

LITERATURE

Ahlmann, H. W: son (1948): Glaciological Researches on the North Atlantic Coasts. Roy. Geogr. Soc., Res. Ser. 1.
– (1953): Glacier Variations and Climatic Fluctuations. Amer. Geogr. Soc., Bowmann Mem. Lect., Ser. 3.
Arctic Institute Greenland Expedition 1958: Field Report 1958 by David C. Nutt, Per F. Scholander, Lawrence K. Coachmann, Willy Dansgaard. Oslo.
Bader, H. (1955): Excavations and Installations at SIPRE Test Site, Site 2. Greenland. SIPRE Report 20.
Bauer, Albert (1953): Campagne au Groenland de 1948. Triangulation côtière de la région de l'Eqe. Rapports scientifiques des Expéditions Polaires Françaises N. III: 1. Annales de Géophys. 9: 1.
– (1954): Contribution à la Connaissance de l'Indlandsis du Groenland. IIe partie: Synthèse Glaciologique. Paris.
– (1955, a): The Balance of the Greenland Ice Sheet. Journ. of glaciol. 2: 17.
– (1955, b): Le Glacier de l'Eqe. Glaciologie Groenland II. Expéditions Polaires Françaises, Missions Paul-Emile Victor. VI. Paris.
Baussart, M. (1958): Essai de détermination par photogrammetrie de la vitesse superficielle d'un glacier du Groenland. Symposium de Chamonix. Publ. A.I.H.S. 47.
Benson, C. S. (1955, a): Scientific Work of Party Crystal 1954. SIPRE Report 24.
– (1955, b): Operation and Logistic of Ice Cap Party Crystal 1954. SIPRE Report 25.
Benson, C. S. and R. H. Ragle (1956): Measurements by SIPRE in 1955 on the Accumulation Markers of Expéditions Polaires Françaises in Central Greenland. SIPRE Special Report 19.
Bishop, Barry C. (1957): Shear Moraines in the Thule Area, Northwest Greenland. SIPRE Report 17.
Bull, C. (1957): Observations in North Greenland relating to Theories of the Properties of Ice. Journ. of Glaciol. 3: 21.
– (1958): Snow Accumulation in North Greenland. Journ. of Glaciol. 3: 24.
Carlsson, W. S. (1939): Movement of some Greenland Glaciers. Geol. Soc. Amer., Bull. 50.
Coachmann, L. K., E. Hemmingsen, P. F. Scholander, T. Enns and H. de Vries (1958): Gases in Glaciers. Science 127.
Dansgaard, W. (1954): The O^{18}-abundance in Fresh Water. Geoch. et Cosmoch. Acta 6: 5/6.
– Nogle meteorologiske og glaciologiske problemer belyst ved målinger af de stabile iltisotoper i vand. Fysisk Tidsskrift 1958 nr. 2–3.
Demorest, Max (1943): Ice Sheet. Geol. Soc. Amer., Bull. 54.
Diamond, M. (1956): Precipitation Trends in Greenland during the past 30 Years. SIPRE Res. Report 22.
Diamond, M. and R. W. Gerdel (1956): Radiation Measurements on the Greenland Ice Cap. SIPRE Res. Report 19.
– (1957): Occurrence of Blowing Snow on the Greenland Ice Cap. SIPRE Res. Report 25.

Epstein, S. (1956): Variation of the $0^{18}/0^{16}$ Ratio of Fresh Water and Ice. Nat. Acad. Sci. Nat. Res. Council. Publ. 400: IV.

Etienne, Erich (1940): Expeditionsbericht der Grönland-Expedition der Universität Oxford 1938. Veröff. des Geophys. Inst. der Univ. Leipzig. Zweite Ser. XIII. Leipzig.

E.G.I.G. (1959): Missiones Aériennes de Reconnaissance au Groenland 1957–58. Rapport interne.

Expéditions Polaires Françaises:
  Publications Préliminaires:
  (1949) No. 5: Campagne préparatoire au Groenland 1948.
  (1949) » 7: Campagne préparatoire au Groenland 1948.
    Météorologie, Transmission radio.
  (1950) » 10: Campagne au Groenland 1949.
  (1952) » 15: Campagne au Groenland 1950.
  (1953) » 16: Campagne au Groenland 1951.
  (1956) » 17: Hivernage au Groenland 1949–50.
  (1953) » 19: Ravitaillement aérien des expéditions françaises au Groenland 1949–50–51.
  (1953) » 22: Hivernage au Groenland 1950–51.
  (1956) » 23: Rapport d'activités.
  (1954) » 24: Campagne au Groenland 1952–53.

(1954): Les observations météorologiques de la station française du Groenland. Conditions atmosphériques en surface de 5 septembre 1949 au 20 juin 1950, par M. Bouché. Fasc. I–II.

(1954): Les observations météorologiques de la station française du Groenland. Conditions atmosphériques en altitude du 17 septembre 1949 au 10 août 1951, par B. Bedel.

(1956): Les observations météorologiques de la station française du Groenland. Conditions atmosphériques en surface du 21 juin 1950 au 15 août 1951. Fasc. I, par B. Bedel.

Finsterwalder, R. (1958): Measurement of Ice Velocity by Air Photogrammetry. Symposium de Chamonix. Publ. A.I.H.S. 47.

Flint, Richard Foster (1948): Glaciological Geology and Geomorphology. The Coast of Northeast Greenland. Amer. Geogr. Soc., Special Publ. 30.

Fristrup, Børge (1948/49): Peary Land. Geogr. Tidsskr. 49.

– : Climate and glaciology of Peary Land. U. G. G. I. A. J. H. S. Assemblée generále de Bruxelles 1951.

– (1952, a): Danish Expedition to Peary Land 1947–50. Geogr. Rev. XLII.

– (1952, b): Die Klimaänderungen in der Arktis und ihre Bedeutung besonders für Grönland. Erdkunde VI.

– (1959): Gletscherundersøgelser i Grønland under det Geofysiske År. »Grønland«.

Frost, Robert E. (1957): A Reconnaissance for a Southern Greenland Ice Cap Access. SIPRE Techn. Report 46.

Georgi, Johannes (1953/54): Bemerkungen zum Klima von Eismitte. Ann. der Meteorol., 6. Jahrg.

Gerdel, R. W. and M. Diamond (1956): White out in Greenland. SIPRE Res. Report 21.

Glen, J. W. (1958): The Flow Law of Ice. Symposium de Chamonix. Publ. A.I.H.S. 47.

Goldthwait, R. P. (1956): Study of Ice Cliff in Nunatarssuaq, Greenland. Ohio State Univ. Res. Found. Report 11, and as SIPRE Report 39.
– (1957): Study of Ice Cliff in Nunatarssuaq, Greenland. Ohio State Univ. Res. Found. Report 17.

Griffith, Thomas M. (1954–56): Glaciological Report, Tuto Area. Univ. of Denver.

Haefeli, R. and F. Brentani (1956): Observations in a Cold Ice Cap. Journ. of Glaciol. 2: 18, 19.

Haefeli, R. (1955/56): Gletscherschwankung und Gletscherbewegung. Schweiz. Bauzeitung 73/74.
– (1957): Le project de la participation de la Suisse à l'Expédition Glaciologique Internationale au Groenland. La Suisse Horlogère 20.

Hamilton, R. A. (1958): The British North Greenland Expedition 1952–54. Scientific Results. Nature 181.

Hamilton, R. A. and G. Rollitt (1957, a): Meteorological Observations at »Northice«, Greenland. Medd. o. Gr. 158, 3.
– (1957, b): Climatological Tables for the Site of the Expedition's Base at Britannia Sø and the Station on the Inland-Ice »Northice«. Medd. o. Gr. 158, 2.

Hansen, B. L. and J. K. Landauer (1958): Some Results of Ice Cap Drill Hole Measurements. Symposium de Chamonix. Publ. A.I.H.S. 47.

Heuberger, Jean-Charles (1954): Forages sur l'Inlandsis. Glaciologie Groenland I. Expéditions Polaires Françaises, Missions Paul-Emile Victor V. Paris.

Hobbs, William Herbert (1941): Reports of the Greenland Expeditions of the University of Michigan I–II. Univ. of Michigan Studies V and VI.

Hofmann, Walther (1958, a): Lagemessung bei der Internationalen Glaziologischen Grönland-Expedition (EGIG). Zeitschr. f. Vermessungswesen 83: 7–8.
– (1958, b): Bestimmung von Gletschergeschwindigkeit aus Luftbildern. Bildmessung und Luftbildwesen 1958: 3.

Holland, M. F. W. (1958): An Expedition to West Greenland 1956. Geogr. Journ. CXXIV.

Holmes, G. William (1955): Morphology and Hydrology of the Mint Julep Area. Southwest Greenland. Mint Julep Reports II.

Holtzscherer, Jean-Jacques (1954): Contribution à la Connaissance de l'Inlandsis du Groenland. Ière partie: Mesures Séismiques. Paris.

Hutchinson, Howard B. (1953): Preliminary Report on the Scientific Program of Operation Icecap 1953.

Kayser, Olaf (1928): The Inland Ice. Greenland I, ed. by M. Vahl, G. C. Amdrup, L. Bobé and Ad. S. Jensen.

Koch, J. P. und A. Wegener (1930): Wissenschaftliche Ergebnisse der dänischen Expedition nach Dronning Louises Land und quer über das Inlandseis von Nordgrönland 1912–13. Medd. o. Gr. 75.

Koch, Lauge (1950): Report on the Expeditions to Central East Greenland 1926–39. Conducted by Lauge Koch. Medd. o. Gr. 143, 1.

La Chapelle, Edward (1955): Ablation Studies in the Mint Julep Area. Mint Julep Report II. A.T.D.I.C.

Langway, Chester C. (1958, a): A 400 Meter deep Ice Core in Greenland. Journ. of Glaciol. 3: 23.

  – (1958, b): Bubble Pressure in Greenland Glacier Ice. Symposium de Chamonix. Publ. A.I.H.S. 47.

Landauer, J. K. (1957): On the Deformation of Excavations in the Greenland Névé. SIPRE Res. Report 30.

Larsen, Helge and J. Meldgaard (1958): Paleo-Eskimo Cultures in Disko Bugt, West Greenland. Medd. o. Gr. 161, 2.

Lichte, H. (1957): Geodätische Messungen auf dem grönländischen Inlandeis. Zeitschr. f. Vermessungswesen, Jahrg. 82.

Lindsay, Martin (1935): The British Trans-Greenland Expedition 1934. Geogr. Journ. LXXXV.

Lister, H. (1956): Glacier Regime in North-East Greenland. Geogr. Journ. CXXII.

Lliboutry, L. (1957): Nos connaissances actuelles sur l'Inlandsis groenlandais. Soc. Hydrotechn. de France. Section Glaciologie. Réunion du 12 Fév. 1957.

Ljungner, Erik (1949): East-West Balance of the Quaternary Ice Caps in Patagonia and Scandinavia. Bull. of the Geol. Inst. of Uppsala XXXIII.

Loewe, F. (1936): Höhenverhältnisse und Massenhaushalt des grönländischen Inlandeis. Gerlands Beitrage zur Geophysik 48: 1.

Matthes, F. E. (1946–50): The Glacial Anticyclone Theory Examined in the Light of Recent Meteorological Data from Greenland I–II. Trans. Amer. Geophys. Union 27: III & 31: II.

Meir, M. F. (1957): Preliminary Study of Crevasse Formation. SIPRE Report 38.

Meldgaard, J. See Helge Larsen & J. Meldgaard.

Milthers, Keld (1953, a): Indlandsisens Oprindelse. »Grønland«.

  – (1953, b): Indlandsisens Produktion. »Grønland«.

Mirrild, W. M. (1957): Foliation, Bubble Trends and Dirt Zones and their Relation to Glacier Flow in Part of North Ice Cap, Northwest Greenland. Geol. Soc. Amer., Bull. 68: 12.

Mirrles, S. T. A. (1932): The Weather on a Greenland Air Route. Geogr. Journ. LXXX.

Nakaya, Ukichiro (1958): Visco-elastic Properties of Snow and Ice in Greenland Ice Cap. Symposium de Chamonix. Publ. A.I.H.S. 47.

Neviere, J. (1954): Campagne au Groenland 1948–1949–1950. Nivellement géodésique de l'Inlandsis. Rapports scientifiques des Expéditions Polaires Françaises N. III: 1. Annales de Géophys. 10: 1.

Nobles, Laurence H. (1954): Characteristics of High-polar Type Glaciers in Northwestern Greenland. Geol. Soc. Amer., Bull. 65: 12.

Nutt, David: See Arctic Institute Greenland Expedition 1958.

Paterson, W. S. B. (1958): The Position of Markers on the Greenland Ice Sheet. Journ. of Glaciol. 3: 24.

Project Mint Julep Reports: I. Introduction and General Reports.
(1955): A.T.D.I.C. Research Studies Institute Air University, Maxwell Air Force Base, Alabama.
(1955): II. Special Scientific Reports.
(1954): III. Snow Studies SIPRE.
(1954): IV. Report of Arctic Construction and Frost Effects Lab.

Ransley, T. J. (1952): Glacier Studies in the Umanak District, West Greenland, 1950. Medd. o. Gr. 136, 2.

Rausch, Donald O. (1958): Ice Tunnel Tuto Area, Greenland 1956. SIPRE Techn. Report 44.

Rigsby, George P. (1955): Study of Ice Fabrics, Thule Area. Greenland. SIPRE Report 26.

Robin, G. de Q. (1955): Ice Movement and Temperature Distribution in Glaciers and Ice Sheets. Journ. of Glaciol. 2: 18.

Saxov, Svend (1958): Bevægelsen af Vestgrønland. »Grønland«.

Scholander, P. F., J. W. Kanwisher, and D. C. Nutt (1956): Gas in Icebergs. Science 123.

Schuster, Robert L. (1954): Snow Studies. Project Mint Julep. SIPRE Report 19.

Schytt, Valter (1955): Glaciological Investigations in the Thule Ramp Area. SIPRE Report 28.
– (1958): Glaciology II. Snow Studies at Maudheim. The inner Structure of the Ice Shelf at Maudheim. Norwegian-British-Swedish Antarctic Expedition 1949–52. Scientific Results IV, Oslo.

Sharp, Robert P. (1956): Glaciers in the Arctic. Arctic 9.
– *and S. Epstein* (1958): Oxygen-Isotope Ratios and Glacier Movement. Symposium de Chamonix. Publ. A.I.H.S. 47.

Simpson, C. J. W. (1955): The British North Greenland Expedition. Geogr. Journ. CXXI.
– (1957): North Ice, the Story of the British North Greenland Expedition. London.

Sorge, Ernst (1933): The Scientifical Results of the Wegener Expedition to Greenland. Geogr. Journ. LXXXI.
– (1935): Glaziologische Untersuchungen in Eismitte. Wissenschaftliche Ergebnisse der Deutschen Grönlandsexpedition Alfred Wegener 1929 und 1930/31, 3.

Tschaen, L. (1959): Groenland 1948–1949–1950. Astronomie-Nivellement Géodésique sur l'Inlandsis. Noveau Calcul. Expéditions Polaires Françaises, publ. 207.
– *et A. Bauer* (1958): Le Mouvement de la partie Centrale de l'Inlandsis du Groenland. Symposium de Chamonix. Publ. A.I.H.S. 47.

Victor, Paul-Emile (1955): Geography of Northeast Greenland. SIPRE Special Report 15.
– (1956): Wringing Secrets from Greenland's Icecap. Nat. Geogr. Mag.

Wager, L. R. (1933): The Form and Age of the Greenland Ice Cap. Geol. Mag. 20.

Wallerstein, G. (1958): Movement Observations on the Greenland Ice Sheet. Journ. of Glaciol. 3: 23.

Waterhouse, R. (1955): Structures for Snow Investigations on the Greenland Ice Cap. SIPRE Report 27.

Watkins, H. G. (1932): The British Arctic Air Route Expedition 1930–31. Geogr. Journ. LXXIV & LXXX.

Wegener, K. und andere (1933–40): Wissenschaftliche Ergebnisse der Deutschen Grönland Expedition Alfred Wegener 1929 und 1930–31. I–VII. Leipzig.

Weidick, Anker (1958): Frontal Variations at Upernavik Isstrøm in the last 100 Years. Medd. Dansk Geol. Foren. 14: 1.

– (1959): Glacial Variations in West Greenland in Historical Time. Medd. o. Gr. 158, 4.

White, S. E. (1956): Glaciological Studies of two Outlet Glaciers, Northwest Greenland 1953. Medd. o. Gr. 137, 8.

– (1958): Preliminary Studies of Motion of an Ice Cliff, Nunatarssuaq, Northwest Greenland 1955. Symposium de Chamonix. Publ. A.I.H.S. 47.

Wilson, L. R. (1955): Minor Surface Features of the Southwest Greenland Ice Cap. Mint Julep Reports. A.T.D.I.C.

Wrigth, J. W. (1939): Contribution to the Glaciology of North West Greenland. Medd. o. Gr. 125, 3.

Studies of Four Glaciers in Greenland

By Børge Fristrup

Abstract

Four Greenland glaciers are investigated, their morphology are studied in relation to physiography, climate and change of climate. A relation is found between the rate of retreat and the temperature of the ice. With exception of the Ice Cap most af the Greenland glaciers are temperate glaciers (in South Greenland) or subpolar glaciers (even in North Greenland), the occurrence of superimposed ice is of importance for the ice accumulation.

Glaciological investigations were carried out in Greenland 1956-58 as a Danish contribution to the International Geophysical Year. The expeditions were sent out from the *Geographical Institute* at the *University of Copenhagen* under the direction of professor *Niels Nielsen*, Ph. D. and the writer, who also supervised all the operations in Greenland. The work was sponsored by the *Rask-Ørsted Foundation* and the *CarlsbergFoundation,* and various kinds of support were also given by the *Ministry of Greenland.* In a tragic accident on the Hurlbut Gletscher, where two men were killed, valuable help and rescue operations were given by the *American Rescue Squadron* from Thule Airbase.

Having regard to the great geographical variation of the Greenland glaciers, especially in respect of the climatology and physiography of the different regions in Greenland, the main programme of the investigations was to study glacier types in relation to geomorphology and the ratio of accumulation/ablation in relation to climate and microclimate. The glacier fronts were mapped in order to observe the oscillations in relation to climatic changes, and marked fix points were established for the purpose of resurveying in future years.

Four special selected glaciers were carefully investigated as representatives for particular geographical provinces, all being local

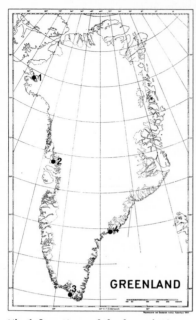

Fig. 1. Locations of the four glaciers: 1, Hurlbut Gletscher. 2, Sermikavsak. 3, Napassorssuaq Gletscher. 4, Mitdluagkat Gletscher.

glaciers outside the Greenland Ice Cap, and all of medium or small size, et being presumed that small glaciers will react more sensitively to less pronounced changes of climate. In selecting the glaciers several desiderata were of importance. All the expeditions were small of 4-6 men, requiring the establishing of no more than one station in each province, and for the same reason the glacier should not be too large or of too complex a form, and when possible the glaciers should not reach the sea, as calculations of production of icebergs had to be avoided. The glacier should be typical for the province, regarding size, type, exposure to prevailing wind direction and the sun and so on. Transport problem in establishing the base camps made it necessary to select glaciers not too far away from the sea. At three of the stations the whole equipment was brought to the shore by ship, while the station at Hurlbut Gletscher was established by sledging with dog teams. All the glaciers were carefully selected with regard of safety, several of the expedition members having had no previous experience of glaciers in Greenland, and real mountaineering should be avoided.

The location and size of the glaciers is given in table 1 and in fig. 1.

Description and morphology of the glaciers

Napassorssuaq Gletscher is situated on Sermersôq Ø, the largest and westernmost of three islands in the entrance to the Sermilik fjord in Nanortalik region; the island is therefore part of the South Greenland granite region with rather high and very steep mountains. The glacier occupies the southern part of a 6 km. long valley, a typical glacier eroded hanging tributary valley 400 m. above sea level and from there ascending to a threshold 1000 m. above the sea. The valley system, which also can be followed to the north on the mainland, is of tectonic origin and afterwards glacier eroded. The glacier itself

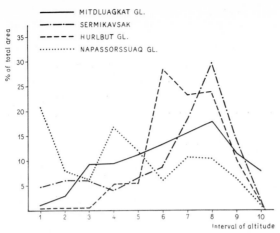

Fig. 2. Curves of frequencies of different height intervals for the four investigated glaciers.

is 3 km. long and 500-900 m. wide, its front terminates in a small lake 495 m. above sea level with a nearly vertical ice cliff, 12-15 m. high; along both lateral parts of the front extensive areas of dead ice were found. No part of the glacier front is afloat, as the lake is shallow. The glacier descends in three or four ice falls, most probably related to differences in the resistance of the substratum, as the glacier is rather thin according to observations of the topography of the region.

The glacier is rather small, which is typical of many of the valley glaciers in the region. According to the classifications proposed by *Ahlmann* (1948) a calculation of the different height intervals was made, the curve is shown on fig. 2. From the general impression gained it is quite evident, that Napassorssuaq Gletscher is a typical valley glacier of a type that is common in that part of Greenland. A study of the curve shows however that the frequencies of the different height intervals do not coincide well with the classification as a valley glacier, the curve represents a transition between valley glacier IV and a piedmont glacier. The explanation of this is that the lower marginal part of the glacier at present is dead ice and is merely a relict of the former greater extension of the active glacier, but still morphologically a part of the glacier. The type described here is very common in Greenland and therefore ought to be called the Greenland valley glacier type as a fifth of the Ahlmann valley glacier types.

The glacier was explored in 1957 by a group of five with *Jens*

Table 1.

Coordinates of base camp	Area	Glacier type
Hurlbut Gletscher..................... lat. 77°23'30"N — long. 67°57'W	188,0 km²	Glacier cap
Sermikavsak.......................... lat. 71°11' N — long. 53°03'W	21,6 km²	Valley glacier
Napassorssuaq Gletscher.............. lat. 60°18' N — long. 45°13'W	2,1 km²	Valley glacier
Mitdluagkat Gletscher................ lat. 65°40'40"N — long. 37°54'W	36,4 km²	Transection glacier

Fabricius as party leader. Glacial meteorological investigations were carried out and surveying of the glacier front. Lateral moraines were not well developed, and there was no terminal moraine as the glacier terminates in the lake. The glacier is rather heavily crevassed with both transversal and longitudinal crevasses.

From a visit by *J. A. D. Jensen* in 1894 a series of photographs shows us the position of the front at that time. Since then the glacier front had retreated 200 m. to 1951 and the retreat has continued so that in 1957 the glacier front has receded 350 m.

Sermikavsak (meaning the paltry glacier) is situated on the western side of Upernivik Ø and was selected as a representative of the great West Greenland region, comprising the area from south of Disko Bugt to the southern part of Melville Bugt. The region contains several well defined glacier types such as the typical cirque glaciers in the basalt region on Disko and Nûgssuaq and the typical valley glaciers in the highly glacierized region between Nûgssuaq and Svartenhuk peninsula. The climate is arctic with cold winters, rather short summers and rather much precipitation. Further investigations will subdivide the region. Sermikavsak is the southern one of the four glaciers descending to Igdlorssuit Sund from the central high mountainous region of the island. The glacier terminates nearly a thousand metres behind the coastline leaving space for outwash plains and terminal moraines. Old moraine systems can also be followed on the sea bottom in front of the glacier valley. The firn area of the glacier is very well defined nearly 1000 m. above sea level, and from there the glacier descends in a tongue 15 km. long and 1 km. wide. Thus the glacier itself completely occupies the upper part of the troughshaped valley and is surrounded by the 2000 m. high mountain chains, the mountains being very steep, and collects much snow during the winter, the result being that numerous avalanches drop down on to the glacier. Sermikavsak therefore receives more snow than it should according to the average snowfall on the region. The glacier thus being partly nourished by avalanches, this is a very characteristic feature of many glaciers in the Umanak Bugt region. In most other parts of Greenland avalanches are somewhat rare, and normally they do not occur in northern Greenland, where the climate is too arid and the snow too powdery and fine grained. Some of the glaciers round Kangerdlugssuaq and Kangerdluarssuk fjords seem to be nearly vertical, and the snow on the ice therefore will move down like an avalanche and come to rest at the snout, making a very large terminal snout frequently in the form of a steeply rising cone. At some of the glaciers the central nearly vertical part of the glacier tongue now, owing to the amelioration of the climate, has melted away so that the glacier is divided into a higher part with the firn area and a glacier tongue descending down the mountain side, and below that an independent cone built up of snow and ice coming down with the avalanches from the upper part. This type is rather frequent here and most probably it will only be so well developed in high latitudes with a low sun and very steep mountains.

Sermikavsak is a typical valley glacier II of Ahlmann, and a characteristic feature is the well developed ice falls.

Investigations there were carried out in 1956, 1957 with *J. Tyge Møller* as group leader. A description of the surveying has been published by *Møller* (1959a) as well as a study of the periglacial landscape in front of the glacier (1959b). Studies of the weather have been published by *Hans Kuhlman* (1959) and according to him, the weather could be divided into four different types, the most dominant was radiation weather (61% of all observations), overcast weather was found in 17,7% and foehn weather in 6,9%. Special investigations were carried out concerning the temperature and wind profiles above the ice. Gravity wind (katabatic wind) was found in 78% of the observations, and round 80% of the ablations was found to be due to radiation.

As by the other glaciers studies of the front oscillations were made. From 1934 to 1953 the front had retreated 600-700 m. and from 1953 to 1957 the retreat was 150 m. giving an annual withdrawal of 34-38 m.

Hurlbut Gletscher is a glacier cap, which is the dominant type in

Fig. 3. The Napassorssuaq Gletscher photographed from the site for the meteorological observations, the base camp is situated near the lake in front of the glacier. Phot. B. Fristrup.

North Greenland, the region being part of the rather monotonous sandstone plateau belonging to the Thule formation. Typical valley glaciers therefore are rare, the only exceptions being Kap York peninsula and round the outer section of J. P. Koch Fjord. The climate is high arctic with severe winters and insignificant precipitation and with very small diurnal temperature variations.

The glacier covers the highest and central part of a plateau between Inglefield Bredning and Olrik Fjord. As seen from the diagram fig. 2 the total area of glacier tongues is very little, and at the present time only one of the tongues really reaches down to the sea at Inglefield Bredning, the front stands on the beach and is above sea at low tide, by high tide there is a small production of ice pieces. Towards Olrik Fjord there are two broader but rather short glacier lobes, which do not reach below 300 m. above sea level. Meltwater canyons have been formed in the ice, indicating that at least some part of the glacier at present is stagnant ice. The total thickness of the glacier cap is less than 400 m., and the drillings with core

Fig. 4. Aerial view of Hurlbut Gletscher. To the left Inglefield Bredning. The glacier in the backgrund is the Heilprin Gletscher descending from the Ice Cap.

samples reveal superimposed ice to at least 15 m. (the deepest core drilling). The firn area is very insignificant, and in some years there will be melting all over the glacier, so that the glacier may be nourished in same way as described by *P. D. Baird* (1952) for Barnes Ice Cap on Baffin Island, e.g. by the refreezing of meltwater and water-percolated snow and ice. Along the edge of the glacier cap proper the ice is very thin, and as is characteristic of many of the glacier caps and highland glaciers in North Greenland there is no terminal moraine along the ice on the plateau; the glacier seems unable to pick material up from the substratum. Cryoconite holes are frequent. Along the glacier tongues are lateral moraines, those moraines on the glacier tongue descending towards Inglefield Bredning being well developed, the blocks are sharp-edged and must have been transported on the surface and not in the ice, the material must have come down with landslides from the mountain sides.

At the present time the glacier has withdrawn and the lateral

Fig. 5. The front of Midtluagkat Gletscher photographed by K. Milthers in 1933.

moraines are longer than the glacier itself. The moraines most probably are very old, and remains of very old moraine systems were
found; the sheltered sand beach, which was used for base camp, in
reality is situated between two old moraines. Because of solifluction
the old moraines are very low and only to be followed by counting
very characteristic blocks such as a white quartzite. The studies
indicate not only that the glacier at a previous time was longer,
but that it was of another form, the lower part was broader of a
typical piedmont or tongued form with the ice from a rather narrow
valley part spreading radially out to the sides. This is typical of
many glaciers in North Greenland, and good examples can be found
at several places, this glacier form most probably was dominant
previous in North Greenland, and most of the present glaciers of
that form may be regarded as relics of another climate. The glacier
retreat is very insignificant, most probably less than 5 m. per year,
and according to photos taken by Dr. *Gilberg* in 1939 the glacier
snout now is more narrow than before.

Mitdluagkat Gletscher is one of the biggest glaciers on Angmagssalik Ø and has been found representative of the East Greenland

Fig. 6. Mitdluagkat Gletscher photographed from the same point in 1958.
Phot. B. Fristrup.

humide climate with a rather heavy snowfall and temperature conditions greatly influenced by the drift ice. The glacier surrounds the
973 m. mountain Mitdluagkat, which in reality is a nunatak in the
glacier. Along the eastern and southern sides the glacier is surrounded by mountain chains culminating in the very steep Vegas
Fjeld, 1084 m. The western and the northern edges of the glacier
are open, and the glacier is drained towards west, i. e. towards
Sermilik fjord. One glacier tongue descends to a flat-bottomed valley
and about a fourth of the discharge from the glacier area runs here
through. The tongue is rather broad and the front is only 4,1 m.
above sea level. Mitdluagkat is a transection glacier according to
Ahlmann's definition.

Midtluagkat Gletscher was studied in 1958 and the normal
routine investigations were carried out, such as surveying the
fronts, glacial-meteorological investigations, ablation measurement
and so on. The period of observations was shorter here than at the
other glaciers according to the ice difficulties in the fjord. Beside
the normal studies a special investigation was made of the runoff

from the glacier, the results have been published by *Larsen* (1959), the diurnal variation of the discharge was very typical with maximum at 17.00-18.00 hrs., and the discharge varied between 2 and 4 cbm./sec. In connection with the runoff studies investigations were also made on some of the ice-dammed lakes. Along the southern, western and northern edges of the glacier were several ice-dammed lakes, and their morphology was studied; in September the river gauge showed a series of tappings from some of the lakes. A special search therefore was established, and two lakes were found to be drained out. The total tapping of one of the lakes has been calculated at between 400.000 and 450.000 cbm. The water drained through or under the ice and a great increase of the water level was found in the river from the glacier tongue. The water from the drained-off lakes appeared not in the glacier port at the front, but far up on the lateral drainage channel, and from there followed the glacier margin down to the river; the water was easy to recognize because of the colour from the suspended material. One of the lakes was tapped through a tunnel at the ice. The lake was so completely drained out, that it was possible to get into the drainage channel and follow the tunnel for a couple of hundred metres. This glacier tunnel was rather big, 5-10 m. high, and 10-30 m. wide, and near the entrance the room in the ice was even bigger forming a large cavern. The water had been drained through this tunnel with great force, many ice-blocks from the collapsed glacier front having been carried by the water stream and now filled the tunnel, at many places is was therefore difficult to find a way through, and in the end we had to give up. The floor of the ice tunnel was ice, covered only by a thin layer of mud and clay; at some places there were narrow crevasses down to a deeper level. The roof of the tunnel was vaulted at the entrance near the glacier port. Here and there the tunnel was divided into different rooms by ice columns formed by water erosion, and supporting the roof. It is most likely that bigger ice tunnels may be found in the ice behind some of the other lakes. The collapse of such ice caverns may give rise to calderons, such were found at several places. The cause for the lake tapping has been discussed by *Larsen,* who also found a very interesting accordance with the discharge curves from the great »jökull-hlaup« from Iceland; characteristic is a rather gentle increase of the discharge to maximum value and then coming to a sudden drop. An observation from a flight over the glacier in late August 1959 shows the ice-dammed lake as re-established, therefore it seems most probable that the

Fig. 7a. The upper part of Sermikavsak seen from the western mountain side. Phot. J. T. Møller.

Fig. 7b. The lower part of Sermikavsak with the glacier front seen from the western mountain side. Phot. J. T. Møller.

tapping was caused by a hydrostatic lifting of the ice near the lake, in connection with a great rainfall and high water level in the lakes.

The Midtluagkat nunatak is an old nunatak, which has been ice free for a long time. The firn area of the glacier is insignificant, and superimposed ice is very important. By a visit in 1933 *K. Milthers* took some phototheodolite exposures, and our photos show a retreat of considerable dimensions; the total withdrawal in 25 years is about 400-500 m., and very impressing is the formation of new nunataks, which now divide the glacier tongue in two lobes emerging below the nunatak, and a new nunatak south of the present one is under development. The new nunatak had no vegetation and the stones and blocks were quite unstable, not having yet found their final position. A number of stone counts were established, and no relations between the longitudinal axes and the former movement direction of the ice were found, the longitudinal axis were only related to the gradient of the terrain and the direction of the solifluction. The nunatak is proof of a lowering of the ice surface of more than 50 m. and the average withdrawal per year of the glacier front is 16-20 m. A retreat of the same order of magnitude was found at several other glaciers visited in the district.

Glacier morphology related to ice temperature

By the investigations we found a greater retreat of the glaciers in South Greenland than in North Greenland. In drilling holes thermo-electric measurements were taken at regular intervals during the summer, some few readings were taken also in winter on the Hurlbut Gletscher. Some of the results will be evident from fig. 8 and 9; it will be seen that the yearly temperature variations continue down to 10-12 m. below which the temperature is nearly constant, and even in September the cold from the previous winter is still present, as ice is a very poor heat conductor. There is a good correlation between the ice temperature and altitude above sea level. From fig. 8 it will be seen that there is a great geographical variation of the temperatures in the ice. Two glaciers: Napassorssuaq and Mitd-luagkat have temperatures very nearly the melting point in August, the temperature vary between zero and $-1°$ at least down to 15 m. The Hurlbut Gletscher is a cold glacier with temperature of $-16°$ at 15 m. depths. While the Sermikavsak seems to be a transition form; this is in good accordance with the difference in geographical latitude, a similar relation between temperature and geographical

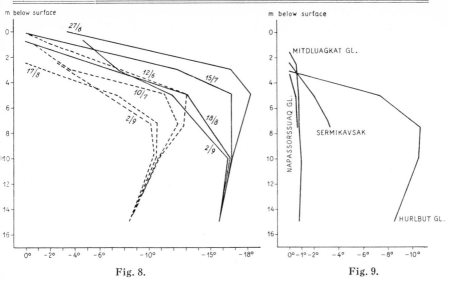

Fig. 8.   Fig. 9.

Fig. 8. Temperature in the ice in August in the four glaciers.
Fig. 9. The temperature variation during the summer time at two different
stations on the Hurlbut Gletscher. The curve to the right is from the station
on the Ice Cap near the highest point of the glacier, and the curve to the left
is from the glacier tongue descending to the Inglefield Bredning.

latitude having been demonstrated by *Benson* (1959) for the Greenland Ice Cap.

According to Ahlmann's definition of glaciers related to temperature the Napassorssuaq and Mitdluagkat may be typical temperate
glaciers belonging to the same type as the Scandinavian and the
Iceland glaciers. According to morphological studies of other South
Greenland glaciers it is possible to say, that most of the local glaciers
in South Greenland belong to this type. The North Greenland
glaciers are polar glaciers according to Ahlmann's definition, the
Hurlbut Gletscher is a polar glacier, where a certain amount of
melting takes place, and studies of the glaciers in Peary Land *(Fristrup* 1949, 1951) show that ice caps in that region also have a
summer melting. Therefore only part of the Greenland Ice Cap and
probably one or two of the largest glacier caps in North Greenland
may be considered as high polar glaciers, all the rest may be
subpolar glaciers, if not temperate glaciers; also the Sukkertoppen
ice cap is a subpolar glacier.

As the yearly temperature variations only affect the upper 10-12
metres of the ice, it will be seen that the cold glaciers in North
Greenland will react only very slowly to changes of climate as far as
the temperature concerns. But they will of course be rather sensitive

to changes in precipitation. As shown by *Diamond* (1956, 1958) there was a slight decrease in annual amount of precipitation from 1920 to 1954 in North Greenland. The cold ice temperatures of the North Greenland glaciers may possibly be the explanation of the question why the northern glaciers in Greenland according to *Lauge Koch* (1928), *Fristrup* (1952) and others seem to have started the withdrawal of the fronts much later than the glaciers in South and Central Greenland. As will be seen from the above mentioned investigations the annual withdrawal is at present less for the North Greenland glaciers than in South Greenland.

BIBLIOGRAPHY

Ahlmann, Hans W:son (1948): Glaciological Research on the North Atlantic Coasts. R. G. S. Research Series no. 1. London.

Baird, P. D. (1952): The glaciological studies on the Baffin Island Expedition 1950. Journ. of Glaciology, II, no. 11. London.

Benson, Carl S. (1959): Stratigraphic Studies in the Snow and Firn of the Greenland Ice Sheet, Thesis, Pasadena.

Diamond, Marvin (1956): Precipitation trends in Greenland during the past 30 years. SIPRE Research Report 22.

Diamond, Marvin (1958): Air Temperatures and Precipitation on the Greenland Ice Cap. SIPRE Research Report 43.

Fristrup, B. (1949): Peary Land. Geogr. Tidsskr. 49.

Fristrup, B. (1951): Climate and Glaciology of Peary Land. UGGI. Bruxelles.

Fristrup, B. (1952): Die Klimaänderungen in der Arktis und ihre Bedeutung besonders für Grönland. Erdkunde VI. Bonn.

Koch, Lauge (1928): Contributions to the Glaciology of North Greenland. Medd. om Grønland 65, no. 2.

Kuhlman, Hans (1959): Weather and Ablation Observations at Sermikavsak in Umanak District. Medd. om Grønland 158, no. 5.

Larsen, Hans Valeur (1959): Runoff studies from the Mitdluagkat Gletscher in SE Greenland during the late summer 1958. Geogr. Tidsskr. 58.

Møller, Jens Tyge (1959a): A West Greenland Glacier Front. A Survey of Sermikavsak near Umanak in 1957. Medd. om Grønland 158, no. 5.

Møller, Jens Tyge (1959 b): Glaciers in Upernivik Ø. With special reference to the periglacial phenomena. Geogr. Tidsskr. 58.

Glaciers in Upernivik Ø.

With special reference to the periglacial phenomena.

By J. Tyge Møller

In the summers 1956 and 1957 a glaciological expedition under the leadership of associate professor, *B. Fristrup,* M. Sc., was sent out to West Greenland and to North Greenland from the Geographical Institute at the University of Copenhagen. The expedition was part of the Danish contribution to the International Geophysical Year 1956—58. The investigations here mentioned have been carried out in Upernivik Ø (Ø = island) in West Greenland. In »Geografisk Tidsskrift« and »Meddelelser om Grønland« have been published some of the results obtained by the team working on the glacier Sermikavsak. The main purpose was glaciological investigations of Sermikavsak. This glacier was visited the first time in the summer 1956, when the work went on for one month. During this time the glacier was reconnoitred, and the surveying was prepaired; further, the meteorological station was established. The next summer the investigations proper were carried out. From the middle of June to the beginning of September the glaciological, meteorological and hydrographical observations were accomplished on Sermikavsak and in the area in front of the glacier, and the ice margin was surveyed. Unfortunately, the hydrographical investigations had to be reduced to some experimental work. In addition to the work mentioned above, Sermikavsak as well as other glaciers in Upernivik Ø were thoroughly photographed in order to make it possible to prove movements and modifications of the glaciers if any future investigation will be carried out in this region. During the work on the glaciers of Upernivik Ø the observations and small surveyings on which this paper has been based were carried out. The glacier Sermikavsak was picked out as an object of the research, because it was necessary to choose a glacier of a suitable

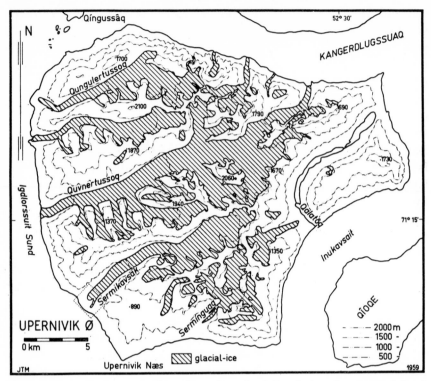

Fig. 1. Upernivik Ø (= island) in West Greenland. Partly based on a provisional map (about 1:50.000) made in 1956 by the Danish Geodetic Institute. The frame round the snout of Sermikavsak indicates the limits of fig. 2.

size and with an easy access and, at the same time, with the snout at some distance from the sea. Sermikavsak fulfils most of these conditions, though it is situated in a pronounced alpine area, in which the glacier is probably the only one that could be taken into consideration.

The *position of Upernivik Ø*, characterized by the snout of Sermikavsak (the poor glacier), is 71° 12' north, 53° 03' west of Greenwich in the Umanak district, West Greenland. To the north the island borders on the big ice-fjord, Kangerdlugsuaq. To the west Igdlorssuit Sund separates the island from Ubekendt Ejland (unknown island), which thus protects Upernivik Ø against the open sea, the Baffin Bay. As a consequence of this shelter the weather in Upernivik Ø may be very fine and sunny, simultaneously with the weather in Ubekendt Ejland being rainy and foggy. The greater part of Upernivik Ø is a very rugged, mountainous region, built up of gneiss and other transformed rocks. An exception is the most

southwestern corner of the island (fig. 1), which consists of a
yellowish sandstone containing layers of coal. The last-mentioned
area differs further from the rest of Upernivik Ø, being a very
rounded, hilly region. The highest part of the sandstone area does
not exceed an altitude of 900 m., whereas the alpine region reaches
an altitude of more than 2.100 m., and but a small part of the island
is below 1000 m. above sea level. Owing to the height conditions
there are plenty of glaciers (of which the most southwestern is
Sermikavsak) in Upernivik Ø. Nearly one third of the whole area
is covered with constant ice and snow. The map in fig. 1. has been
based on a provisional map (approximately 1 : 50.000), executed
by the Danish Geodetic Institute by means of topographical maps
and air photographs taken in 1953. Furthermore, the figure has
been supplemented by the author. It shows the extension of the
glaciers and the height conditions indicated by contour lines with
an equidistance of 500 m. With regard to the distribution of ice-
covered land and ice-free land the map in all probability gives a
true picture of the conditions in Upernivik Ø; however, the use
of air photographs implies the risk of overestimating the extent
of the ice-covered areas, because it is very difficult to distinguish
between constant snow and real glaciers. The precipitation and the
melting-off in the period of photographing is of great importance.
For instance, some of the air photographs were taken so early in
the spring that the snow still covered the highest parts of the island.
In 1957 it was the general impression that the extent of the glaciers
had been reduced since 1953, when the photographs were taken.
The great melting-off in the summer 1957, caused by the sunny
weather, in connection with the very small precipitation the previous winter contributed to reducing the glaciers in the period
mentioned above.

   Four glaciers valleys, of which Sermikavsak is the most south-
western, debouch on the west coast of Upernivik Ø. The direction
of the valleys is about north east—south west. From the Igdlorssuit
Sund west of Upernivik Ø it is possible to get a view to the interior
of the island, and the approach to this is only possible through
glacier valleys and melt-water gullies. Between these the slopes are
so steep that only in few places it is possible to walk along the
shore. The glaciers debouching into the Kangerdlugsuaq descend
steeply to the sea. In fact, there is only an easy access to the valleys
of Sermikavsak, Serminguaq (the small glacier) and Qalatog. The
last-mentioned valley is a river-valley, which drains off two small

glaciers and the oblong lakes which at a height of 250 m. separate
the rest of the island. It is a conspicious feature of most of the
glaciers in Upernivik Ø that especially the western parts solely
receive affluxes of ice from the southern sides of the valleys. Furthermore the south eastern ice lobes are covered with gravel and
rocks and are stretching more towards west than the rest of the
glacier. These distinctive features are caused by the height conditions of the island and also by the fact that the glacier valleys
are situated in a northeastern—southwestern direction. Even if
the midnight sun is shining for several months in this part of
Greenland the southern sides of the glacier valleys have a very
small chance of being reached by the sunbeams because the sun
only rises very little above the horizon. The glacier valleys are cut
so deep in their south western parts the the the southern sides of the
valleys are permanently in shade. (The drawing-back of the contour lines from the coastline has to be noticed). Owing to this only
the icestreams from the southern slopes can exist under the present
climatic circumstances. In any other place the snow will melt away
before a glacier can be formed. The lateral glaciers from the northern sides of the valleys have only been slightly developed. In the
central parts of Upernivik Ø the shade conditions are of smaller
importance, because the entire area, owing to the height, is exposed
to the sun. The central parts of the island are covered by an icecap with some nunataks, which have probably never been eroded
by glacial ice.

The ice-cover of Upernivik Ø can be divided into three glacial
areas. The two northern glaciers seem to originate from the same
small ice-cap. Only the northernmost branch has a name in the
maps, Qungulertussoq. According to the inhabitants in Igdlorssuit,
the only village in Ubekendt Ejland, the name is standing for »the
glacier with the sour plants« (*Cochlearia officinalis?*). The glacier
immediately south of Qungulertussoq wast just called »the central
glacier«. South of this the greatest glacier in Upernivik Ø is situated.
It is named Quvnertussoq (the heavily crevassed glacier). This is
a suitable name, because the surface all the way to the snout is cut
up into small pieces by several systems of crevasses. Quvnertussoq
is the only glacier which has more than one outlet of some importance and, furthermore, the only one which stretches out to the
coast; however, the production of this glacier is very small; for
instance, in the summer 1957 it calved only once. Sermikavsak is
the most sharply delimited glacier in Upernivik Ø, having only a

slight connection with the glacier system from which Serminguaq originates. The last-mentioned glacier has, as mentioned above, been reduced since 1953. Thus, the very narrow glacier stretching out between Sermikavsak and Serminguaq in 1957 had disappeared or was at least completely covered with gravel and rocks.

As far as the *climatic conditions* in Upernivik Ø are concerned it just has to be mentioned that the dry and sunny weather charac- terizing the Umanak Bay is predominant here too. High tempera- tures occur frequently in connection with foehns (in Greenland called »Southeast«), which in summer are able to raise the tem- perature to a little below 20° centigrade (as an average of a period of 24 hours), while the normal maximum temperature is 10—12° centigrade. The high temperatures in connection with the extremely low humidity manifests itself in a increasing of the melting-off, which is normally determined by the great incoming radiation. The precipitation seems to be very vayring too; thus, it should be mentioned that in 1956 the snow in the middle of June melted off to a line about 400 m. above sea-level, while this limit in 1957 moved to 1000 m. in the shaded side of the valley and 1200 m. in the sunny side. Of course, these limits have to be regarded as the result of all the weather conditions in the year in question and not as the result of an exceptional great melting-off or small precipita- tion. As far as the latter is concerned, it is obvious that only a small part of the precipitation is falling on the very surface of the ice. A great part of the supply of snow to the glaciers is coming from the steep sides of the valleys in the shape of avalanches.

In the summer 1957 it was tried to estimate the size of the run- ning-off by placing a small dam across a little melt-water river coming from the most south-western part of the glacier. Just be- hind the dam, with a known profile of the flow through, a self- recording river-gauge was placed. The discharge which was re- corded close to the shoreline was very delayed (2—4 hours) in spite of the short distance from the glacier. The discharge was at its minimum about 2 o'clock p. m. (G.M.T.). After this point it rose steeply to the maximum at about 11 o'clock p. m. (G.M.T.) and the next day steadily decreased to the minimum. With regard to the time, all the melt-water rivers followed the same scheme. The effects of the foehn on the run-off appeared through the recordings of the water-level, the maximum of which, reached in the evening, remained almost constant through the whole night. The next morning the increase started from this level, the maximum of the

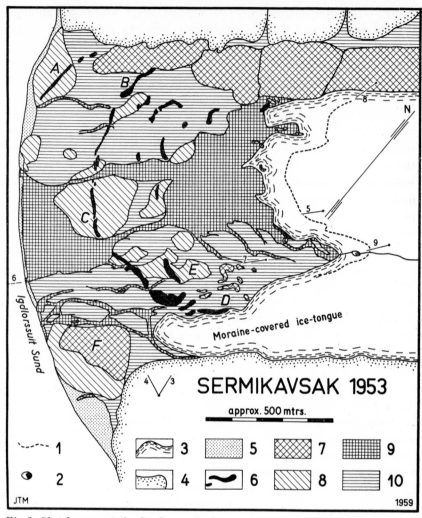

Fig. 2. Sketch-map of the landscape in front of Sermikavsak (the poor glacier) 1953; partly based on air photographs. The place and the direction in which the figures 3-9 have been taken are indicated by a dot, a line and the number of the figure. Signs: 1, the ice margin 1957; 2, debris cone; 3, the ice margin 1953; 4, solid rock; 5, beach ridge; 6, terminal moraines; 7, moraines containing glacial ice; 8, moraines not containing glacial ice and not eroded by melt-water rivers; 9, outwash plains 1953; 10, outwash plains formed by melt-water rivers before 1953.

day before. This process was repeated through the entire foehn-situation and, finally, the small dam usually was washed away by the continuously increasing stream. These observations can only be used as a hint of the progress of the run-off. When the weather was clouded the water-level curve was nearly straight for a whole

period of 24 hours. It was impossible to place instruments in the
two water-courses through the terminal moraine BCD (fig. 2), as
the stream was violent enough to transport rocks of a weight of
25 kg or more. Almost the entire run-off from Sermikavsak is
streaming through these openings in the terminal moraine; however, the discharge is constantly varying, because the situation of
the melt-water rivers to the east of the moraine BCD is steadily
changing. Thus, the importance of one of the openings in the terminal moraine is increasing at the expense of the other. — Behind
the beach ridge at the coast of Igdlorssuit Sund some ice and snow
was left in the summer 1957. Here the upper layers of the snow
had been transformed into needle in vertical position, a not unusual
phenomenon of rime; however, in this case the length of the needles
was up to one meter.

The *glaciological investigations proper* solely included the lower
parts of Sermikavsak and the area between the snout and the
shoreline at Igdlorssuit Sund. The glacial ice-cover named Sermikavsak stretches over an area of 22 sq.km. The north-eastern part
of the glacier consists of an almost rectangular basin about 7 km.
long and 2 km. wide. In its south-western part the basin has an
outlet (fig. 1) 1 km. wide and terminating in the snout 500—1000
m. from the shoreline. The glacier is on all sides surrounded by
high mountain ranges which rise to about 500—1000 m. above the
surface of the glacier. As already mentioned, Sermikavsak only
receives glacial affluxes from the southern side of the valley, where
several cirques are situated. Some nunataks in the shape of high,
narrow mountain ranges are found in the inner part of the glacier
basin. From the western part of the basin and through the outlet
the glacier is descending past a number of ice-falls, each of a height
of 200—300 m. The ice-falls, in connection with the narrowings in
the upper end of the outlet and the glacial affluxes from the branch
valleys, have caused the division of the glacier into several systems
of crevasses. Opposite the cirque, at a distance of 6 km. to the
northeast of the snout, no less than three systems of crevasses were
found, because in this place the glacier turns aside, sliding down
over an ice-fall. Owing to the crevasses, Sermikavsak is only accessible in the lower parts. At the glaciers north of Sermikavsak the
climbing conditions were much worse. Near the snouts, or at least
just east of these, great systems of crevasses and ice falls make
the glaciers almost unapproachable. The crevasses on Quvnertussoq reach the snout that is rising vertically from the sea.

Fig. 3. *The snout of Sermikavsak 1957. In the background the big northern lateral moraine. In front of the snout the northeastern outwash plain. Between this and the southern slope of the valley are seen som ice-filled mounds, partly formed by melt-water erosion. To the right the big debris cone and below that a small part of the moraine-covered ice lobe. In front of the central part of the snout an area furrowed parallel to the direction of the valley.*

In the lower parts of Sermikavsak the surface is rather plain. Only at the sides of the valley some deep, though short, lateral crevasses existed. In the direction of the movement of the glacier lie some parallel melt-water gullies, which in several cases disappear through glacier mills and continue their course under the ice. Remainders of collapsed meltwater-gullies were found on the surface at a few places, as for instance in the northern part of the glacier where the deep cut in the snout (fig. 2) is probably a collapsed melt-water tunnel. A part from this place in the northern, most recessed part of the snout, the ice margin consists of very even slopes. Most of the glacier is almost white, having but small amounts of gravel scattered on the surface. Still, near the bed the glacier is black with mud (fig. 3). This comparatively clean part of Sermikavsak consists of a broad lobe in the middle with narrower lobes on each side. The lobes are separated by melt-water gullies, which at several places have eroded gorges to a depth more than 25 m. below the surface. In the summer 1957 no traces of any big melt-water streams under the ice could be found. The only real glacier outlet was found in 1953 as well as in 1957 in the snout near the most south-western part of the arrow pointing towards the north. This ice cave was in 1957 about 1½ m. high and 1½ m. wide, whereas a glacier outlet in the snout of Quvnertussoq was 10 m. high and 20 m. wide. Contrary to the northern two thirds, the third of Sermikavsak nearest to the southern side of the valley is characterized partly by being covered with moraine materials, partly by stretching out to a line much nearer to the shoreline than the rest of the glacier. As a consequence of the dark colours of the moraine materials on the ice surface, this ice lobe looks very much like a lateral moraine. However, in several steep slipping surfaces on the northern side of the dark ice lobe the ice can be seen very clearly.

As mentioned above, the glaciers in the valleys of east-western direction in Upernivik Ø are characterized by their southernmost moraine covered ice lobe, which is stretching much more towards west than the rest of the glacier. The length of the ice lobe and the cover of moraine material on the surface of this lobe is due to the fact that the lobe is situated in the shades of the northern side of the valleys, the melting-off thereby being considerably reduced. Further, the greater part of the supply to the glaciers is coming from the southern slopes of the valleys; this causes a greater transport of ice and, consequently, of moraine material to the southern ice lobes. The increased amount of moraine material is more insulating, resulting in a further reduction of the melting-off (Kuhlman 1959). A consequence of this is that the snout of the moraine-covered ice lobe of Sermikavsak is situated about 400 m. nearer to the shoreline than the rest of the glacier. This ice lobe is still moving, a fact which became evident when, in 1956, a surveying point was placed on this part of the glacier, then considered as a tolerably stable lateral moraine. During the summer 1957 the point had moved, whereas the cairn built over the point was intact. Probably the ice in this lobe is moving very slowly, even compared with the rest of the glacier. The southern ice lobe of Sermikavsak seems to behave as a medium between the central parts of the glacier and the northern lateral moraine, which is described later on.

The moraine systems of Sermikavsak have but a small extent. Although the glacier has several glacial affluxes no medium moraines are visible. Lateral moraines, or at least the results of a glacial erosion in the sides of the valley can be seen on the slopes

Fig. 4. *The coast at Sermikavsak 1957. In the front the southern side of the valley. To the left the moraine area southwest of the moraine-covered ice lobe, which lies hidden under the valley-side. To the right the moraine-system BCD emphasized by a dotted line. In the upper part of the picture the outmost part og the northern lateral moraine (A) and the isolated moraine islands near the shoreline. Further, the beach ridge in front of the western outwash plain.*

near the shoreline (fig. 2 and fig. 3). The northern lateral moraine can be followed to the westernmost ice-fall at a distance from the shoreline of about 5 km. towards north east. It appears clearly that the sides of the valley have been greatly eroded. At several places thin layers of gravel and rocks, in the course of time deposited on less steep parts of the southern slope, have been covered with vegetation. To a height of about 50 m. above the ice surface big scars of recent date have been cut in the vegetation and the debris by the glacier. The most powerful erosion takes place in the outmost parts of the turns in the outlet from the inner glacier basin, for instance near the ice-fall situated at the westernmost cirque valley. Quvnertussoq has several medium moraines, which all come from the smaller branch glaciers in the southern side of the valley. The moraine deposits on the glacier surface are joining as the ice is approaching the shoreline and, in this case too, they are the cause of the dense cover of moraine material on the southern parts of the glacier. Lateral moraines along this glacier are only found at the northern side of the valley. According to the air photographs the glacier north of Quvnertussoq reached in 1953 as far as to the shoreline, while in 1957 the snout had retired about 200 m. This was partly du to an actual withdrawal of the glacier, partly due to the fact that the small, shallow creek in front of the snout was going to be closed by a beach ridge in which the material, originating from the glacial erosion, was transported to the sea by the melt-water rivers. In front of the glacier valleys on the west coast of Upernivik Ø fans of deposits are stretching out in Igdlorssuit Sund. The deposit fans in front of Sermikavsak and the two northern glacier valleys rise a little above sea-level. The southern part of the glacier (the central glacier) north of Quvnertussoq is completely covered with rocks and gravel. The shoreline to the north and to the south of the creek just mentioned has been formed by moraine material (partly originating from the moraine cover of the glacier and partly from the lateral moraine), which has been pushed out into Igdlorssuuit Sund in continuation of the sides of the valley. The southern slopes of the deposit fans in the sea in front of Qungulertussoq are thus protected by the southern moraine-covered ice lobe of this glacier, while the snout otherwise is situated at a distance of about 500 m. from the shoreline. In profile the deposit fans and lateral moraines stretching out into the sea from the shoreline look like beaks.

In 1957 the glacier Serminguaq had retired so much that almost no clean ice surface could be seen below the level of 500 m. Apparently, this glacier has never reached any considerable size, and the northwestern lateral moraine has developed but little. In the lower part of the southwestern slope the bed-rock is greatly scarred by glacial erosion. The last glacier visited in the summer 1957 stretches to the river Qalatoq. This glacier has lateral moraines on both sides. The snout has retired from the position which appears from fig. 1. The two lakes above Qalatoq receive the greater part of their water supply from the glacier which looks like a hand with a pointing finger. Judging from the vegetation in the valley, the water-level in the lakes may oscillate about 1 m. In some years it looks as if the ice does not melt away (1953?). However, in the summer 1957 the ice had melted away, and the water had the colour of light emerald green cause by the great quantity of materials washed out by the melt-water rivers.

During the research-work in the summer 1957 the snout at that time was surveyed (Møller 1959). However, owing to lack of time the surveying could not be continued beyond this. The map figure 2 has been worked out on the base of air photographs 1953 (about 1 : 40.000) which have been enlarged to about 1 : 6.000. Of course, the map must only be regarded as a sketch, because it has not been possible to adjust the air photographs with regard to horizontal level. In the scale here available (about 1 : 18.000) the errors are after all insignificant. Moreover, a certain weight has been attached to representing the morphological elements instead of producing an exact topographical map. — It has to be mentioned that no error of any importance has been found when it was possible to compare the map with later measurements. It was rather difficult to choose signs for the map. First it was tried to apply the signs used in the Danish morphological maps; however, the moraine landscape mentioned here and those in Denmark cannot be immediately compared. Therefore, in this map only few and simplified signs have been used and, as far as possible, the importance has been attached to grouping the morphological elements as in the Danish literature on morphology (Rosenkrantz 1939 and Schou 1949).

The bed-rock north of Sermikavsak consists of gneiss. The wall of rock is rising very steeply to a height of more than 1200 meter above sea-level with a very rough and inaccessible surface, which in the upper parts has probably never been eroded by glacial ice. The sides of the valley are cut up by numerous melt-water rivers supplied from snow drifts on the top of the mountains (only the two greatest of the melt-water rivers have been marked in fig. 2). The southern slope of the valley in fig. 2 consists of sandstone containing coal. The rather soft sandstone rises in rounded hills to about 900 m. above sea-level. Apart from some deep canyons, especially on the south coast, the sandstone area is covered with vegetation. The southern part of the valley in front of Sermikavsak is characterized by the yellow gravel and rocks from the sandstone area.

The lateral moraine along the northern side of the valley of Sermikavsak is clearly seen in fig. 3. — The direction in which the picture has been taken appears from fig. 2 (small arrows marked by the number of the picture). The distance between the place where the picture has been taken and the northern lateral moraine is about 1500 m. The highest part of the lateral moraine (just northeast of the snout) rises about 200 m. above sea-level. It appears from the figure that the slope of the moraine facing the glacier is very steep, too steep to consist of gravel and rocks only. The lateral moraine follows the northern side of the valley at a distance of 6 km. from the shoreline towards north east, steadily decreasing in height. In the eastern part the lateral moraine consists of two mounds parallel to each other. Nearest to the glacier stands the high, steep mound mentioned above. Between

Fig. 5. A view from the central part of Sermikavsak towards southwest 1957. In the foreground a small terminal moraine. In front of the snout and furrowed parallel to the valley an area corresponding to the withdrawal of Sermikavsak since the air photographs were taken in 1953. In the background and to the right outwash plains behind which the terminal moraine BCD can be seen; further, Igdlorssuit Sund (= sound), Ubekendt Ejland (unknown island) and to the left Nugssuaq (the great peninsula). The bamboo pole is 2 m. long and placed 45 m. above sea-level.

this and the valley slope lies a low, rounded mound completely covered with vegetation. The hollow between the mounds is at several places partly filled up with water. The mounds are probably lateral moraines originating from different periods of the life of the glacier. The content of moraine material in the mounds is probably almost equal; however, the mound nearest to the glacier contains no doubt great quantities of glacial ice, which acts as a cement in the northern moraine and favours the steepness of the slope, facing the glacier. This lateral moraine filled up with ice looks just like the southern moraine-covered ice lobe; however, contrary to this, the northern lateral moraine is a completely isolated mound which does not take part in the movements of the glacier. The moraine material in the lateral moraine is probably more equally dispersed in the ice than that of the southern ice lobe, which is covered with a relatively thin layer of moraine material. Probably, the high northern lateral moraine is a remainder from a period when the glacier had much larger dimensions. At this place the great content of gravel and rocks has had steadily increasing insulating effect, resulting in a very slow melting-off. Owing to its age, the low mound mentioned above does not contain glacial ice; therefore, it has shrunk to become insigni-

Fig. 6. Sermikavsak August 1934 (Reginald Orcutt phot.). It is possible to catch a glimpse of the terminal moraine BCD (fig. 2 and 4) in the right part of the figure.

ficant. It was obvious that the younger moraines contain large quantities of glacial ice; consequently, the surface was cut up by numerous fissures produced by the melting-off, whereas the older moraines without glacial ice have an undisturbed surface and are of very small dimensions. — It has to be emphasized that the ice mentioned here is glacial ice, and not the phenomenon permafrost, which was not examined at this occasion —. Though the northern lateral moraine has probably formed a part of Sermikavsak and participated in the life and movements of the latter, the moraine is now quite different from the rest of the glacier. It looks so much like a lateral moraine that it seems justifiable to name it thus. This is supported by the fact that, southwest of the snout, the cover of vegetation is increasing and the height of the mound falling with a decreasing distance to the shoreline. Near this the lateral moraine is a low mound covered with vegetation and with the same aspect as the mound between the high moraine and the slope as mentioned above. In fig. 2 the westernmost part of the lateral moraine has been marked with an A; it can further be seen in fig. 5 outmost to the right. In this part the surface of the moraine has not been cut up by fissures and shrinkings, which normally disclose an underground melting-off. Behind the northern

lateral moraine melt-water rivers are running which receive their
water supply from snow drifts on the mountains north of Sermikavsak through the melt-water gullies in the steep slope. The melt-
water rivers carry large amounts of gravel which is deposited
between the slope and the moraine, at a few places eroded by the
rivers, (fig. 2 and 3), whereupon the streams carry the gravel out
to the plains in front of Sermikavsak.

On the surface of the glacier several small moraines, medium
moraines are found which at a close examination appear as ice
mounds with a thin cover of moraine materials. In the right part
of fig. 6 it is possible to catch a glimpse of several great, dark
moraines, most likely the recent terminal moraines (near D, fig. 2).
Some moraine formations (5—10 m. high), which partly are remainders of melt-water erosion, are seen in the figures 2, 3 and 7.
All of them appear to contain glacial ice. In several moraines the
ice has melted away. Like the lateral moraines without glacial ice
these formations are very small (less than 1 m.) and are difficult
to see in the field. In continuation of the moraine-covered southern
ice lobe an isolated, hilly area is situated (fig. 2 and 4 entirely to
the left). The eastern part of this area is obviously containing
glacial ice and rises to a height of about 50 m. in contrast to the
western, ice-free parts of the hills, which only rise to about 10 m.
above sea-level. Across the valley in front of Sermikavsak several
systems of mounds — probably terminal moraines — are situated.
The mounds can be seen very clearly when the landscape is regarded from above, as in fig. 4 (taken from a point about 200 m.
above sea-level on the southern slope of the valley). Apart from
the terminal moraines from C to D, all the mounds are very small,
only rising 2—5 m. above the surface. As mentioned above, considerably greater quanities of moraine material must have been
available in the southern parts of the valley. The terminal moraine
is here of compartively great extension, and the moraine material
is rather coarse. This distinction between the different parts of the
terminal moraines is clearly seen in fig. 4. It is possible to find
two systems of terminal moraines from different periods (A and
BCD, fig. 2). East of the system BCD there is no possibility of
recognizing terminal moraines, because the surface has been disturbed too much by the melt-water rivers. The terminal moraine
BCD is very well preserved, partly as a consequence of the large-
grained material, partly because it has been protected by remainders of moraine areas situated to the east. The terminal moraine A

Fig. 7. Moraine mounds in the southern part of the valley 1957. Contain glacial ice and are partly formed by meltwater-erosion. The person is a little below medium height.

must originate from a period when the snout of the glacier partly has been situated at some distance to the west of the shoreline.

The dating of the terminal moraine is difficult without special investigations. It is possible to make an estimate of the age through an examination of the extent and the age of the vegetation in front of and behind the terminal moraines. However, this method is questionable, because the surface has been eroded so much by the melt-water rivers. The best judgment of the state of the front can be obtained on the basis of air photographs from different periods of the life of the glacier. In august 1934 the American explorer Reginald Orcutt from New York passed by the west coast of Upernivik Ø. He photographed Sermikavsak just when the boat was outside the southern part of the valley. The original negative has been lost during the Second World War, and only a small, rather poor copy has been available. From this copy (fig. 6) it clearly appears that at that time the front of Sermikavsak was situated at the place of the terminal BCD, perhaps a little behind the recent moraine. Especially the southern parts of the terminal moraine (fig. 2, D) are very easy to recognize because of the large, marked rocks. Some dark, high moraines, obviously containing large

amounts of glacial ice, are seen near the snout (fig. 6). The greater
part of the remainders of these moraines are now rather small,
as it appears from fig. 4, and at short distances they are difficult
to see among the rocks and the melt-water gullies. The terminal
moraines formed in the summer 1957 are all very small too in spite
of their content of glacial ice. A small crescent-shaped mound,
behind which some melt-water has been dammed up, is seen to
the left in fig. 5. The size of the mound appears from the bamboo
pole (2 m. high) placed to the right. In several cases stratified clay
has been deposited in the water behind the mound and later become visible when the glacial ice in the moraine has melted away,
allowing the water to run off. Small terminal moraines are very
frequent in front of Sermikavsak — as it appears from fig. 2 —
near the northern part of the snout. On the other hand, none of
the moraines formed in 1957 reach the size of the terminal moraines
from the 1930ies mentioned above.

Investigations of *the movements of Sermikavsak* were one of
the main objects of the expedition. Originally it was intended to
survey a row of bambo poles drilled into the ice surface in the
lower parts of the glacier. However, the poles were only surveyed
once, partly caused by the lack of time, and partly because the
northern lateral moraine was very difficult to climb, and it was
very hard to get a view of the glacier from anywhere else. On a
rough estimate, the speed of the southern moraine-covered ice lobe
on a part with the rest of the front is about 2—5 m. in one year.
In the middle of the white ice lobe the speed must be about 15—
25 m. in one year at some distance from the front. Unlike these
poor estimates it has been possible to make a judgment of the withdrawal of the snout during the last years, based upon Reginal
Orcutt's photograph, air photographs and the map of the snout
1957 (Møller 1959). In 1953 the distance between the terminal
moraine BCD and the snout was 600—700 m., while during the
years 1953—57 the snout has withdrawn about 150 m. further
towards north east. — These figures do not apply to the southern,
moraine-covered ice lobe —. As will be seen, the average withdrawal is about 30—40 m. in one year (the exact figures are 34
and 38 m. respectively) for both periods in question. While some
importance can be attributed to the absolute size of the withdrawal, the withdrawal in the individual year and in the different
parts of the snout is probably very varying. Thus, the southern
moraine-covered ice lobe seems to have been stationary in the

Fig. 8. The front of Sermikavsak near the northern lateral moraine 1957. In June the ice stretched out to the right in the picture. In the background the moraine area (F) southwest of the moraine-covered ice lobe. Notice the rucksack and the rounded rocks.

period 1934—57. The very procedure of the melting-off implies the possibility of rather great variations. As mentioned above, several places in the lower parts of the snout are covered with mud and sand, while the rest of the snout is rather clean and white. A certain content of moraine material in the ice will accelerate the melting-off, owing to the dark colours of the surface, especially in this area with the great incoming radiation. If, on the other hand, the content of moraine material rises above a certain limit the material will gradually act as an insulating cover, and the melting-off will decrease again (Kuhlman 1959). By a certain, constant content of moraine material in a certain part of the glacial ice the melting-off will increase in the start and then decrease steadily, because the concentration of moraine material in the ice is gradually rising. This is revealed at several places on the snout of Sermikavsak by the flat shape of the lowest parts of the ice. In a longitudinal section the glacier has the shape of a duck's head with a beak. This low, flat part of the snout is then exposed to erosion from the numerous, steadily alternating melt-water streams. As soon as the moraine materiale has been washed away the erosion and the increased melting-off (caused by the removal of the material) may make the withdrawal go on in jerks in the course of a few days, even a few hours. Thus, the snout of the glacier retired 5 m. in three days from the small mound (fig. 5), which was a terminal moraine in the beginning of the summer 1957. The northern part of the snout in fig. 2 was entirely flat. The narrowing in the northern part of the snout has been caused by the collapse of a melt-water tunnel in which the outermost parts have melted away. In the summer 1957 the narrowing had disappeared; however, the contour lines in the former tunnel allow to follow it as a valley towards north east. At some distance to north east of the snout the tunnel passes into a melt-water gully, which separates the northernmost ice lobe from the rest of the glacier.

Just in front of the glacier is an area which is furrowed parallel to the direction of the glacier (fig. 5). These furrows are not a result of the melt-water erosion, because the moraine material here is coarse and the area is protected against the melt-water rivers which, coming from the gullies on both sides of Sermikav-sak, unite in an acute angle in front of the snout. Therefore, there is an almost undisturbed area between the rivers and the snout. It is difficult to explain how the furrows have been formed; how-ever, the complete lack of melt-water erosion can be interpreted to the effect that the area still remains as when the ice left it. The distance from northeast to southwest in the area corresponds to the withdrawal of the glacier in the period 1953—57. If so, the furrows are probably remainders from the time when the snout reached so much further to south west that the ice was still moving across the area. As the ground is quite filled up with water it is very difficult to move here. Probably some glacial ice is still left in the area. Corresponding furrows are seen in the moraine area C (fig. 2 and 4). Judging from the lastmentioned picture, the furrows are situated on both sides of the terminal moraine from 1934. It is likely that the glacier had stopped for some time at the now visible terminal moraine after a brief advance a little further towards south west. The furrows do not seem to be the result of solifluc-tion, because the gradient of the terrains in question is very small, and no signs of a separation of the moraine materials are seen.

Being dispersed irregularly in the glacier, the moraine material has probable been carried to the snout in jerks. This explains the big concentration of moraine material seen in fig. 6. Great distur-bances in the surface in front of Sermikavsak have only been

Fig. 9. Debris cone (9 m. heigh) between the white and the moraine-covered ice lobe 1957. To the left it is possible to catch a glimpse of the steep northern side of the southern ice lobe. Notice the sharp-edged rocks.

found near the northernmost, narrow ice lobe (fig. 7). The rocks which are of considerable size must, judging from their rounded shape, have been transported in the bottom of the glacier. They came to the surface of the snout along shear planes a few metres above the bottom of the valley. Very small mounds, which have to be considered as shear moraines, are seen just in this part of the snout (fig. 2). The snout of Sermikavsak stood in the summer 1957 entirely to the right of the picture, which was taken in August. The withdrawal is partly attributable to the melting-off, partly to the melt-water erosion caused by the river running between the glacier and the northern lateral moraine. The moraine below the big rock above to the right is filled up with glacial ice and is an offshoot of the northern lateral moraine. — On the other hand, a very great part of the moraine material is transported on the surface of the glacier, down to which the rocks probably fall from the high, steep slopes of the valley. All the time the transportation takes place on the surface, and at last the moraine material has simply been left back on the bottom of the valley as the glacier draws back. Therefore, a very big part of the erratics are sharp-edged (fig. 9); this is for instance the case in the southern part of the moraine BCD, where it is possible to catch a glimpse of the big rocks in fig. 4. The presence of the large quantity of edged rocks on the surface of the southern ice lobe and, moreover, the distribution of the erratics in the valley seem to indicate that the cover of moraine material on the southern parts of the glaciers facing Igdlorssuit Sund has been caused by rocks fallen down to the ice surface from the southern slopes and especially from the steep slopes along the southern glacial affluxes.

A debris cone (fig. 9) is situated in the melt-water gully between the southern moraine-covered ice lobe and the rest of the glacier. Small debris cones have been noticed at several place in Upernivik Ø. About 10 m. above the bottom of the valley on the steep snout of Qungulertussoq stood a row of small cones at the same level and all about half a metre high. These cones, which were not subjected to any close examination, were covered with gravel. In reality, they correspond to the moraines on the surface of a glacier and are an insulation-phenomenon. This is no do doubt the case of the debris cone at Sermikavsak too. Here is only one large cone, 9 m. high and containing a great lump of glacial ice, covered with gravel. The cone can be seen in the air photograph of 1953, in which the shape of the lump appears to be an isolated, but very irregular formation. In the summer 1956 the lump looked like a cone when regarded from certain angles, and in 1957 a very regular cone had been developed. While, in 1953, the cone was situated to the north east of the snout, this had in 1957 retired so much that the cone then stood just west of the snout very close to the moraine-covered ice lobe (seen to the left in fig. 9 as a steep, dark wall). Probably the debris cone has been formed by a big lump of glacial ice, isolated either by a fall or by melt-water erosion. As the ice has melted away the content of gravel has slipped down to the surface around the lump and in this way formed the recent cone as the only possible result, provided the base of the lump, if only approximately, had the shape of a circle. The characteristic result has at any rate been caused by the original shape of the ice lump. The debris cone contained still in 1957 some glacial ice.

The greater part of *the valley in front of Sermikavsak* is characterized by the melt-water rivers. Fig. 2 shows areas in which the melt-water rivers ran in 1953, as well as areas formed by rivers before 1953. The rivers are detained by the terminal moraine BCD, which has caused the formation of the outwash-plain in which the rivers are constantly changing beds (fig. 3 and 5). The breaking-through of the north-western melt-water river is seen to the left in fig. 5. Just after the rivers have broken through the terminal moraine the water is spreading and covers a great area, shaping another outwash-plain to the south west of the terminal moraine. This outwash-plain has been formed because the melt-water rivers are restrained in their outlets into Igdlorssuit Sund. The tidal difference at the west coast of Upernivik Ø is about 2 m. When the sea-level is rising the wave action takes place at increasing levels; in this way a beach ridge can be formed in a very short time (Møller 1958). The top of the beach ridge is about half a metre above the surface of the western outwash-plain. The melt-water rivers are only able to keep very few outlets in the beach ridge. Fig. 4 was taken at high tide. The water from Igdlorssuit Sund has flown through the outlets and is covering small areas behind the beach ridge, where melt-water deposits have been shaped by numerous melt-water rivers. The surface of Igdlorssuit Sund is covered with a thin layer of melt-water containing outwashed clay. The limpid salt water is stirring up at the lee side of the icebergs. The limpid water flowing out from the melt-water river in the lowest part of the picture originates from glaciers and snowdrifts several kilometres from the shoreline in the sandstone area. This river, following the southern side of the valley, changes bed from time to time and is sometimes situated south of the moraine hill F (fig. 2). But few moraine areas have not been eroded by the melt-water rivers. The undisturbed moraine areas are scattered in the landscape as islands, especially in the shelter of terminal moraines containing heavy materials. Especially the areas in the northern side of the valley very near to the shoreline look like moraine islands (old moraine landscapes, »hill islands«). The moraine island A is covered with vegetation, and a tomb has been found in the southern part.

The above comments on the investigations in question should only be regarded as a description of some observations in an interesting, but small-sized marginal landscape. Even if it is tempting to compare the marginal landscape in Denmark with that in Greenland this is obviously impossible, because the glacial formations in front of Sermikavsak compared with the corresponding formations in Denmark (terminal moraine, outwash plains, old moraine landscapes and marginal moraines) have entirely different dimensions in proportion to each other and to the glaciers which have created the formations. Still, perhaps, the attention has to be drawn to the moraines in which the content of glacial ice is of very great importance as compared with the content of real moraine material.

SUMMARY

Owing to the shade conditions the alpine valley glaciers in Upernivik Ø receive their supply from branch glaciers on the southern sides of the valleys. For the same reason the lower parts of the glaciers consist of a broad, almost white ice lobe to the north of a narrower lobe covered with moraine material. The last-mentioned lobe has not retired as much as the rest of the snout because of the insulating moraine cover and the shade conditions. Along the northern side of Sermikavsak a high, lateral moraine is stretching, probably a rest of the glacier, now entirely isolated and motionless. The size of the moraines depends on their content of glacial ice. Thus, the northern lateral moraine at several places rises to 200 m. above the bottom of the valley, while the moraines without glacial ice are very small. A debris cone in front of the southern part of the snout consists of a big lump of glacial ice containing moraine material. The moraines in front of Sermikavsak cannot be compared with moraines in Denmark before their content of glacial ice has melted away whereupon they are very small (less than $1/10$ of their former height). The ice mentioned in this paper is glacial ice, not permafrost.

Several systems of small terminal moraines are situated in front of Sermikavsak. Based on photographs from different periods of the life of the glaciers the withdrawal can probably be estimated at about 30–40 m. on an average in one year. The area in front of Sermikavsak is characterized by melt-water rivers; even some undisturbed moraine areas are still left as islands in the outwash plains. Some of the moraine islands are furrowed parallel to the direction of the valley. The furrows are still existing, probably because the withdrawal has gone on for only a short time. The furrows do not seem to be the result of solifluction. Owing to the content of dark moraine material in the glacial ice, the melting-off is increasing until the relative content of moraine material attains a certain limit, whereupon it acts as insulation, and part of the ice will remain for some time as a motionless rest covered with moraine materials. As a consequence of the uneven distribution of these materials in the glacier the moraines are scattered as heaps of unequal size in front of Sermikavsak. Rounded rocks and gravel have been transported to the surface along shear planes in the entire extent of the snout; especially in front of the southern parts of the glacier large quantities of edged rocks have been left back, originally fallen down to the ice surface from the steep slopes of the valley and then transported on the surface of the glacier.

LITERATURE

Bishop, B. C. (1957): Shear Moraines in the Thule Area, Northwest Greenland. SIPRE Research Report 17.

Engeln, O. D. von (1957): Geomorphology. New York.

Fristrup, B. and Jensen, Ad. S. (1950): Den arktiske Klimaforbedring og dens Følger. Geogr. Tidsskr. 50. København.

Geodætisk Institut: Grønland 1 : 250.000 og 1 : 50.000. København.

Grønland i Tohundredeaaret for Hans Egedes Landing. (1921): Medd. om Grønl. 60–61. København.

Kuhlman, H. (1959): Weather and Ablation Observations at Sermikavsak in Umanak District. Medd. om Grønl. 158: 5. København.

Madsen, V. (1928): Oversigt over Danmarks Geologi. Danm. Geol. Unders. V: 4. København.

Møller, J. T. (1958): Et tidevandsfænomen i lille målestok. Geogr. Tidsskr. 57. København.

Møller, J. T. (1959): A West Greenland Glacier Front. A Survey of Sermikavsak near Umanak in 1957. Medd. om Grønl. 158: 5. København.

Noe-Nygaard, A. (1955): Geologi, processer og materialer. København.

Rosenkrantz, A. (1939): Danmarks Geologi. København.

Schou, A. (1949): Atlas over Danmark I. København.

Weidick, A. (1959): Glacial Variations in West Greenland in Historical Time. I. Medd. om Grønl. 158: 4. København.

Runoff studies from the Mitdluagkat Gletcher in SE-Greenland during the late summer 1958.

By Hans Valeur Larsen.

Since 1956, glaciological investigations have been carried out in Greenland under the leadership of *Børge Fristrup*. The expeditions have been sent out from the *Geographical Institute* at the *University of Copenhagen* and are part of the Danish IGY work. In 1958 an expedition worked on the Mitdluagkat Gletscher (gletscher = glacier) on the island Angmagssalik Ø, East Greenland. The main object of this expedition was studies of the glacier variations in relation to change of climate; in addition, some special glacial-meteorological research-work was carried out and, in connection with these studies, an investigation of the runoff from the glacier.

I wish to express my gratitude for all the help and advices given to me in my studies, first of all to the leader of the expedition, *Børge Fristrup*, who made it possible for me to carry out my investigations, and a special thank to *Jens Fabricius*, who assisted me in the field. I also wish to thank the other members of the expedition for their valuable help. Further, I take this opportunity to express my gratitude to the *Danish Technical Highschool*, the *Hydrological Laboratory,* to which I am much indebted for having lent the necessary instruments and for the advices which I got there from amanuensis *B. A. Christensen*.

The glacier which had been chosen was called the Mitdluagkat Gletscher after the peak Mitdluagkat (973 m.). The landscape is alpine (fig. 1), and the glacier may be classified as a transection glacier (Ahlmann's classification system). Its total area is *about* 30 sq. km. The greater branch is a tongue towards west, narrowing in the approach to the front. The latter is situated at a distance of about 0,8 km. from the sea (Sermilik Fjord). Most of this tongue is drained off to the front, in the bottom of which a stream emerges through a gate. The water level at this point was on the

6th of August computed (by levelling) to 4,10 m. above mean sea level. From there the stream runs meandering in a flat-bottomed valley, which has a width of about 200 m. (fig. 1).

For the investigation of such a glacial river several methods are useful; however, the chemical ones may be preferable, *Sögnen* (1954). The principle of these is to add an indifferent saline solution to the river above violent stream turbulences and to measure the time required for the »saltwave« to pass a point further down and the concentration of the latter. This method is preferable when the stream is very turbulent, which is generally the case of glacial rivers; however, its application offers rather great difficulties to unexperienced persons. Furthermore, as it was possible for me to borrow the necessary instruments for the following method this was adopted:

It is a well-known fact that there is a certain relation between the discharge and the water level of a watercourse. By means of a self-recording river-gauge (fig. 2) the water level was automatically recorded. The type of instrument was A. W. 1. R. Fuess no. 1033; it was fixed upon a triangular wooden tube. Inside this a float was hanging, following the water movements up and down. The movements were drawn on a recording paper, wrapped round a rotating cylinder driven by a clockwork.

In plate I the thinner curve (H) indicates the water level at any time from 4th August to 17th September, copied directly (after the necessary corrections) from the above mentioned recording paper, while the thicker curve (Q) indicates the discharge, computed from fig. 3 (see below).

The position of the river-gauge is 250 m. from the outlet, as shown by »H« in fig. 1; the difference of the water level between the two points is about 1 m. Part of the stream does not pass this place, but forms a separate branch. However, the size of this is comparatively small, and, as it was evident that its slope was nearly the same as that of the main stream, the error brought in by recording the level only at »H« is bound to be insignificant. From time to time the position of the river-gauge had to be controlled by levelling to a point on the solid rock; however, the deviations from the mean instrument height were small — less than 16 mm. difference between the highest and the lowest position. Also the relative position of the pen had to be controlled at least twice a week.

For the determination of the velocity of the current it is necessary to find a place where the stream is smooth, deep and undivided

Fig. 1. The glacial river, seen from the glacier.

and the place so far upstream that the changes in the sea level will not affect the current (the tidal amplitude was 2,5–3,5 m.). The chosen point is indicated by »Q« in fig. 1 about 420 m. downstream from »H«, 2,40—2,45 m. above mean sea level. The distance along the stream from »Q« to the sea is about 360 m. at high tide and about 200 m. longer at mean sea level. The type of instrument was »Flügel Lüth 4251« current-meter; a signal is given every time a propeller has rotated 20 times. The discharge was measured 5 times at different water levels, and a diagram of the water level as a function of the discharge (log. scale) was drawn (fig. 3). The five values are shown to be situated approximately on a straight line. The upper (dotted) part of this could not be determined in this way; however, the tapping-off from an ice-dammed lake on the 2nd of September made the extension possible:

The quantities of water tapped off could be calculated, and they are clearly represented by the area »A« in plate I (cf.: *Brüchner* (1895)); the dotted line below »A« indicates the probable values of the water level if no tapping took place. The curve in fig. 3 was extended in a way to satisfy the different water-level values by differentiating the area »A«; however, the extended part of the curve is, of course, given with far less accuracy.

About 50 per cent of the drainage area concerned is glacier-covered; consequently, the conditions of the glacier, especially in

Fig. 2. The river gauge in position. In the background: the glacier outlet, the height of which is 4 m.

dry periods, dominate the discharge. This is rather uniform (plate I) — although slightly diminishing — from the beginning of the investigation period until about the 29th of August. The amplitude is big and very regular (the high discharge values on the 23rd of August are probably caused by tapping from a certain reservoir in the glacier). Later, the amplitude is diminishing, and from the 2nd of September the discharge is extremely irregular, and the daily variation has almost disappeared.

In the period with pronounced daily rythm the high water occurred at about 5 or 6 p. m. and the low water at about 10 (or 9) a. m. The corresponding discharge values were about 4 cu. m./sec. and 2 cu. m./sec. — i.e. a very big amplitude (67 per cent of the mean discharge) and only a small delay of the dicharge maximum, compared with the probable hour for the daily maximum of melting on the glacier.

This short delay of the discharge might go to show that only a small and local area is drained off to the stream in question; however, a comparison between the total discharge in a certain precipitation-free period and the readings of the ablation poles, shows that the intake area is not less than 5,6 sq. km. and not more than 19,6 sq. km. with a most probable value of 8 sq. km. Consequently, the area drained off to the river is not inconsiderable, when the total size of the glacier and the narrowness of the (lower part of the) glacier tongue are taken into consideration. Consequently, the pronounced daily variation in August and the short delay of maximum and of minimum must be due to an effective draining from the glacier surface; the great number of (small) crevasses in the upper part and of wells in the lower part seems to confirm this; so does the fact that but few slush accumulations existed and that the extension of the firn was very small, as the greater part of the glacier surface was bare ice or firn ice.

No doubt, the daily amplitude was much smaller earlier in the year and the delay of discharge much bigger owing to the greater extension of firn and snow.

The radiation and the meteorological conditions are often clearly reflected in the curve of discharge; and as the temperature of the glacier at all depths, according to *Fristrup*'s investigations from the uppermost 15 m., was about the melting point the refreezing of melt-water must be insignificant. The month of August was mostly radiation-dominated — great incoming radiation in day-time and great outgoing radiation at night — while September was dominated by the precipitation and by the ice-dammed lakes.

Fig. 4 illustrates the influence of the radiation and of the meteo-rological conditions. In this figure 6 days have been given as samp-les. As stated above, the curves called »Q« indicate the discharge, »t« indicates the temperatures at the coast-camp, 25 m. above sea-level, read on an Assman aspiration psychrometer; the tempera-tures on the glacier were lower according to the difference of alti-tude. The greater part of the glacier, drained off to the stream, is situated at about 300—500 m. above sea-level. The cloudiness is indicated by a fat, black gurtle near the top of the figures; a width of 8 units means 8/8 cloudiness. The letters »H«, »M« and »L« refer to the cloud base »high«, »middle« and »low«. »Weak, »middle« and »strong« refer to the winds, but are only to be understood rela-tively, as »strong« merely means force 4 or more (Beaufort scale). Finally, the actinograms have been copied to give an idea of the in-coming radiation (it should be noticed that in reality the ordinate-axis is slightly bent). The actinagraph was placed on a nunatak on the outlet of the glacier, and, therefore, the undoubtedly rather big multible reflex between the sky and the glacier higher up cannot fully be read from the actinagrams; partly for this reason, and partly because no zero-point correction of the actinagrams has yet been made, no ordinate-scale has been put in.

The period with daily rythm is seen clearly to reflect the radia-

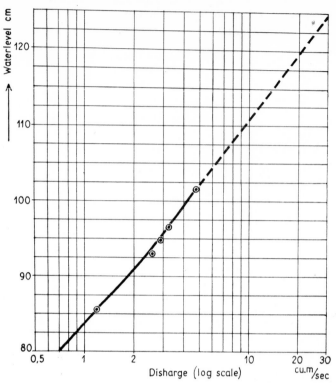

Fig. 3. The water level at point H as a function of the discharge.

tion conditions and, in addition, the temperature conditions. The 20th of August was cloudless, and the temperature maximum occurred at about 11 a.m.; the discharge maximum occurred at 5 p.m. (3,4 cu. m./sec.), the discharge minimum at about 10 a.m. (1,5 cu. m./sec.); consequently, the amplitude was 78 per cent, and the delay of maximum in relation to the incoming radiation and to the temperature maximum was about 5—6 hours. It should here be remembered that at a negative radiation equilibrium the surface temperature of the glacier may be several degrees lower than that of the overlying air.

The 11th of August shows similar conditions; however, a cloud layer has reduced the loss of radiation during the night, causing high discharge values the following day; the minimum of these were 2,6 cu. m./sec. (at 10 a.m.) and maximum 5,3 cu. m./sec. (at 5 p.m.). The high maximum temperature can only be responsible for the high discharge values in the late afternoon and in the evening. The winds, being weak all the time, could not have any great influence on the discharge.

On the 9th of August the maximum of incoming radiation occurred at about noon or 1 p.m., at the same time as the occurrence of the temperature minimum. Nevertheless, the rythm of discharge is pronounced on this date too, the maximum being only an hour later than normally. The discharge amplitude was 72 per cent of the mean value, i.e. only slightly less than that of the 20th of August.

On the 26th of August a rather dense cloud layer caused a small insolation in day-time and a small loss of radiation by night; furthermore, the temperature variations were insignificant; the discharge amplitude was only 33 per cent.

During the last third of the investigation period the discharge is completely dominated by rain and by tapping from ice-dammed lakes, the latter causing the flood values on the 2nd and on the 5th of September (see below). The daily rythm of discharge was insignificant. In plate I the curve composed by black steps illustrates the recorded precipitation at the coast; the figures above the single steps indicate the precipitation (mm. water) in the periods in question. The precipitation on the upper parts of the glacier was undoubtedly bigger — how much is not known. The increase of the discharge on the 14th of September is no doubt due to the abundant precipitation just before, although part of this appeared in the form of snow — especially on the upper parts of the glacier — and, consequently, hampered the runoff. The delay was only 4—6 hours, probably because the mountain slopes already were waterlogged, causing an instant runoff. On the 10th and 11th of September, however, the discharge was delayed considerably more, partly because the slopes were not saturated at that time, and partly because most of the precipitation was snow, except for the lower parts of the glacier.

Tapping from ice-dammed lakes

On the 2nd of September a flood was observed in the glacial river. The water poured down along the southern edge of the glacier tongue, making a cascade when passing the front. Fig. 5 has been photographed from the glacier at nearly the same point as fig. 1 and shows how the stream flooded the river-bed. At about 4 p.m. the flood suddenly decreased, and after a few minutes stopped totally. At the southern edge of the glacier, at a distance of about

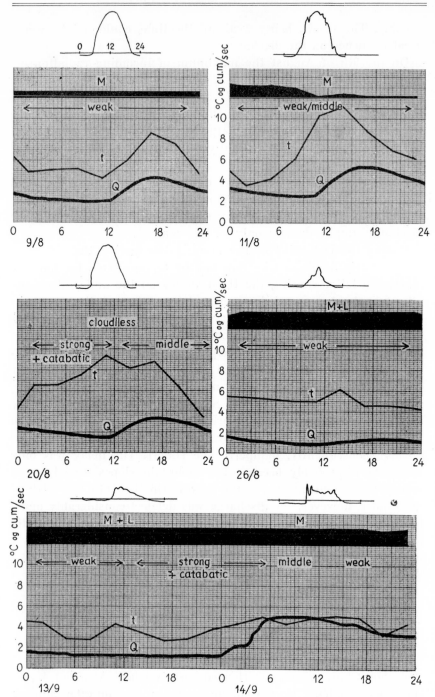

Fig. 4. The influence of the radiation and the meteorological conditions on the discharge.

Fig. 5. The flood on the 2nd of September. Water is running down from the lake being discharged in the lateral groove along the glacier, compare with fig. 1.

4 km. from the front, we found an ice-dammed lake which, no doubt, had caused the sudden flood. At a height of about 5 m. above the water surface there was a mark showing the level of the water before the tapping. The total quantity of water tapped off was computed at about 400.000—450.000 cu.m.

On the 5th of September another tapping took place from a lake situated between the one mentioned above and the glacier front. This lake was totally emptied, as shown in fig. 6. The large discharge values around this date are difficult to explain, the precipitation being too small to cause them. It is possibly a question of a series of small tappings from the numerous ice-dammed lakes along the glacier-edges.

It is easy to reconstruct the emptying of the latter lake, the distance from this to the lateral groove, shown in fig. 5, being very short. In fig. 6 is shown the gate-hole, through which the water had undoubtedly forced its way down. I may have used an old subglacial tunnel, as the hydrostatic pressure grew to become high enough.

Fig. 6. The dry bottom of the lake, tapped off on the 5th of September. Notice the person and the gatehole.
(Fabricius fot.).

The explanation of the tapping on the 2nd of September is much more complicated. It is impossible to say whether a certain syphonic mechanism has acted, or whether the hydrostatic pressure had become high enough to enable the water — in lifting part of the ice — to force its way under the ice through a sub-glacial channel already used; it may be a combination of both processes, cf.: *Glen* (1954); however, the syphone theory explains probably in the best way the sudden cease of the flood.

Of course, the tapping-off from these small lakes must be interpreted in another way than that from the big ice-dammed lakes, well known from Iceland, *Arnborg* (1955), *Okko* (1956), *Thorarinsson* (1939, 1957); however, it is interesting to observe that both types show the typical tapping-profile in the curve of discharge: a relatively gentle increase until the maximum value, and then a sudden drop.

Conclusion

This rather superficial treatment of the material leads to the result that in the month of *August* the *discharge* was primarily *determined by the radiation*, whereas the winds were mostly so weak that the temperature and the humidity had no appreciable effect on the discharge. In *September* the discharge shows great variations, in the first place due to *tappings from ice-dammed lakes*.

secondly because in this month the discharge is dominated by *precipitation* (and the somewhat more powerful winds). Further, it appears that periods with big daily variations of the radiation equilibrium also have big amplitudes of discharge; inversely, on a day and night with small radiation variations the amplitude of the discharge is insignificant.

As will be seen from the above, a small glacier like the Midt. luagkat Gletscher is excellent for making studies of the runoff and, thereby, for getting an impression of the magnitude of the melting at different hours of the day and of the night. Especially in summer, when the extension of snow and firn is small, it is possible in this way to study the influence of radiation and of meteorological factors. Our interpretation possibilities were additionally favoured by the fact that the glacier in question is in recession and that, consequently, the firn cover has a small extension. A further study of the material will undoubtedly give a more exact picture of the relation between the melting, on one side, and the radiation and the meteorological factors, on the other side.

LITTERATUR

Arnborg, Lennart (1955): Hydrology of the glacial river Austurfljot. Geogr. Ann. 37.

Brüchner, E. (1895): Untersuchungen über die tägliche Periode der Wasserführung. Petermanns Mitt. 41.

Glen, J. V. (1954): The stability of ice-dammed lakes. Journal of Glaciology 2 : 15.

Hughes, T. P. & Seligman, M. G. (1939): The temperature, meltwater movement and density increase in the neve of an Alpine glacier. Monthly Not. of Roy. Astr. Soc., Geogr. Suppl. 4 : 8.

Klebelsberg, R. v. (1913): Die Wasserführung des Suldenbaches. Zeitschr. f. Gletscherkde., 7.

Okko, Veikko (1956): Glacial drift in Iceland. Acta Geographica 15.

Schytt, V. (1949): Re-freezing of the melt-water on the surface of glacier ice. Geogr. Ann. 31.

Søgnen, R. (1954): Discharge measurements by means of a salt solution. U.G.G.I., Ass. d'Hydr., Ass. Rome 1954, III.

Thorarinsson, S. (1939): The ice-dammed lakes of Iceland. Geogr. Ann. 21.

Thorarinsson, S. (1957): The Jökulhlaup from the Katla area in 1955 compared with other Jökull in Iceland. Jökull 7.

Wallen, C. C. (1948): Glacial-meteorological investigations on the Kârsa glacier in Swedish Lappland. Geogr. Ann. 30.

White, Sidney E. (1956): Glaciological studies of two outlet glaciers in N.W. Greenland. Medd. om Grønland 137: 8.

An outline of the climate of Denmark

By Kr. M. Jensen

Abstract

This article contains a summary of the average temperature conditions, the quantities of precipitation and the wind conditions. Further, an analysis is given of the distribution, over a rather great number of years, of these climatical elements. A representation is given of the diurnal temperature trend and of the diurnal quantity of precipitation at a certain station in the period 1946–1949; thus, we get an impression of the seasonal alternations of the weather conditions.

Thanks to its geographical position, Denmark is among the regions of the globe where *the balance between incoming and outgoing radiation* for the whole year shows a considerable deficit, calculated for the ground and the superjacent troposphere as an entity. Expressed in average values, the energy deficit resulting from the radiation amounts to about 40.000 cal./sq.cm. per year in our regions. The total incoming atmospheric radiation to the ground proper is about 85.000 cal./sq.cm. per year, which proves that the above-mentioned deficit is of a considerable size and of great importance for the temperature conditions in the country.

The compensation of this deficit principally takes place as follows: by condensation of the water vapour in the atmosphere and by advection. As stated below, the size of the precipitation varies from a little more than 400 mm. till about 800 mm. annually, and the average for the whole country is estimated at about 650 mm. The evaporation amounts to about 350—450 mm. annually; this gives a condensation excess of about 250 mm., corresponding to a heat transfer to the atmosphere above Denmark of approximately 15.000 cal/sq. cm. per year; in this way about one third of the radiation deficit is covered; the rest of the deficit it compensated by a supply of energy through a transfer of warm air-masses.

The day-to-day temperature of the atmosphere is thus determined partly by situations with great radiation, partly by the varying heat conditions of the air-masses. The periods with the radiation as a predominant factor and with still or gently moving air have an intensive heating of the ground surface and of the superjacent air during daytime and, under such conditions, a strong nocturnal cooling. However, a radiation fog may hamper the outgoing terrestrial radiation in the last hours of the night, resulting in an asymmetric course of the daily temperature curve. During these periods the mean daily temperatures do not deviate much from the average values for a great number of years; however, as a result of the above-mentioned fogs they may be a little superior to the normal in summer. What characterizes these situations is the relatively big diurnal temperature amplitude and the rather regular course of the diurnal temperature cycle with its maximum at 2—3 p.m. and its minimum just before sunrise. Such conditions are created when big high-pressure systems stay for a rather long time with their nucleus above or in close proximity to Denmark, resulting in long-lasting, bright weather with wind-forces of a few metres per second. The effects of these anticyclones are accentuated in spring, when a steady heating of the air takes place, giving rise to a relative desiccation, which, in its turn, causes small cloud formations and creates better conditions for the in- and outgoing terrestrial radiation.

As the greatest vertical temperature differences in the air layer near the ground occur during these *high-pressure situations* they are of decisive importance to the micro-climate with all its bio-geographical effects. Thus, the frequency of the high-pressure plays a great role in the Danish climate. They are most frequent in January/February, in May and in September/October; however, their occurrence in proportion to the total number of weather types does not vary much from month to month. A quantitative description is given in the analyses which *Hess* and *Brezowsky* have made of the so-called »Grosswetterlagen«. According to their calculations, »high pressure above Central Europe« (abbr.: HM) occurs in 11% of the total number of days (1891—1950) with its maximum, 17%, in September and its minimum, 7%, in April. Most often this group has its centre to the south of Denmark, while other high-pressures are situated farther to the north and are designated »heigh pressures above Fenno-Scandia and the northern Atlantique« (abbr. HF and HNF). The latter high-pressures occur in 7% of the total number of observations with their maximum of 12% in May and their minimum of 2,5% in July.

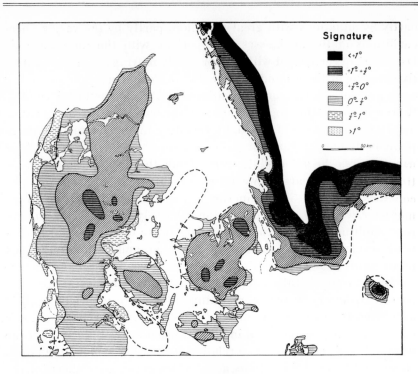

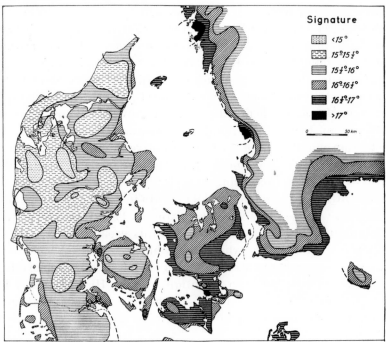

However, much more often the weather is subjected to the influences of *the moving air-masses*. These masses, when passing above Denmark, have such a great influence on our temperature conditions that the diurnal temperature cycle is almost completely dominated by the alterations of the heat content of the air-masses; consequently, the diurnal temperature variations conditioned by the radiation only manifest themselves to a slight degree. It is the heat accompanying these air-masses which compensates a great part of the negative balance between incoming radiation and outgoing radiation; however, the supply of energy is by no means the result of a constant transport to the region of warm air-masses. Thus, the alternations are frequent between the flow of cold, Arctic or Polar air-masses and warm, Tropical air. The most common air circulation takes place in connection with passages of cyclones, and the geographical position of Denmark on the western side of the Eurasian continent is favourable for the intrusion of the cyclones departing from the North Atlantic Polar Front. Around these frontal depressions a definitive wind-change normally takes place. During a passage of a cyclone north of Denmark we first get eastern to south-eastern winds with a supply of Polar Continental air-masses (cP air), which in winter may result in severe cold. Thereafter, the wind turns towards south-south/west after the passage of a warm front, and the region receives Tropical Maritime air (mT air). Finally, in the course of a day or two the wind turns towards west behind the cold-front which delimits the warm sector with the Tropical air-masses, after which the weather conditions are dominated by Polar Maritime air-masses. In certain cases the Polar Maritime air is replaced by air-masses of a more Arctic character, conveyed to us by the north wind. In the cases where the centre of depression wanders straight south of Denmark a wind-change takes place from eastern to northern or, perhaps, north-western winds. However, this change does not bring about the same pronounced alterations of the air temperature as does the front passage.

As appears from the above-mentioned air-masses, the passages of cyclones are often accompanied by great temperature fluctuations. This is especially the case in winter, the season with the greatest number of cyclones above Denmark. Further, the centres of the cy-

← Fig. 1. The two maps p. 224 indicate the average temperatures (not reduced) for January and July. With a view to a judgment of the level-conditioned influence on the temperatures it should be mentioned that it is only small regions in central East Jutland, South Funen and Central Zealand which reach an altitude higher than 150 m. above sea-level (Partly from "Danmarks Klima").

clones often pass over Denmark in winter, resulting in big differences between the northern part of the country, where the Polar-Continental air-masses may reign uninterruptedly, and the southern part, which may be under the influence of Tropic or Polar Maritime air-masses. This difference is particularly noticeable, when occluded depressions are resting above Denmark with back-bent (east-west orientated) frontal systems. If so, North Jutland may have strong, eastern wind with air-temperatures below the freezing point, while the southern part of the country has temperatures up to 10° C.

While, as mentioned, the big primary depressions in winter often pass immediately above or in close proximity to Denmark they move, in summer, far to the north as a consequence of the displacement of the Polar Front in a northern direction; however, the region is touched by the accompanying frontal systems. As for the temperature variations which may follow these front passages, they are relatively small.

Not only the passages of cyclones are followed by moving airmasses above Denmark; also the high-pressure situations may supply »foreign« air-masses in such cases where the centre of the highpressure is situated at a rather big distance to the north or to the south of Denmark.

Summer as well as winter there are pronounced differences between *the temperatures of the coastal areas* and those of *the interior,* partly as a natural consequence of the differences of the levels (the maximum height is 174 m. above sea-level), partly on account of the Maritime-Continental contrast. In the average values these differences only amount to 1°—2°, whereas in special situations they may reach 10°—12°. The mean monthly temperatures vary for all Danish stations, as appears from the maps, p. 224, between 0° in January/February and about 15°—16° in July. The map of the January temperatures most clearly shows the difference between the areas close to the coast and the interior, both in Jutland and in the bigger Danish islands. A far-reaching maritime influence from west and from south-west also appears from this map, which shows a rather slow decrease of the mean temperature from the west coast of Jutland and towards the interior, while the transition is very sharp in the other coastal regions of Denmark. In the month of July the mean temperature is, on the whole, increasing from the north-western part of the country towards south and east; one of the causes of this is an advance of warm air-masses from south-east of a distinct continental character — the so-called heat-waves; however, the contrast between the interior and the coasts is less perceptible in this season than in the rest of the year.

In order to further illustrate the *temperature conditions* in the *various parts of the country* the figures on p. 228 have been worked out; they indicate the variations of the mean temperatures of the individual months for a station at the west coast (Nordby on Fanø), for a station in the interior of Jutland (Herning) and finally for a station on Bornholm in the Baltic (Hammershus). Further, these figures show the mean minimum and the mean maximum as well as the absolute minimum and the absolute maximum for the single months. These diagrams as well as the maps p. 224 represent the continental effect in the interior of Jutland in relation to the west-coast station. In the winter half-year the differences between the monthly averages of the two stations are about 1°; however, the variations in the single months are smaller on Fanø than in Herning, and the amplitude between the absolute maximum temperature and the absolute minimum temperature is far greater in Herning than on Fanø in all the months of the year; this is one of the principal causes of the different biological effects of the climate in these parts of the country. The cycle of the average temperatures is practically identical at the two above-mentioned Jutland stations, both of which, however, deviate rather much from the station on Bornholm. What especially distinguishes Hammershus from the other stations is the much smaller variation of the mean temperatures of the winter months, (November—March); this is due to the moderating effect of the Baltic on the trend of temperature. During winter-gales from north-east with a supply of Arctic-Continental air-masses the temperatures, in most cases, are higher in Bornholm than in the rest of the country, as long as the Baltic is not frozen; normally, this freezing does not take place until February—March and only in the years when the winter is sufficiently severe. The milder temperatures are a result of the fact that the air-masses from north-east are heated by the relatively warm waters of the Baltic, whereas, in these cases, the air-flow towards the other parts of the country arrives via Sweden, a fact which contributes to maintain the continental character of the air-masses with severe cold. On the other hand, the slow heating of the waters of the Baltic and the melting of the ice after the winter, result in relatively low temperatures in the months of spring. Both April and May are considerably colder in Bornholm than the corresponding months at the Jutland stations, as appears from the diagrams p. 228.

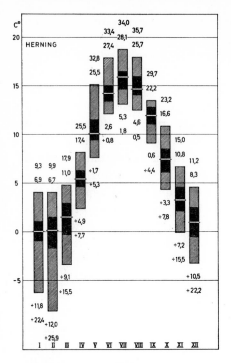

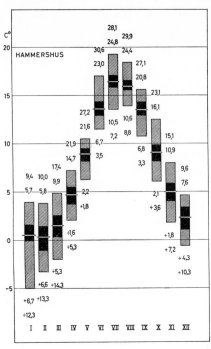

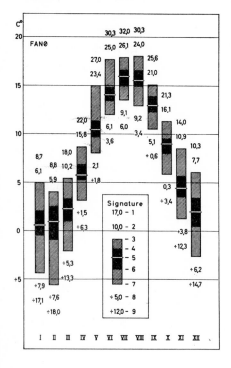

Fig. 2. Diagrams showing the temperature conditions at the three meteorological stations: Fanø (island at the south-west coast of Jutland), Herning (Central Jutland) and Hammershus (in Bornholm in the Baltic). The positions of the stations are shown in the map page 233. Each column represents the distribution of the mean monthly temperatures and of the maximum temperatures and minimum temperatures; thus, the signs stand for:

1. Absolute maximum of observed temp.
2. Mean maximum of observed temp.
3. Maximum of mean monthly temp.
4. The temperature exceeded by 25 % of the mean monthly temperatures.
5. The temperature exceeded by 50 % of the mean monthly temperatures.
6. The temperature exceeded by 75 % of the mean monthly temperatures.
7. Minimum of mean monthly temp.
8. Mean minimum of observed temp.
9. Absolute minimum of observed temp.

(all stations from 1873—1920)

The climatic variations within the frontiers of Denmark in a biologically important period are apparent from *the frequency of frost days* in the two spring months April and May. From the map p. 230 it will be seen that the central parts of Jutland are very much exposed to temperatures below the freezing point at the time when the spring-sown crops are sprouting, whereas the risk is less in the coastal regions. In the interior of Jutland the risk of frost, on an average, begins already about the 10th of October and continues until about the 10th of May. Along the west coast the corresponding period is from about the 10th of November till about the 15th of April, i. e. almost two months less; in East Denmark this period stretches from about the 1st of November till about the 20th of April. In this relation the delayed arrival of the winter-time in Bornholm is also evident from the fact that the frost-danger does not occur until about the 20th of November.

During the three summer months: June, July and August, it is extremely seldom that the minimum temperature drops below the freezing point, and even September is almost frost-free. In May and October the average frequency of frost occurrence is a few days per month. Thus, the unsymmetrical trend of the Danish temperature climate in relation to the summer solstice is distinct, because the slow rise of temperature in spring happens after spring equinox, while the corresponding decline of the temperature does not arrive until after the autumnal equinox. This fact is partly due to the influences of the surrounding waters and, at least as much, to the effect of the maritime air-masses. In the winter months, January—February, the temperature drops below freezing point in twenty days per month, on an average, and in March and December for about half the number of days; however, there are great fluctuations from year to year, as appears, for instance, from the diagrams on planche I.

The average situations hitherto described in this exposé only give a summary of the temperature conditions in Denmark; therefore, the planche I may be useful as an illustration of *the temperatures observed* during a certain number of years. In the diagrams is shown the diurnal variation of the air-temperature for an inland-station (Studsgård in Jutland; the position is shown in the map p. 233), where we may expect great amplitudes for the whole year as well as for single days; thus, we will get the strongest possible impression of the temperature variations.

A study of the four years mentioned (1946—1949) clearly shows a fundamental difference between the trend of temperature in winter

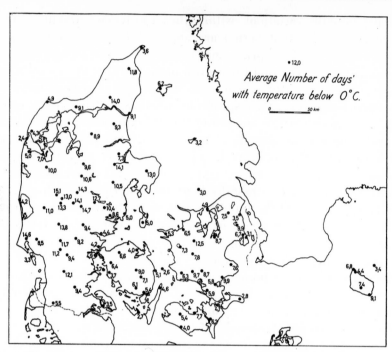

Fig. 3. The average number of frost days in the months April and May (i. e. the number of days with minimum temperatures $\leqq$ -0,1° C.).

and in summer. In the winter half-year the daily temperature range is normally much smaller than in summer; further, in this season the big jumps of the temperature from day to day are much more frequent. Further, in winter the readings reveal a more pronounced, though irregular periodicity of the trend of temperature. This periodicity manifests itself in a temperature rise stretching over two— three days, followed by a decline during the subsequent four—five days, corresponding to a passage of big low pressures with distinct and widely extended frontal systems (example: January—March 1946). In such situations the cloud-layer in connection with the low noon altitude of the sun in winter is greatly contributing to provide a small diurnal temperature amplitude. In the period 1946—1949 this winterly trend of temperature was rather pronounced already from the first half of November, and it ceased as abruptly in the latter half of March.

Another feature characteristic of the winter time appears in the first half of March 1949, when we have a cold wave with constant eastern winds and dry air; this allows the nocturnal terrestrial ra-

diation to go on unhampered, and the angle of incidence of the sun-
rays is now so great that a considerable insolation also takes place in
daytime. In the diagram the period in question appears with relatively big diurnal temperature amplitudes and with temperatures
varying from 0° to - 10 ° C. Similar situations are seen in February
1947 and 1948; they express a pronounced continental feature of the
Danish climate with far reaching biological effects.

The four winter situations represented in the diagrams further
express the great variations of the levels of the temperatures from
year to year. These variations are due to the shifting position of the
tracks of depressions in relation to the European Continent and to
the extent of the continental high pressure from the central Eurasia
towards Western Europe. In the winter 1946—1947 the mean temperatures for a rather long period (almost three months) are between
0° and -10°, whereas 1949, apart from a brief period, had mean temperatures on the positive side of the zero point (3° to 5°). The continental type, of which 1947 is representative, occurs, on an average,
fifteen to twenty times per century, and the most important continental winters in this century have been 1928/1929, 1939/1940, 1940/
1941 and 1941/1942. These ice-winters have left traces of distinct
biological effects; for instance, the agriculture has encountered difficulties with the winter crops at places where the snow has not
protected the surface against the dangerous radiation and the cooling.

The rest of the year, from the end of March to the end of October,
normally has a trend of temperature with much bigger diurnal temperature amplitudes than in winter; however, on the whole, the
temperatures oscillate more regularly in the neighbourhood of the
same mean values from day to day. Roughly, a distinction can be
made between a period with evenly rising temperatures in spring
(April and the beginning of May) and a period with corresponding
decreasing temperatures in the autumn (the end of September and
October). However, the transitions between these seasons are normally not as sharp as at the beginning and the end of the winter.
Characteristic of the early summer are the stable weather conditions with enormous temperature ranges (15°—20°), which often
occur in the month of May as a natural consequence of the relative
desiccation of the air (see also p. 223). Thus, May is the month which
has the smallest cloud-layer and the biggest possibilities of insolation
and terrestrial radiation, and the nocturnal terrestrial radiation is
only slightly restrained by fogs. On an average, May is also one of
the most favoured months as regards the duration of sunshine,

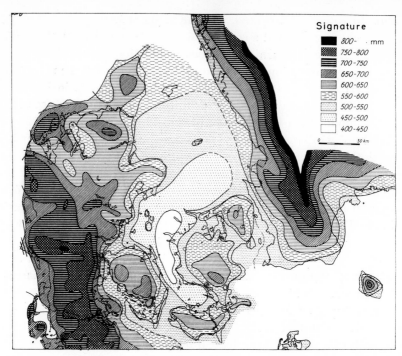

Fig. 4. Precipitation map of Denmark, showing the average yearly precipitation
in mm. (Partly from "Danmarks Klima").

though the number of sunshine hours only differs slightly from that
of June and July.

When similar stable weather periods occur in the summer months
Denmark is often exposed to a heat-wave under the influence of
Continental air-masses (cP or cT air-masses), arriving from Eastern
Europe and from South-Eastern Europe; 1947 is a good example
of such a »continental« summer with big diurnal temperature amplitudes and relatively few disturbances of depressions from West. In
contrast to this, 1949 had but few high-pressure periods and frequent passages of the small depressions from the Atlantic Polar
Front. Long high-pressure periods in the autumn months September
and October procure Denmark with an »Indian summer« as shown
in the planche I for the first half of the month of September
1949. However, in this season a lively cyclonic activity is normal,
followed by considerable quantities of precipitation (especially in
October) in connection with a general decrease of the temperature
resulting in an increasing relative humidity.

The average annual rainfall in Denmark varies from 415 mm to

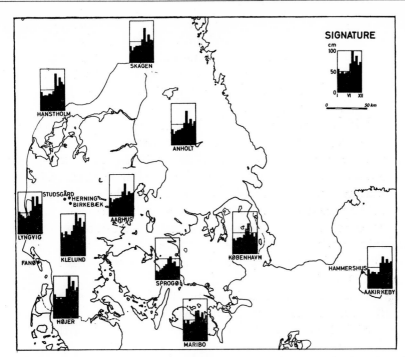

Fig. 5. Diagrams of the average distribution of the precipitation for the individual months for a number of stations.

810 mm., quite a considerable variation within such a relatively small region. From the map showing the annual rainfall over Denmark it further appears that the distance between maximum in Central Jutland and minimum around the Great Belt is only 125 km. The greater part of the precipitation falls in connection with the cyclonic passages and but a small part as a consequence of local thunder storms. The passage of the warm front from a depression system is followed by rain all over the country, whereas the cold front most often manifests itself by short, though heavy rainfalls of a more showery character. These frontal systems first reach the western part and the southern part of the country, and here fall the biggest quantities of precipitation, partly as a result of an increasing friction when the air-masses move from sea to land, partly as a consequence of the increasing altitude of the land. Eastern Jutland and especially the region around the Great Belt are in such cases situated in a pronounced rainlee; however, these questions have not yet been submitted to a close examination.

The curves representing the monthly averages of rainfall (fig. 5) for a number of Danish stations further show that it is the autumn months which are dominating in Western Denmark and in Southern Denmark with pronounced maxima in August and in October. As August is the harvest month for the majority of the Danish grain crops this maximum may cause considerable difficulties for the agriculture, to whom the rainfall distribution, from an agricultural point of view, is by no means favourable. The average number of rainy days in August is 13—17; however, there may be periods with several days without precipitation, facilitating the drying of the crops. The spring months April and May have but 10— 12 days with precipitation and are to be reckoned among our least rainy months. This has extremely unhappy consequences for the agriculture when a draught period occurs simultaneously with continuous winds; if so, the country is exposed to an extensive wind-erosion at a time when the spring-cereals have just been sown or when the first sprouts have come up, so that there is no vegetation for retaining the soil-layer.

As far as the annual distribution of rainfall is concerned, a distinction can be made between two types with even transitions; one type for Western and Southern Denmark, where each of the first six months of the year has 40—50 mm. of precipitation, and where the autumn months reach 70—90 mm. As a contrast to this we have a North-East-Danish type, surrounding the whole of the Kattegat; in the map p. 233 Sprogø in the Great Belt is most representative of this type. Here, seven of the months of the year have 20—30 mm. of precipitation, and the maximum in July/August does not reach far beyond 50 mm. The general feature of the daily precipitation at Studsgård in the years 1946—1949, as appears from the planche I is that the whole winter period and the early summer have small precipitation quantities with an average of about 5 mm. per rainy day. In summer the thunder-storm situations manifest themselves thereby that a few days reach a precipitation of about 40 mm.; in the autumn months (September and October) big quantities of precipitation of 10— 20 mm. often fall for several successive days (for instance: September 1946, September 1948, and October 1949). Further, it is evident that the precipitation principally occurs on days with a thermal shift of the weather, as a natural consequence of its being attached to moving depressions.

Fig. 6. Relative frequencies of wind directions in the months January and July. The circle indicates 10% of the total number of wind observations. The figure to the right of the wind rose represents the relative frequencies of observations with calm.   →

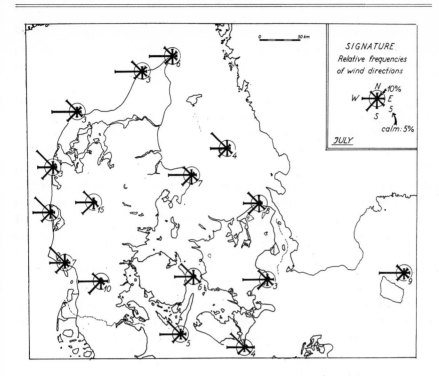

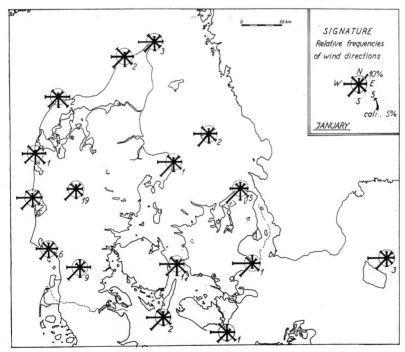

A couple of examples will give an illustration of *the variations of the monthly values of the precipitation*. The two stations treated in the planche II fall within the West-Danish and the East-Danish precipitation type, respectively; at the same time Birkebæk (in Central Jutland) is the locality of Denmark where the biggest annual precipitation has been measured: 1276 mm. in the year 1882, while on Anholt (in Kattegat) has been measured the smallest annual precipitation: 305 mm. in 1879.

The two sets of curves have certain common features: Thus, the first five months of the year have rather steeply rising curves as compared with the summer months and the autumn months; this shows a rather small distribution of the monthly values in the first half of the year. Especially August and October have great variations of the quantities of precipitation from year to year. The contrast between the two stations finds its best expression in the fact that the precipitation at the Jutland station is far greater than at the East-Danish station in all the months of the year, and especially in the summer months and in the autumn months the bigger precipitation quantities are much more frequent at Birkebæk than on Anholt. Already in June and July it can be seen that the deviations of the curves in their upper parts are more and more increasing, and in August—November the dominance within the big precipitation quantities at the Jutland station is conspicuous. In the months December—May the distribution pattern is fairly the same for both regions — though in the neighbourhood of rather different mean values.

The position of Denmark in the central part of the westerlies at about 55° N.L. involves a very varying *atmospheric pressure;* this is a consequence of the moving depressions, already mentioned, and their frequent alternance with periods of high pressure. Thus, it would be a rather poor information to indicate the decline of the average atmospheric pressure from 762 mm. in Southern Denmark to 760 mm. to the north in January, and from 760 mm. to 758 mm. in July. If these indications were of general validity Denmark should be under constant influence of western winds in the air-layers above the friction-layer, while the observed winds should show deviations towards south-west, in conformity with the size of the friction. From the maps showing *the wind directions* which have been observed, on an average, with no regard to the wind force (p. 235) it appears that winds from the western sector are the most frequent; however, it is also a question of a considerable number of observations of winds from other directions, especially from east; this is particularly true of the winter half-year, where the high-pressure over Eurasia may give rise to eastern winds of long duration. Winds from the south and from the north are, on the contrary, in absolute minority in all seasons.

At all places the biggest *wind-forces* are measured in winter and in the autumn; however, the variations from month to month are but small. The calm most often occurs in the interior of the country; like the other wind-observations these indications may be greatly defective owing to local conditions around the weather stations.

However, when taking into account the small extent of our country and the insignificant variations of altitude it is interesting to note the relatively big climatic differences, both from region to region and from year to year. However, a summary like this only gives a rough outline of the conditions, whereas a detailed analysis would be needed for describing and for finding the causes of the multiple variations.

LITERATURE

D. D. M. I. = Det Danske Meteorologiske Institut.
Danmarks Klima. Udgivet af D. D. M. I. 1933.
Månedsoversigten over Vejrforholdene. Udgivet af D. D. M. I.
Meteorologisk Årbog: Danmark. Udgivet af D. D. M. I.
Nautisk-Meteorologisk Årbog. Udgivet af D. D. M. I.
Ugeberetningen over Nedbør m. m. Udgivet af D. D. M. I.
Vejrberetningen. Udgivet af D. D. M. I.
Deutsche Planungsatlas, Band Schleswig-Holstein. 1956.
P. *Hess* und H. *Brezowsky:* Katalog der Grosswetterlagen Europas. Berichte des Deutschen Wetterdienstes in der US-Zone. 1952.
A. *Ångström* (1958): Sveriges Klimat. Stockholm.

The Danish Village: Its Age and Form

By Viggo Hansen[*]

Abstract

With the aid of the great Danish land register of 1688 and old maps, the author studies the changing form of two villages in North Jutland. He maintains that the nucleated form of the Danish village immediately prior to the enclosures[1] of the late eighteenth century was the result of two distinct processes operating from premedieval times. The first was a normal process of internal growth of population with an associated extension of arable land; the second was a periodic concentration of population from peripheral settlements onto a central site.

BRØDSLEV

The township of *Brødslev,* forming part of the parish of *Ingstrup* in the province of Vendsyssel, North Jutland (fig. 1), occupies a gently undulating morainic plateau whose soils are derived from sandy boulder claw (fig. 2). During Late Glacial times most of the present site was an island, and the many short valleys, now dry, that cut into the plateau appear to have originated then. When man settled in the area, his expanding arable fields occupied the level extents of glacial soils, while the steep slopes and somewhat damper bottoms of the small valleys were grazed by livestock. At the junction of these contrasting physical and economic landscapes the settlement, with its loosely grouped farmsteads and associated paddocks, arose.

When the great land register of 1688 was compiled, *Brødslev* township comprised eighteen farmsteads and five cottages. The farms, which were not equal in size or status, fell into three distinct groups (Table I). The first group contained five whole farms

---

[*] English translation by dr. *Harry Thorpe,* Department of Geography, University of Birmingham.

1. For at description of the Danish village before and after enclosure and of the associated documentary evidence vide *Thorpe, H.,* The influence of inclosure on the form and pattern of rural settlement in Denmark, Insittute of British Geographers, Transactions and Papers, No. 17 (1951), London, 1952.

The two investigated villages are localized to the northern part of Denmark, north of the sound Limfjorden, in the landscape called Vendsyssel. The remoteness of the area may be the explanation of some old features in the agricultural organization. While many Danish villages several times have been affected by an equation of the farm area between all complete farms, this does not seem to be the case here.

Fig. 1

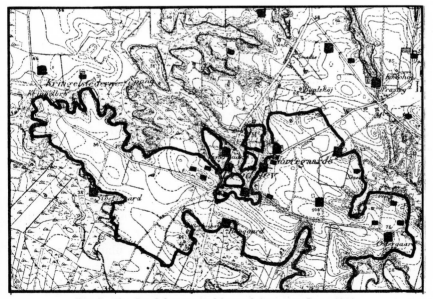

Fig. 2. The Brødslev township and farmsteads c. 1810.

(Gårde), the second group five half farms *(Bol)* and, finally, came eight quarter farms *(Halve Bol)*. It is interesting to find that although stall-feeding of livestock was essential throughout the winter, only the five whole farms *(Gårde* Nos. 1—5) and the five half farms *(Bol* Nos. 6—10) had specific rights to cut hay in the meadows.

To the east and west of the village lay the common fields divided into 38 shots, each with a distinctive name (Fig. 5). While the shots varied in length according to the nature of the terrain, their width appears to have fallen into certain well-defined groupings. The standard Danish land measure in use at the time was the Zealand *ell*, equivalent to a little over 2 feet, and the widest shot ranged from 450 to 470 *ells* (930—975 feet). Each shot was divided into a number of parallel strips, representing allocations of land to individual farms, and from Table II it will be seen that in a great many shots the number of strips was either 7 or a multiple thereof (e.g. 14 or 21). Taking measurements from the more regularly shaped and subdivided shots it is clear that the original width of a standard strip must have been 21.6 Zealand *ells* or 24 Jutland *ells*, which coincides remarkably with the customary *Dobbeltager* (double-acre) recorded in old Danish provincial laws from 1241 onward. Even more common in *Brødslev* was the single acre of 12 Jutland *ells*, being half the width of the *Dobbeltager*.

On the extreme western edge of the common fields lay three shots with very distinctive names — *Vestervang, Søndervang* and *Nordervang* (fig. 5) – suggesting that they were the fossilized remnants of the West Field, South Field and North Field of an ancient threefield system. It is highly significant that the strips in these shots belonged only to the five complete farms, and to *Bol* No. 6 and *Bol* No. 7. Moreover, the land register records that allocations of strips in these shots were measured »from the *Toft* (paddock)«, on the strength of which the author concludes that this is a reference to the former existence of a settlement, probably a village or hamlet, on this site. This settlement probably included only the five whole farmsteads, as the two *Bol* possessed only small strips. It is believed that the three-field system was only introduced into Denmark 1000 A.D., consequently *Old Brødsted*'s pattern of common fields cannot be older than that. Yet the place-name ending suggests that the settlement itself may have originated as early as 500 A.D., and there may then have been two or three small farm clusters of which nothing is now known.

Table I.
The Brødslev farmers in 1688.

	Areal tdr. skp. *area*	Deraf toften *the paddock*	Jord der		Rettigheder til eng *with meadows*
			hviler *not yearly sown*	bruges årligt *yearly sown*	
Gård 1	14.4[1])	2.6	6.7	7.5	+
— 2	17.5[2])	0.3	13.2	4.3	+
— 3	23.1	1.5	7.2	15.7	+
— 4	30.0	6.3	17.1	12.7	+
— 5	27.6	4.0	14.2	13.4	+
Bol 6	14.1	1.4	8.2	5.7	+
— 7	15.2	1.1	9.7	5.3	+
— 8	8.6	—	4.7	3.7	+
— 9	11.3	0.6	7.3	4.0	+
— 10	10.4	0.5	8.1	2.3	+
— 11	6.6	—	3.6	3.0	
— 12	14.7	0.2	7.6	7.1	
— 13	7.6	0.5	5.3	2.3	
— 14	6.4	0.4	4.2	2.0	
— 15	6.4	0.1	1.5	4.7	
— 16	5.7	0.1	1.6	4.1	
— 17	4.7	0.3	3.1	1.6	
— 18	10.5	2.5	7.5	3.0	
Hus 19	0.2	0.2	0.2		
— 20	0.2	0.2	0.2		
— 21	0.2	0.2	0.2		
— 22	0.1	0.1	0.1		
— 23	0.3	0.3	0.3		

[1]) 4.0 tdr. land waste due to sand movement.
[2]) 2.3 tdr. land waste due to sand movement.

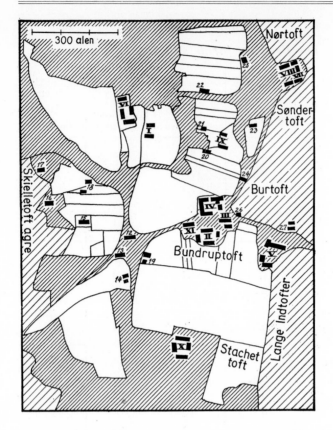

Fig. 3.
The Brødslev
farmsteads and
paddocks 1796.

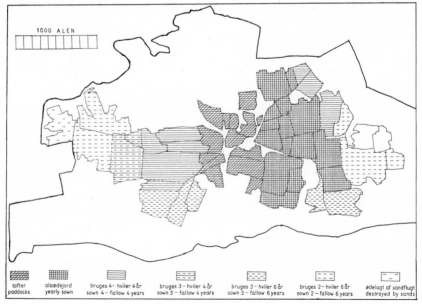

| tofter paddocks | alsædejord yearly sown | bruges 4- hviler 4 år sown 4 - fallow 4 years | bruges 3 - hviler 4 år sown 3 - fallow 4 years | bruges 3 - hviler 6 år sown 3 - fallow 6 years | bruges 2- hviler 6 år sown 2 - fallow 6 years | ødelagt af sandflugt destroyed by sands |

Fig. 4. Field rotation 1688.

It is possible that this three-field system, based on a rotation of winter seed (rye), spring seed (barley or oats) and fallow, may not have been successful for more than a few centuries. There are good grounds for supposing that the climate deteriorated in late medieval times (from 1300 A.D. unward) and subsequent records describe the non-existing of a winter seed in North Jutland. Accordingly the farmers in *Old Brødslev* may have been driven to extend their arable land, the only opportunity for such expansion being to the east as shifting sand handicapped activity on the west. As population continued to increase, more and more land was taken in on the east until some time in late medieval times it became desirable for the settlement, now boasting seven farmsteads, to move to a new site more central to its fields. Thus, *New Brødslev* was created (Fig. 3). Shortly after this event, two additional farmsteads, represented by *Bol* No. 10 and No. 12 whose land lies mainly to the west of the new settlement, are believed to have been incorporated into the community. The new village now had nine farmsteads, of which all but one had the right to cut hay in the meadow, while No. 12, which was only small, had probably been fashioned out of No. 10.

This still omits us two more farmsteads (Nos. 8 and 9) with meadow rights to be explained. But an old record of 1553 confirms that there were two additional settlements, called *Hauenbye* and *Hauen Torp,* in the parish of *Ingstrup.* The place name ending *-by* would date the former to Viking times (800—1000 A. D.), while *-torp* is considered medieval (1000—1200 A.D.). A search for further information about these two hamlets has been unsuccessful, but on the enclosure map there are two shots with the significant names of *Hauen* (*Haugen* or *Hoven*) and *Gammeljord* (Old Land) (Fig. 5). Reference to the land register shows that only farmsteads Nos. 8, 9 and 14 participated in *Gammeljord* which lay on the eastern periphery of the common fields in 1688. Perusal of the air photograph provides unmistakable evidence of the existence of a »lost« village or hamlet to the south of *Gammeljord,* which might conceivably be the *Hauenbye* of 1553. If this assumption is correct, it would appear that the deliberate destruction of *Hauenbye* and the incorporation of its farmsteads and its land in *Brødslev* probably occurred soon after 1553.

So far we have accounted for the five *Gårde,* the five primary *Bol* and *Halve Bol* Nos. 12 and 14, leaving six small *Bol* to be explained. Of these, No. 18, which held land only in a few of the more recent

Table II.
The Brødslev strips in 1688.

Skifte Shot	Antal Agre Number of strips	Areal td.skp. Area	Rotation br.-hv. Rotation sown-fallow	Markbetegnelse på udskiftn.kort Name on 1796 map
1 Vestervang	21	8.1	ødelagt	Vang, Steenbroe
2 Søndervang	26	19.2	2–6	Sievers Ager 16–30
3 Nordervang	20	7.5	2–6	Bloe Fald
4 Musback	5	1.6	3–4	–
5 Sives Agre	14	7.4	3–4	Sievers Ager 1–15
6 Ramses Smeder	17	4.7	4–4	Randers Smeder
7 Skielle Toft	14	8.4	4–4	Skielle Toft
8 Rørkilde Agre	4	3.0	4–4	Roe Kild
9 Westerby Lang	27	15.3	4–4	Bye Langer
10 Mands Agre	7	3.4	4–4	Bye Langer
11 Huos Agre	19	6.7	3–6	Was Ager
12 Bloch Agre	4	1.0	3–6	Tingweis Fald
13 Syndhøys Agre	8	4.3	3–6	Tingweis Fald
14 Syndkiers Agre	7	4.0	3–6	Sønderkiers Agre
15 Nørtoft Agre	19	8.6	årlig	Berhøjs Agre 1–16
16 Brøndager	4	2.2	årlig	Berhøjs Agre 17–18
17 Bagskov Agre	10	1.7	3–3	Pungen
18 Bagstaad Agre	11	3.2	3–3	Basken
19 Blokken	6	2.1	årlig	Østen Burtoft
20 Søndertoft	5	1.7	årlig	N. f. Burtoft
21 Bugtoft	19	5.5	årlig	Burtoften
22 Hørmederne	10	1.5	årlig	Hørmeder
23 Øster Bylang	17	5.1	årlig	Byelanger
24 Boetoften	9	3.1	årlig	Steen Ager Nr. 1
25 Steens Fald	22	9.7	årlig	Steen Ager 2–20
26 Bremager	14	6.1	3–3	Brem Ager
27 Gammeljord	8	2.2	2–6	?
Morbacke	3	0.4	2–6	?
28 Stache Indtoft	21	5.0	årlig	Indtoften
29 Indtofts Føder	21	5.6	årlig	Fæder Ager
30 Lange Indtofter	14	11.0	årlig	Indtoften
31 Haugen	4	6.4	2–6	Hoven
32 Sanden	53	20.4	2–6	Lerager og Sandet
33 Leerager	31	8.7	årlig	Rosager
34 Skiftet Østen Dalen ...	38	15.7	årlig	Agrene Østen Dyb Dal
35 Hjorthede	7	2.5	3–6	Joos Hede
36 Fangen	11	3.1	3–5	?
Tvende Agre	2	0.4	årlig	?

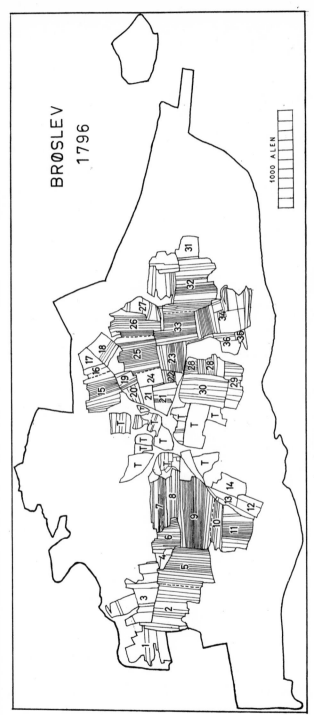

Fig. 5. The Brøslev shots 1688 (compare Table II).

1. Vestervang.
2. Søndervang.
3. Nordervang.
4. Musback.
5. Sives Agre.
6. Ramses Smeder.

7. Skielle Toft.
8. Rørkilde Agre.
9. Westerby Lang.
10. Mandsagre.
11. Huos Agre.
12. Bloch Agre

13. Syndhøys Agre.
14. Syndkiers Agre.
15. Nørtoft Agre.
16. Brøndager.
17. Bagskov Agre.
18. Bagstaad Agre.

19. Blokken.
20. Søndertoft.
21. Bugtoft.
22. Hørmederne.
23. Øster Bylang.
24. Boetoften.

25. Steens Fald.
26. Bremager.
27. Gammeljord.
28. Stache Indtoft.
29. Indtofts Føder.
30. Lange Indtofter.

31. Haugen.
32. Sanden.
33. Leerager.
34. Skiftet Østen Dalen.
35. Hjorthede.
36. Fangen.

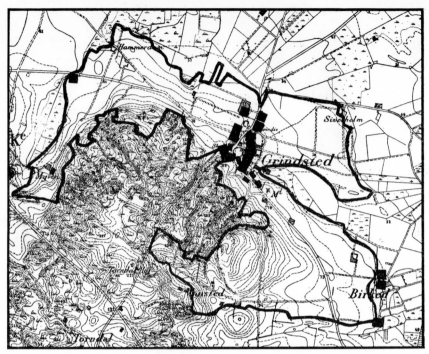

Fig. 6. *Grindsted township 1688 and the farmsteads c. 1810.*

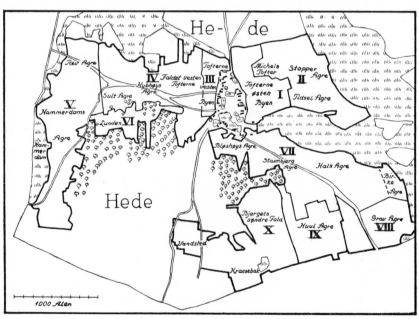

Fig. 7. *The Grindsted common fields 1688.*
I: Stokbrofald; II: Hauensfald; III: Tofteagre (toften); IV: Tofteagre; V: Hammerdams Agre; VI: Hundalsfald; VII: Bløshøys Agre; VIII: Græsfald; IX: Skovensfald; X: Bjergefald.

shots, was certainly a very late addition to the community, while the remainder (Nos. 11, 13, 15, 16 and 17) were clearly the same five *Halve Bol* to which reference was made in the record of 1553. The latter affirms that shortly before 1553 five *Bol* were built from a farm in *Brødslev* that had belonged to the priest in *Ingstrup*. Consequently, at the end of the sixteenth century at least 17 farmsteads were to be found in *Brødslev*, while by 1688 the addition of No. 18 had increased this by one.

GRINDSTED

The hamlet and township of *Grindsted* in *Hammer* parish is bordered on the south by the steep hill slopes of *Hammer Bakker* and on the north by low-lying Late Glacial plains whose surface is waterlogged in many places (Fig. 6). The intermediate area, which forms a platform of sandy boulder clay, is of relatively high fertility and intensive arable land-use. The oval village green, around which the farmsteads are grouped, is a common feature in eastern Denmark and closely resembles the German *Rundling* (Fig. 7). When the great Danish land register was prepared in 1688 the settlement comprised five whole farms (*Gårde*), seven half farms (*Bol*), four quarter farms (*Halve Bol*) and thirteen cottages (Table III). Four whole farms and three *Bol* had rights to cut hay in the meadow, while all farms could cut grass and reeds in the bogs.

The common fields were divided into three great fields (*Vange*), called *Stokbro Mark*, *Vestermark* (West Field) and *Søndermark* (South Field); each of these contained a varying number of shots, which in turn were subdivided into many parallel strips (Fig. 7). The strips contiguous with the eastern edge of the settlement belonged to *Gårde* 2, 3 and 4 and to *Bol* 1 and 5, while those on the western outskirts of the village belonged to *Gårde* 6 and 7 and to *Bol* 8, 9, 10 and 12 (Fig. 8). At some time past these strips had clearly served as paddocks (*Tofter*) until a subsequent redistribution of strips led to their incorporation in the common fields. In *Stokbro Mark* and *Vestermark* the allocation of strips to individual farms appears to have been quite haphazard and many farms held two or more contiguous strips, apparently the result of careful exchange of property over many years. Only in *Søndermark* do we find shots whose strips reveal an orderly allocation to individual farms. For example, in *Bløshøys Agre*, the largest and oldest of the shots in *Søndermark*, one finds a remarkable regularity of distribution; making allowances for a few exchanges of property,

Table III.
The Grindsted farmers and their land in 1688.

| Nummer i 1688-matr.s | | Matr. 1796 | Toft [1] | Areal [2] | Hø i læs og knipper loads of hay taxed | |
Brugerliste *Farmer no.*	Ekstrakt *Farmstead no.*	*Number*	Pad- dock [1]	total area [2]	i eng in meadow	i mose in bog
1	7	XV	Tv	31.2	3	4—3
2	4	II	Tø	30.4	6.5	5—8
3/4	3	III	Tø	22.3	—	23—0
5	2	IV	Tø	39.1	6	11—4
6/7	6	XIV	Tv	32.2	5	7—3
8	5	I	Tø	13.2	1.5	$2^{1}/_{2}$—0
9/10	1	V	Tø	15.6	—	3—5
11/12	14	IX	—	13.6	—	$7^{1}/_{2}$—6
13/14	8	VIII	Tv	15.4	—	6—11
15	10	X	Tv	19.6	1.5	3—6
16	12	XII	Tv	14.4	1.5	3—3
17	9	XIII	Tv	10.0	—	8—4
18	13	XI	—	6.0	—	$6^{1}/_{2}$—4
19	16	XVI	—	5.5	—	5—1
20	11	VI	Ts	5.5	—	6—11
21	15	VII	Ts	5.3	—	1—1

[1] *Tø = paddock to the East, Tv = to the West, Ts = to the South.*
[2] *Area in tønder and skæpper (1 tønde = 8 skæpper = 1,363 acres).*

Table IV.
Succession in strips in Bløshøys shot.

1688-rækken: 8 – 8 – 12 – 6 – 7 – 3 – 3 – 3 – 1 – 9 – 6 – 7 – 4 – 2 –
korrigeret: 8 – 10 – 12 – 6 – 7 – 4 – 3 – 2 – 1 – 9 – 6 – 7 – 4 – 3 –

1688-rækken: 2 – 8 – 10 – 12 – 6 – 7 – 5 – 5 – 5 – 5 – 6 – 7 – 4 – 3 –
korrigeret: 2 – 8 – 10 – 12 – 6 – 7 – 4 – 3 – 2 – 1 – 6 – 7 – 4 – 3 –

1688-rækken: 2 – 8 – 6 – 7 – 4 – 3 – 2 – 1 – 6 – 7 – 4 – 3 – 2 – 1 –
korrigeret: 2 – 1 – 6 – 7 – 4 – 3 – 2 – 1 – 6 – 7 – 4 – 3 – 2 – 1 –

1688-rækken: 13 – 10 – 12 – 6 – 7 – 4 – 3 – 2 – 2 – 6 – 7 – 7 –
korrigeret: 8 – 10 – 12 – 6 – 7 – 4 – 3 – 2 – 1 – 6 – 7 – ? –

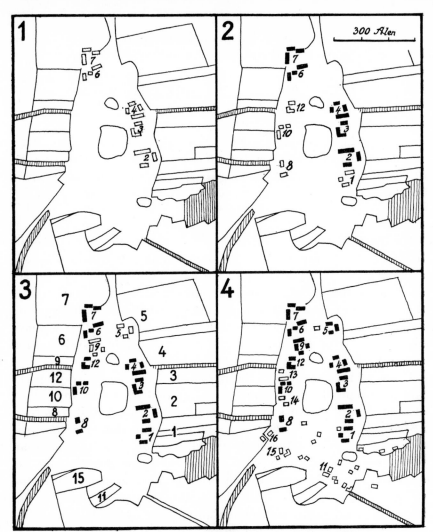

Fig. 8. Suggested growth of Grindsted until 1688 (1800).
1: c. 1200 A.D.; 2: after 1300; 3: 1553; 4: 1688-1800.

one arrives at the following succession, reckoned from east to west
— farms 1, 2, 3, 4, 7, 6, (9), 12, 10 and 8 (Table V). Both the
farmsteads in the village and the paddocks had the same succession,
with the single exception that *Bol* 5 is represented here, but not
in *Bløshøys* shot (compare Fig. 8). Reference to this practice of
Solskifte, or the sun-distribution of strips from east to west within
a shot, has been found in Danish provincial laws of the thirteenth
century.

Table V.

B. *The farm sizes in Grindsted after deduction of the latest great fields: Birkeagre, Skouens Fald, Bjergefald and Hundals Fald.*

Nr.	2	3	4	7	6	1	5	12	10	8	9
Areal	28.4	20.0	28.4	22.5	27.7	10.3	12.2	9.7	9.1	9.4	9.4
Nr.	14	11	13	15	16						
Areal	3.0	3.0	2.7	0.3	0.5						

C. *The acreage (in Tønder and Skæpper) of the five old complete farms (Gårdene) and the five older bols (Bolene) in the five supposedly old fields.*

	Hammerdam	Hauensfald	Tofteagre	Bløshøy	Græsfald
Gårdene	14.3	20.7	30.4	35.4	13.2
Bolene	20.6	5.6	10.3	11.0	4.4

As there is no firm evidence of *Solskifte* in the other ancient fields, it would appear that the redistribution of strips in *Bløshøys* shot took place at a later date than in the other old fields. It may also follow that *Bløshøys* shot is younger than the others. One is then tempted to ask at what time and for what reason did this late redistribution of *Bløshøys* shot take place? Could it be that we have here evidence of the extension of *Grindsted*'s field system as a result of common agreement between all farmers?

From an investigation of the relationship between *Gård* property and *Bol* property in each shot, it is clear that the *Gårde* were allocated three to four times as much land as the *Bol*. But at *Grindsted* a striking exception to this rule could be seen in *Hammerdam Agre*, the most westerly of the shots, where the *Bol* owned no less than 60 % and the *Gårde* only 40 % (Table VI). One can discount the suggestion that this was a compensation for remoteness from the village. The most reasonable assumption would be that the *Bol* had a priority to this part of the arable land, possibly because an earlier settlement had existed on this site. Unfortunately, there are no precise records of a village having disappeared here, but there is strong circumstantial evidence that a settlement called *Hammer* once stood on this site. *Grindsted* lies in *Hammer* parish, but although there is an isolated church called *Hammer Kirke*, a hilly area called *Hammer Bakker* and a pond called *Hammerdam*, there is no village of that name. It is not unlikely that such a village did exist in medieval times (1000—1200 A.D.), when the church was built, but subsequently disappeared. The reason for its disappearance might lie in the general deterioration of climate at the beginning of Late Medieval times c. 1300 A.D., when more stormy

Table VI.
Acreage in each shot and of each farmstead in 1688.

Nr.	Ialt	Stokbro-fald	Hauens-fald	Tofteagre	Hammer-dams agre	Hundals-fald	Bløshøys agre	Græsfald	Skouens-fald	Bjerrefald
G 2	39.1	2.6	5.4	4.2	—	0.7	10.3	4.4	3.6	5.2
— 3	22.3	3.6	5.0	3.3	—	1.2	7.2	2.6	—	1.1
— 4	30.4	5.5	5.5	6.2	3.6	0.2	4.4	0.7	—	1.6
— 7	31.2	—	2.0	8.1	2.2	0.2	8.3	2.3	3.2	5.1
— 6	32.2	1.0	2.6	8.4	8.3	3.3	5.2	2.5	1.0	—
B 1	15.6	1.2	1.1	1.3	1.7	0.1	2.6	2.0	3.7	1.3
— 5	13.2	5.4	2.1	1.2	2.3	0.1	1.2	—	0.2	0.5
— 12	14.4	—	—	1.1	5.6	0.1	1.5	0.4	2.5	1.7
— 10	19.6	—	0.7	1.7	5.4	3.1	2.1	1.1	—	7.4
— 8	15.4	—	0.6	2.3	0.4	1.5	2.6	0.3	4.7	3.0
— 9	10.0	—	0.7	2.3	4.6	0.4	0.4	0.4	—	—
— 14	13.6	—	—	—	2.1	1.6	—	0.6	1.0	9.1
— 11	5.5	—	1.2	—	—	0.1	1.2	0.2	—	2.4
— 13	6.0	—	—	0.6	3.0	0.2	1.1	—	0.5	1.1
— 15	5.3	—	—	—	0.3	0.4	0.7	—	2.2	1.6
— 16	5.5	—	—	—	—	—	1.4	—	—	3.4

conditions prevailed. A rise in the level of ground water in and around *Hammer pond* might easily have made tillage very difficult, or even impossible, for the *Hammer* folk, and induced them to move the village to a more favourable site. Rather than establish an entirely new site, it was decided to extend the existing hamlet of *Grindsted* by establishing a western row of farmsteads facing the older eastern row (fig. 8–2). As a compensation for the loss of *Hammerdam* shot, agreement was reached with the *Grindsted* folk, whereas all farmers tilled the *Bløshøys* shot in common.

While these changes were taking place, another *Bol* (No. 1) had been added on the eastern side of the settlement, so that by the end of the fourteenth century the enlarged village of *Grindsted* had ten farmsteads (in order Nos. 1, 2, 3, 4, 7, 6, 9, 12, 10 and 8, in order to their place in the village). At a later date *Bol* 5 was built, and the settlement now consisted of eleven farmsteads as stated in the record of 1553 (fig. 8–3). Since then the fields have continually been extended by the addition of more strips, usually by individual activity. Especially has this been so in the steeper and less fertile parts of *Hammer Bakker,* once all the level land of the plateau had been pressed into cultivation. Finally between 1553 and 1688 growth of population resulted in the formation of one more *Bol* (No. 14) and four more *Halve Bol* (11, 13, 15 and 16) (fig. 8–4).

LITERATURE

Aakjær, S.: Maal, Vægt og Taxter i Danmark. Nordisk Kultur XXX, Sth. 1936.

Dahl, S.: Torna och Bara. Studier i Skånes bebyggelse- och näringsgeografi före 1860. Lund 1942.

Eneqvist, E.: Nedre Luledalens byar. Geographica Nr. 4. Uppsala 1937.

Evers, W.: Ortsnamen und Siedlungsgang im mittleren Ostfalen zwischen Leine und Fühse. Berichte zur Deutschen Landeskunde, 1951.

Ewers, W.: Das Hof und Dorf Problem auf Grund neuer Untersuchungen im mittleren Ostfalen. Petermanns geogr. Mitt., 1952.

Hansen, C. Rise og Axel Steensberg: Jordfordeling og Udskiftning. Undersøgelser i tre sjællandske Landsbyer. Det Kgl. Da. Vid. Selsk. Histor.-filol. Skrifter, Bind II, Nr. 1, Kbh. 1951.

Hannerberg, D.: Byamål, tomtreglering och odlingsgång. Lund 1955.

Hannerberg, D.: Råberga och Alm, 2 Närkesbyar. Ymer 1957.

Hannerberg, D.: Skånska bolskiften. Veberöd. Sv. Geogr. Årsbok 1958.

Hatt, G.: Oldtidsagre. Kgl. Da. Vid. Selsk. Arkæolog.-kunstihistor. Skrifter, Bind II, Nr. 1.

Hatt, G.: Nørre Fjand. An early village site in West Jutland. Samme, Bind II, Nr. 2.

Klitgaard, C.: Hvetbo Herred I–II, Aalborg 1906–07.

Larsen, H.: Nogle Oplysninger og Bemærkninger om de danske Landsbyer. Aarbøger f. Nordisk Oldkyndighed, 3. Række, Bind 8, 1918.

Larsen, H.: Trevangsbruget i Jylland. Samlinger til Jysk Hist. og Topografi, 5. Række, Bind 1, 1932/34.

Lauridsen, P.: Om gamle danske Landsbyformer. Aarbøger f. Nordisk Oldkyndighed og Historie, 1896.

Müller-Wille, W.: Die spätmittelalterlich-frühneuzeitliche Kulturlandschaft und ihre Wandlungen. Berichte zur Deutschen Landeskunde, 19 Band, 2 Heft, 1957.

Niemeier, G.: Gewannfluren, Ihre Gliederung und die Eschkerntheorie. Petermanns geogr. Mitt., Band 90, 1944.

Niemeier, G.: Die kulturgeographische Fundierung der Ortsnamenforschung. Erdkunde, Band IV, 1950.

Nordholm, G.: Geografiska studier över de nordeuropeiske byarnas grundformer. Svensk Geogr. Årsbok, 1931.

Oberbeck-Jacobs, U.: Die Entwicklung der Kulturlandschaft nördlich und südlich der Lössgrenze im Raum um Braunschweig. Jahrbuch der Geogr. Gesell. zu Hannover, 1957.

Steensberg, A.: Store Valby. En sjællandsk landsby, der blev genfundet. Fra Nationalmuseets Arbejdsmark, 1953.

Vahl, M.: Landbebyggelsen i Danmark. Svensk Geogr. Årsbok, 1930.

Vahl, M.: Landbebyggelsen på Øen Falster. Geografisk Tidsskrift 1931.

Wulff, D. H.: Statistiske Bidrag til Vendelbo Stifts Historie i det 16de og 17de Aarhundrede. Aalborg 1872–74.

Morphology and habitation
in eastern Himmerland, NE. Jutland

By Viggo Hansen

Abstract

A certain region of the Danish peninsula Jutland is studied from the aspect of habitation, the development of which is compared with the different relief features and with the progress in agricultural technics.

Himmerland is the name of a province and a peninsula in northeast Jutland, bordered on the east by the Kattegat and on the north and west by the Limfjorden. A high watershed, running nearly north-south in the middle of the peninsula, separates two distinctly different landscapes. To the west lies a system of elongated hills and shallow valleys with smooth running rivers in the bottom, and the base level is the level of the sea. The small streams are surrounded by wet meadowland and bogs only recently reclaimed, and the glacial soils are leached and the yields rather low.

To the east of the watershed the landscape is split up into steep-sided »peninsulas« and »island«s by interjacent deep, flat-bottomed valleys of different geneses. These valleys reach very close to the watershed, from where the streams have cut deep gorge-like, v-shaped valleys in the glacial sub-soil. The gorges open directly into the flat valley bottoms, from where the slope is so slight that the river beds in their further course mostly are canalized as a protection against flooding. The base level thus is not the level of the sea, but rather the point where the streams reach the flat valley bottom.

These barely sloping valley bottoms have a different origin. Danish geologists consider some of them to be pre-quaternary river beds, in which tectonic forces may have played a part. During the ice-age the subglacial rivers followed the previously made valleys or cut new ones in the substratum of cretaceous limestone. When the ice melted away the cold arctic sea invaded the deep valleys and converted the northeast part of Himmerland into an island and fjord landscape. Remnants of the arctic sea are still to be found as narrow terraces at a level of 60 feet in the northeast and at 30 feet near Komdrup. After an uplift of the land the sea once more transgressed the same area in the Litorina transgression, beginning at about 5000 B. C. But this time the sea penetrated much deeper into the former valleys (see fig. 1), dividing up the land into islands and peninsulas.

In the still waters of the inner fjords sands and muds were deposited, while wave erosion formed the more exposed beaches, particularly along the east coasts. The previous shore lines now lie at a level of 13—14 feet in the southwest and at 20 feet in the northeast. The general uplift of the land after the transgression of the Litorina Sea has been greater in the northeast than in the southwest, thus resulting in the formation of shallow stagnant lakes and ponds in the inner fjords, which have long since been filled up with layers of peat.

On more exposed sites the erosion forms, caused by wave action, dominated. The waves of the Stone-Age sea have cut high nearly vertical cliffs into the flanks of the outer »islands« and »peninsulas«, while in other places the wave currents deposited pebbles and gravels as beach ridges and recurved spits which later became the basis of agricultural settlements.

The rural habitation in the area fall into three groups:

I. Villages on the inner morainic plateaux.
II. Villages on terraces and raised beach ridges.
III. Villages on dry sites in the Stone-Age sea.

I. The villages on *the morainic plateaux* again fall into two groups. An older group with place name terminations in -inge and -sted can be dated back to pre-Viking times (300—700 A. D.), and these villages apparently have preferred more sandy soils. A younger group with place name terminations in -by and -torp was founded between 1000 and 1200 A. D., and these mainly tilled more loamy or clayey soils. Both groups of villages show a preference for more undulating land than for even surfaces.

II. *The terrace site* is a most conspicuous feature in the settlement pattern. In many places there are elongated villages with the farmsteads lying in ribbons on narrow strips of land which rise some feet above the wet meadows, and often they have an old cliff behind. Some of the terraces are remnants of tunnel valley-bottoms, while others are late-glacial or Stone-Age beach terraces. This site at the

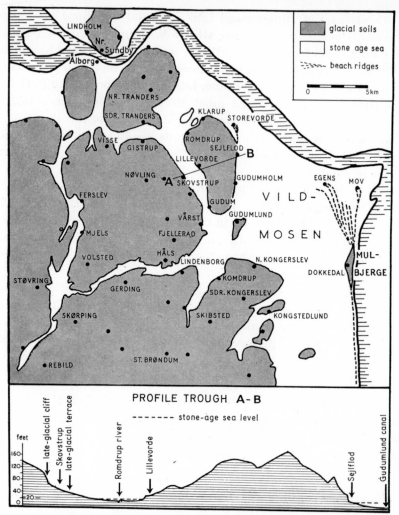

Fig. 1. Map of Eastern Himmerland, showing the supposed maximum extent of the habitations in proportion to the level of the Litorina sea. Scale: 1:250.000.

foot of an old overgrown cliff, yet raised some feet above the wet ground, is favourable for several reasons, favourable for land use, when arable fields occupied the upper glacial soils and the wet meadows were grazed by the livestock, and favourable for fresh-water supply, because rain water, which rapidly seeps down through the porous limestone-subsoil, again emerges at the foot of the cliff.

III. The villages on the marine foreland of *the raised Stone-Age sea* are very few (see map), but all of them show the same features

and originated in the same way. All three are placed on the tip of
recurved spits formed through wave action during the postglacial
uplift of the land. The spit on which Storevorde lies, clings to a
late-glacial raised beach, while the other two (Mov and Egens) are
bordered on all sides by marine foreland. The placing is very clear,
both are on the tip of a fan-shaped system of recurved spits, built
of materials from the island of Mulbjerge. The fan represents two
different age groups of spits, an older to the west and a younger to
the east. The ends of the spits were chosen for village sites, partly
because there were more extensive areas with silty soil outside and
in the lee of the spits. In addition the site may previously have been
chosen as a harbour for a fishing population because of deep water
close to it. From archaeological findings it is known to have housed
a fishing population prior to the agricultural reclamation.

The three villages on the spits are undatable from their place
names, but they are mentioned in old chronicles from the 13th century. *Storevorde* was then named *Vdræ Wardhæ*, meaning *Outer
Ward*, while *Egens* was called *Eigenshaffue (Oak-ness forest)*.

Until now only clustered habitations have been mentioned, because
they are more easily datable; but scattered farms may also have
existed in earlier times, even though such farms generally are supposed to be younger than villages and most often originating from
the end of the eighteenth century onward.

Detailed studies of the newer development in habitations have been
made of a specific region in the east central part of the map section,
namely the three parishes of Sønder Kongerslev, Nørre Kongerslev
and Komdrup, together comprising a peninsula with glacial soils and
the adjoining raised sea bottom from the Stone-Age with soils of
sand, silt and peat.

The development in the three parishes is illustrated by five different maps (figs. 2—6), on which are shown the boundary lines
between the parishes, the twenty and forty feet contours and the
habitation for each of the years. The source of the first map (fig. 2)
is the great Danish land register of 1688. From this it will be seen
that each parish comprised a clustered village (on glacial soil), and
in addition there were three solitary farms (on the edge of the glacial soil). Sønder Kongerslev is on a slope of a dry, late-glacial valley
(not shown on the map) with easy access to the meadowland to the
east. There was at that time an open green in the middle of the village maybe as a later development from a single row of farmsteads.
The place name termination dates it back to 500 A. D., but it may be

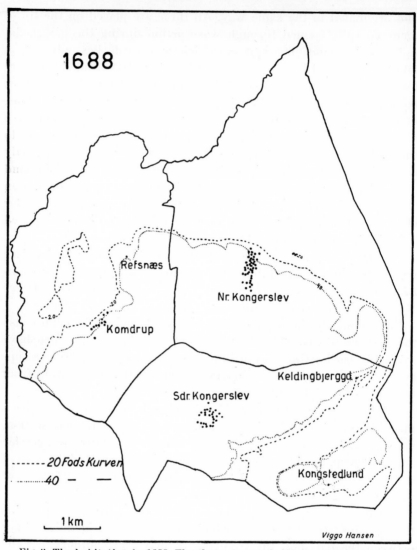

Fig. 2. The habitation in 1688. The three clustered villages are dominating.

much older, because there is a cluster of Bronze Age barrows just to the south of the village, meaning perhaps an uninterrupted farmers' settlement from at least 1000 B. C.

Nørre Kongerslev village to the north of Sønder Kongerslev bears the same name as this one, but still it may be at least a hundred years younger and founded somewhere about 600—700 A. D. The farm grouping is here perpendicular to the old coast line, indicating

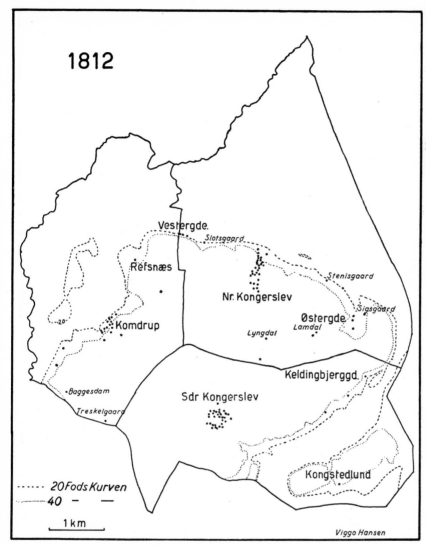

Fig. 3. The habitation in 1812. Most of the new-built farms are situated between the twenty and forty feet contour lines.

that the raised sea bottom must have been usable, if only in part, at foundation time. This is supported by archaeological investigations showing that the uplift of the land was not yet complete at the beginning of the Christian era, and because of the climatic deterioration with an accelerated growth of peat mosses round 400 A. D., which made the bog land immideately to the north of the village unusable at least until 600 A. D.

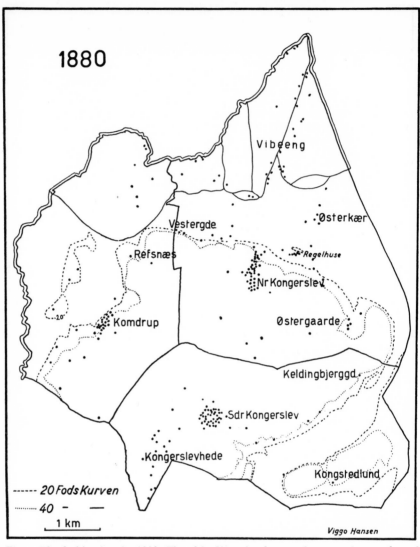

Fig. 4. The habitation in 1880. The thin lines in the meadows to the north and the extra line along the parish boundary indicate the position of the water courses at the beginning and the middle of the 19th century.

Komdrup village is the younger of the three and goes back only to Medieval times (1000—1200 A. D.). The farmsteads are here grouped on a line parallel to the Stone-Age shore line, indicating a more intensive use of the low-lying meadow lands, which at that time had dried so much that livestock grazing was of importance.

Of the three solitary farms at least two (Kongstedlund and Refs-

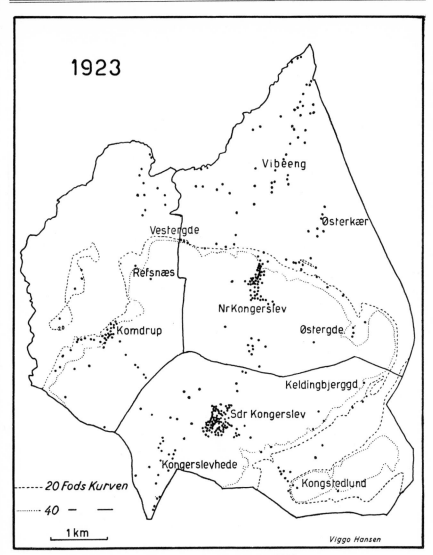

Fig. 5. The habitation in 1923.

næs) can be dated back to the fifteenth century. They were owned and lived on by noble families and had separate enclosed fields, while the villages at that time had their land lying in common.

The nex map (fig. 3) shows the situation in 1812, some twenty years after the passing of the Enclosure Act, when each farmer had been allotted his share of the common fields and now was allowed to move the farmstead out of the village. From the map it will be seen that several farmers made use of this opportunity. But it is also evident that except for a few (Lyngdal and Lamdal) the farmers moved to certain preferred places, inasmuch as most of them built their new farms between the twenty and the forty feet contours. Just here is a narrow brim of a terrace, an abrasion plane made by erosive wave forces in Stone-Age times. The special attractions of these places are evident from the formation of not only single farms, but even small hamlets like Østergårde and Vestergårde, something between a village and a single farm. Exposed sites were never chosen, not even by the farmers who moved into the central plateaux, as indicated by the place names like Lyngdal (heather valley) and Lamdal (supposedly: long valley), and the other ones had found similar sheltered places.

The time after 1840 was a prosperous one for Danish farmers, and as the population increased as never before, there was an ever growing demand for more land. Fortunately it was possible to meet this demand, because at that time there was still a lot of waste or little used land in the former commons, still mostly growing coarse grasses and heather because of insufficient manure, and because chemical manures were unknown. Another reserve of land in this region were the wide areas of wet meadows that only needed draining to turn the svamps into good agricultural land.

Favourable prices for grain and livestock produce in the years after 1840 were an effective stimulus for converting all formerly waste land into productive agricultural soil by means of more rational methods in the use of manures and fertilizers and in drainage.

Fig. 4 (1880) pictures the result of 40 years' efforts to meet the demand for agricultural land. On the high lands a new habitation grew up on former heathland, Kongerslevhede, while at the same time the empty space between the old villages had to some extent been filled up with farms that moved out of the villages. To the north the low lying meadows were tilled and inhabitated, and two new settlements had sprung up here (Østerkær and Vibeeng). The farmsteads are more and less linked to the canals and open ditches which are also followed by a system of new roads. The nearness to the open canals and to other streaming waters is not only due to better drainage near these, but also to meet the demand for fresh water. For many years at first the water in the ground was saline, and the fresh water problem was only solved by digging open canals or in other cases by laying down pipes from boring on the high land.

The result of this land reclamation in the later part of the nineteenth century was a rapid increase of farmland as well as of new farmsteads, as shown in the table.

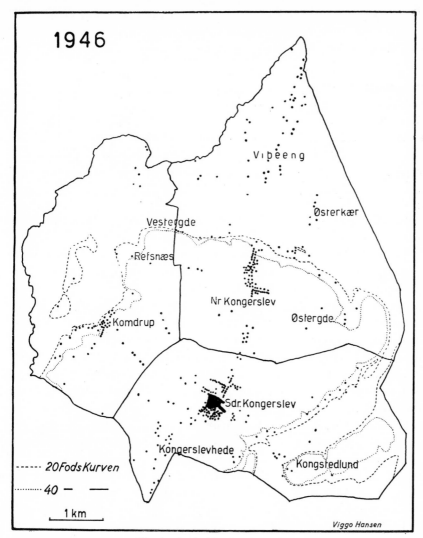

Fig. 6. The habitation in 1946.

It is astonishing to see how the number of complete farms is unchanged from 1850 to 1895. All new holdings are classified as small holdings, the number of which has increased from 43 to 101, and this increase is even confined to the two Kongerslev parishes. The 28 new holdings in Kongerslev parish are the result of heath reclamation in Kongerslevhede, while the 41 new holdings in Nørre Kongerslev parish are on reclaimed meadowland. Similar holdings on former meadowland in Komdrup parish, shown on the map but

Number of complete farms (F.) and small holdings (H.)
1850 to 1895.

	1850		1860		1873		1885		1895	
	F.	H.	F.	H.	F.	H.	F.	H.	F.	H.
Sønder Kongerslev.......	17	12	18	13	16	29	17	35	16	40
Nørre Kongerslev........	29	25	31	28	29	38	29	61	29	66
Komdrup	19	6	19	8	19	7	20	6	20	5
Total	65	43	68	49	64	74	66	102	65	101

not in the table, are cottages (without farmland) on land owned by Refsnæs manor.

The twentieth century shows a continuous increase in the number of farms and at the same time an acceleration in the general displacement of old farms from the villages into their own plot on the plateaux. New holdings increased by 34 from 1904 to 1940, of which 12 were in Sønder Kongerslev, 11 in Nørre Kongerslev and 11 in Komdrup. But now most of them are State-subsidied, half of them on land below the twenty feet contour, the other half on high lands, mostly roadside houses (see fig 5 and 6). There is also a general change of location for many older holdings, away from remote places towards the roads with better transport facilities. The dependence on free fresh water surfaces is no longer urgent, because Vibeeng and Østerkær now get their water supply in pipes from Nørre Kongerslev. It is also obvious that special relief features no longer play a part in the choice of building sites. New holdings are now more or less located along road sides, and predilectively on high spots, where older farms are seldom found.

The village itself experiences a radical change in the course of the twentieth century. Old farms move into their fields (often after a fire), and small houses grow up on theirs sites. But the change is not uniform in all three villages. In Komdrup the influence is only slight, in Nørre Kongerslev rather more pronounced, while Sønder Kongerslev has undergone a complete change. From a purely rural habitation of farmsteads and cottages it has been transformed into a trade and service centre, not alone for the three parishes but also for a big area to the east of the village. The railway came in 1900, and one of the results was the development of a peat industry which took its raw materials from the extensive Lille Vildmose bog in the

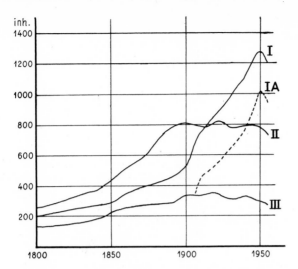

Fig. 7. Diagram showing the development of the rural population 1801—1955. I: Sdr. Kongerslev. I A: Kongerslev, railway town. II: Nr. Kongerslev. III. Komdrup. The railway from Hadsund via Kongerslev to Aalborg was opened in 1900. The rural population has been stagnant ever since the turn of the century, or even decreasing.

east. This industry had a new boom during the Second World War, and when the supply of peat was nearly exhausted, hundreds of hectares of the bog were reclaimed and made into arable land.

Today only a trained eye can find the old village site in Sønder Kongerslev, behind the shopping centre with its many new streets. This new development, which really began with the opening of the railway in 1900, has only affected the town population in Sønder Kongerslev, while the rural population has been stagnant ever since the turn of the century, or even decreasing (see fig. 7). This is a quite normal development for Danish rural districts owing to urbanization and to mechanization in farming.

Even if only a small area has been dealt with in this paper, it more or less reflects what has happened in most Danish rural districts: the reclamation of heathland, the drainage of waterlogged areas, the dispersal of farms and small holdings, the transformation of the old village structure and population flight from rural areas, and the growing up of local urban centres. It is only a question of difference of degree, and the area discussed may be regarded as a pattern of most Danish regions.

LITERATURE

Hansen, Viggo (1947): Tre østhimmerlandske Sogne. Et bebyggelsesgeografisk Studie. Geografisk Tidsskrift. Bd. 48.

Hansen, Viggo (1954): Morfologi og bebyggelse i det østlige Himmerland. Kulturgeografi, Århus.

Jessen, Axel (1920): Stenalderhavets Udbredelse i det nordlige Jylland. Danmarks geologiske Undersøgelser, II Rk., No. 35.

Mertz, E. L. (1924): Oversigt over de sen- og postglaciale Niveauforandringer i Danmark. Danmarks geologiske Undersøgelser, II Rk., No. 41.

Mikkelsen, E. (1943): Lille Vildmoses Stratigrafi og Vegetationshistorie. Meddl. f. Dansk geologisk Forening, Bd. 10, H. 3.

Milthers, V. (1948): Det danske Istidslandskabs Terrænformer og deres Opståen. Danmarks geologiske Undersøgelser, III Rk., No. 28.

Nielsen, A. C.: Sønder Kongerslev Sogn. (Kl. Gjerding, Bidrag til Hellum Herreds Beskrivelse og Historie, Ålborg 1890-92).

Pedersen, Henrik (1928): De danske Landbrug 1688. København.

Rasmussen, A. (1924): Komdrup Sogns Beskrivelse og Historie. (Fra Himmerland og Kjær Herred, XIII).

Steensberg, A. (1940): Den danske Landsby. (Vi og vor Fortid, Nr. 1), København.

Statistisk Tabelværk, udgivet af Statens statistiske Bureau og Statistisk Departement, København.

Land Use on Outwash Plain and Moraine Landscape in Denmark.

By Aa. H. Kampp.

Danish agriculture as a whole attaches the greatest importance to intensive cattle breeding. For this reason, the cereals have at present a far less predominant situation in Danish farming than in most other countries, and the grain areas cover less than half of the arable land. The remaining part is covered with grass, green fodder and roots.

The arable land is intensively utilized. One of the results of this is that the system of fallow has been abandoned. As a rule, the crops in one field alternate in a fixed succession. If all the fields are of equal size the farmer will have the same area of each crop every year. Manure is added, and a greater profit is drawn from the nutrient by changing the crops from year to year in order not to exhaust the soil by using always the same crops and, consequently, the same set of nutrient in one field. At least once in the rotation, in the root field, weeding is done, and in the grain-field the weed is chemically destroyed. In this manner the soil keeps its fertility, the farm-work is dispersed as evenly as possible, and parasites do not become predominant.

Field-rotation systems in Denmark.

On the basis of a series of inquiries, a representative investigation has been made dealing with the field rotation in different regions of Denmark (Kampp, 1956 b). The 8-field rotation is the most common in the greater part of Denmark, corresponding to the utilization for the whole country: barley, oats, mixed grain, rye or wheat, grass, and roots, each of the two lastmentioned often being cultivated in two fields, or seed crops may be grown. The 7-field rotation is common where only one field is grown with root crops, especially in Vendsyssel, while the 6-field rotation seems to be predominant in North-West Jutland with its bullock-feeding farms, where seed crops are very rare. If kohlrabi (swedes) is a fixed link in the field rotation 7—8 years seem to be the smallest possible distance considering the *Plasmodiophora brassicae.* The same rule holds good for clover and oats (*Tylenchus*), wheat and barley *(Fusarium).*

Examples are given from 11 to 5 field rotation; however, the whole problem is complicated by the "camouflaged" rotation, for example this one: 1. wheat; 2. a. sugar beet; 2. b. kohlrabi; 3. a. barley; 3. b. oats; 4. grass; 5. grass, where, in reality, 2 and 3 are grown as 4 different fields. As to oats, barley, kohlrabi and sugar beets it is a question of a 10-year rotation, though called a 5-field rotation.

The character of the field rotation is usually inherent with the wish of being able to provide fodder for the live-stock and, therefore, the system may vary in accordance with the number of stock. In the few farms in Denmark where agriculture is stockless and, consequently, without roots or grass, the number of fields may, of course, be reduced. This may be the case too where meadows render rotation-grass superfluous. The number of rotation-fields may also change according to the fluctuations of the market for seed crops, permanent grass or lucerne. However, the number seems neither to depend upon the fertility of soil (except where large meadow-areas and marsh-areas exist) nor on the situation in relation to towns (apart from Copenhagen), as vegetables and fruits are principally grown in special farms (Kampp 1952). Other cash crops, as outdoor vegetables on ordinary farms, are grown, according to the owners' interests, regardless of the town distance, because the increase of the rate price for long carriage is compensated by the lower price of the land and, partly, of the labour.

However, the number of rotation fields is only a frame within which it is possible to vary the system a good deal in conformity with the fertility of the soil, the capability of the farmer and the prices of different farming products. In some regions there are 2 or 3 different rotation systems at the same farm, as a rule in order to make it possible always to have roots or grass near the stables, so as to ensure an easy contribution of roots to the cows and the bullocks in the stable. Further, this rotation system allows to pro-

vide the small calves grazing in the field with milk, which it would
be difficult to transport over a long distance, and to take them to
the stable when the weather is cold or rainy. The application of
more than one rotation system may also be due to pronounced
differences in the soil fertility of the farm-land. However, owing
to the mechanization, there is a tendency, for the whole country,
towards an adoption of the largest possible fields. "Free rotation"
is used, for instance, to grow roots in fields with much weed and,
especially, to be able to grow the seed crop which obtains the most
advantageous price at the market.

On the outwash plains in Western Jutland the use of the rotation
fields (but hardly their number) may be fixed according to meadows and other natural pastures outside the rotation. The West
Jutland farmers, however, not rarely overestimate the benefit which
may be drawn from these sour meadows, often situated at a long
distance, and from where one may get, rather labouriously, a few
cart-loads of second-class hay, or where the heifers may graze
during three or four summer months.

Two examples of field rotation.

Below are given two examples of the utilization of arable land
in Denmark, the first one from agricultural region I, the second
one from region VII (fig. 1, Kampp 1959). The two examples have
been chosen from the ordnance survey maps M 2905 and M 3101
as typical of farms situated 1) on outwash plain transformed into
farm-land (with rather poor soil fertility) and 2) on moraine landscape with the most favourable conditions for cultivation.

The two farms are *Overgård* on an outwash plain in Western
Jutland and *Grønvang* on the fertile, undulating East Jutland moraine landscape, some few kilometres east of the main ice margin
from the last Ice Age (Würm). In fig. 1 Overgård is marked O
and Grønvang G, on a map showing the 7 agricultural regions of
Denmark. This map is based on the yield capacity of the soils, as
explained in a previous paper (Kampp 1959).

Each of the seven regions has a peculiar combination of crops
and livestock. Characteristic features of the farming area are in
region I: Mixed grain, rye, and potatoes; in II: grass, oats, rye,
and bullocks; in III: oats, barley, and mixed grain; in IV: mixed
grain, rye, oats, and potatoes; in V: barley, oats, wheat, rye, potatoes, and orchards; in VI: barley, oats, wheat, and bullocks; in VII:

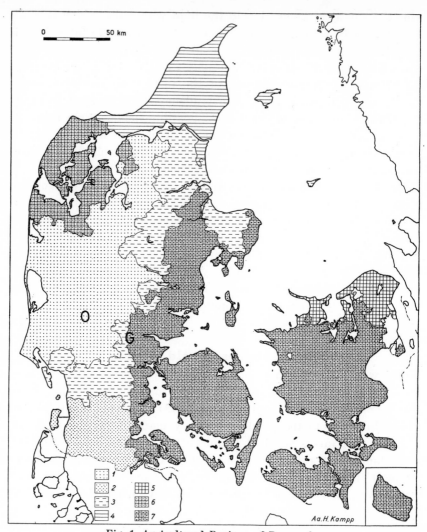

Fig. 1. Agricultural Regions of Denmark.

barley, wheat, and beets, five sixths of the seed-producing area of the whole country, and a large part of the nursery garden and orchard areas. The yields per unit of area are low in regions I and II, medium in III and IV, fairly high in V, and high in VI and VII. With the exception of region II, where the density of live-stock is smallest, it generally increases in the regions in the order mentioned above. As for the breed of cattle, Shorthorns dominate in II and VI, Shorthorns and Black and White Danish Dairy Cattle (SDM) in I, SDM in IV, Red Danish Dairy Cattle (RDM) in V and VII.

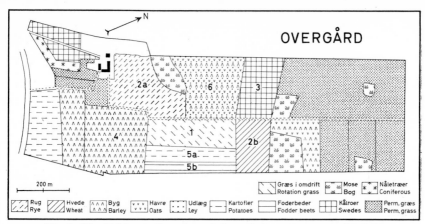

Fig. 2. The field rotation plan of Overgård on the outwash plain,
Ringkøbing county.

Region III is a rather peculiar area with various breeds. The yield
of butter per cow is much less in the regions I, III, and IV than in
the regions V, VI, and VII.

Fig. 2 shows the field-plan of *Overgård*, Ørbæk village, Hoven
parish, Nørre Horne district, *Ringkøbing county*. The land-register
numbers are 3a and 4a with a total of 65,7 hectares (apart from
road areas). The farm has been on copyhold till about 1800; however, it has only belonged to the owner's family since 1927. The
present buildings are from 1900 (the eastern wing was rebuilt in
1933, the northern one in 1942).

The depth of *the soil* varies from 25 to 40 cm. In the southernmost fields (inclusive of 2a and 4) the soil consists of podsolized
sand with an extremely low content of humus; the subsoil is leached
sand. The remaining fields have a blackmoulded, sandy soil, originating from outwash sand with superposed, swamped bog. Peat has
been dug until recently in the bogs and is at present (1959) dug in
the north-eastern one. Next year this area will be tilled. The 4 permanent grass fields to the north were raw humus until 1935. The
adjacent parts of the kohlrabi fields and of the mixed-grain fields
is land which was reclaimed in 1931. The last-mentioned field will
from next year be permanent grass.

The 6-field rotation only includes the numbered fields and runs
as follows: 1: grass for hay; 2: grain (the species depending upon
the soil humidity and acid reaction); 3: kohlrabi; 4: grain (as 2);
5: beet and potatoes (depending upon the soil); 6: grain with ley.
The permanent grass fields which lie untouched for at least 10

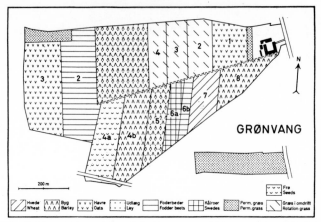

Fig. 3. The field rotation plan of Grønvang on the young morain landscape,
Vejle county.

years have all been fenced in for grazing, except the small one east
of the stable, which has been mowed for the pigs; the other two
small ones are used for the calves. All other fields are without any
hard and firm rotation; the farmer only changes between a grain
species and a root crop. The fields south of the garden bear evidence
of having been, years ago, under the meadow irrigation system of
the water course Omme Å.

In 1958 the barley yielded (as normally) 35 hkg. per hectare, oats
20 (one field gave 0, the oats being used for grazing because of an
infection with crane fly larvae). Owing to this parasite, rye has
not been grown for 10 years. Wheat has not been grown until
this year.

Livestock: 26 dairy cows (SDM breed, artificial insemination is
used), 35 young stock, 4 sows with 11 suckling pigs (June 1959),
70 bacon pigs, 50 hens. The yield of butter per cow per year has
varied, during the last five years, from 141 kg. to 185 kg.

Implements: 1 tractor with plough, harrows, potato-planter,
potato-lifter, horseshoe, drill, reaping machine and a binder. Milking-machine is used.

Staff: 1 farm hand all the year round, 2 in the summer; the
farmer's wife gives a hand in weeding the beets, harvesting grain
and potatoes.

Fig. 3 is a field-plan for *Grønvang* 1959. The larger part of the
farm-land, immediately at the farm, has land-register no. 5a in
Balle village, Bredsten parish, Tørrild district, *Vejle county.* Apart
from roads, it amounts to 43,9 hectares. The rectangular area south

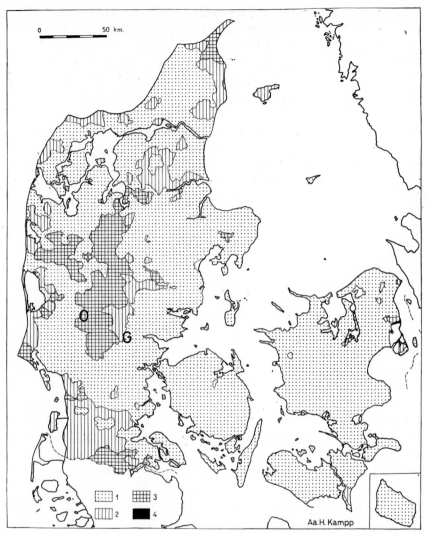

Fig. 4. The principal cereal by area (1951) in each Danish parish: 1. two-rowed barley; 2. oats; 3. rye, and 4. wheat.

of Bredsten (land-register no. 4b, 2,9 hectares) was bought at the occasion of the parcelling-out of Bredstensgårde in 1937. A small area, land-register no. 7c, about 3 km. south of the farm, amounts to 0,6 hectares with calcareous tufas and is, consequently, not taken into consideration in this paper. The area south of the East-West going road is let; two houses have been constructed. This gives a total agricultural area of 46,2 hectares. The farm was taken over on copyhold from the estate Engelsholm by the present owner's family more than 200 years ago and was bought free about 160 years ago. The buildings are from 1890—96; however, they were enlarged and modernized in 1930—31.

The soil is a clay mull of varyring depth (about 45 cm. nearest to the farm and decreasing to the west to 20 cm.). Subsoil of sandy clay forms a 0—50 m. broad belt along the northern boundary. In the remaining part of the area the subsoil is boulder clay, except in a few small, former bog depressions, distributed over the land, with peat as subsoil. In field 1 (barley) and partly in 4, immediately north of the field-path, an accretion bog, amounting to 1 hectare, has now been totally reclaimed.

Besides the three *permanent grass* plots, which have been fenced and are used for grazing, there are *two rotation systems*. The fields nearest to the farm buildings, numbered 1—8, are principally used for grazing. A 4th-year grass bed has been used till now. Field no. 2 has 3rd-year grass, no. 3 2nd-year and no. 4 1st-year grass. The ley in no. 5 is for 3 year old grass. The sugar beet is for fodder only. The ley in no. 8 is orchard grass (*dactylus glomerata*) and red clover, planned for one year only. The farmer will alter this rotation; in 1960 it will run as follows: 1: 1st-year grass (orchard grass + red clover); 2: barley with ley (as 1); 3: oats; 4: 3rd-year grass; 5: 2nd-year grass; 6: 1st-year grass; 7: roots; 8: barley with ley (as 1).

The other rotation system consists of 4 fields. There is no fixed rotation; however, common practice, being the result of a long-time experience in the preparation of the fields, is used from one year to another. The ley in the barley is white clover, red clover and Italian rye-grass for seed; the sugar beets are exclusively used for fodder. Half of field no. 4 is covered with Italian rye-grass for seed, the other half with barley, just as in 1958. According to the original plan it ought to have been white and red clover for seed; however, owing to trade depression, these crops were not sown. The seed areas are interchanged, so that in the next turn, 1963, 4a will carry clover, and, in its turn, red and white clover will be interchanged in 1967. This arrangement involves for each field an interval of 8 years between two crops of Italian rye-grass and 16 years between two crops of red clover etc. The yields were in 1958: barley 40 hkg. per hectar; oats 36; no wheat. Normally the yields are: barley 50—52, oats 48—50, wheat 52—54.

Livestock: 2 brood mares, 34 dairy cows (RDM breed), sometimes 1 bull; however, as a rule artificial insemination is used;

35 young stock, 20 sows with 70 suckling pigs (June 1959), 100 bacon pigs and 200 hens. The yield of butter per cow per year has varied, during the last five years, from 191,2 kg. to 225 kg.

Implements: 1 tractor with plough, harrows, horsehoe, fluid-sprayer and harvesting implements. The farm is equipped with milking-machine.

Staff: 1 married cattle-man, 1 married farm-hand, 1 younger farm-hand, 2 in the summer.

Likewise, nearly all the neighbouring farmers are working with rather large live-stock and, accordingly, have 1—2 fields with beet and rather large grass areas.

Some of the most obvious differences between the two farms are that potatoes, mixed grain, and rye are only grown on the podsolized sand at Overgård (O), while seed crops are only grown on the fertile clay at Grønvang (G). G. has a larger area of rotation-grass, beet and kohlrabi than O. Consequently, it is not surprising to find that O. has only 84,5 live-stock units in spite of its 66 hec-tares (1,3 per hectare), while G. has 149 units on 46 hectars (3,2 per hectare) and consequently, a larger staff. The two different cattle breeds are also characteristic of the respective regions. The average yield of butter per cow per year is on O.: 173 kg.; on G.: 201,2 kg.

The utilization illustrated by crop predominance maps.

How typical the crops on the two farms are of the respective regions appears from fig. 4 and fig. 5: O. is situated in the rye/potato-region, G. in the barley/kohlrabi-region. Fig. 4 indicates the principal cereal by area in 1951 in each Danish parish: 1. two-rowed barley; 2: oats; 3: rye, and 4: wheat. About 200 detailed agricul-tural maps exist at the Geographical Institute of the University of Copenhagen. A few examples have been published (Kampp 1939, 1952, 1956 and 1959).

The two-rowed barley covered in 1951 a bigger area than any other cereal in most of the parishes of Denmark, especially the islands and the eastern part of Jutland. As Denmark is situated in the oat-region of North-West Europe oats was predominant in the first part of the century in Jutland with the exception of the rye-regions, which were especially found in the moist South-West Jut-land and more northern outwash plains and other sandy soils; however, because of the higher yields and the higher prices of

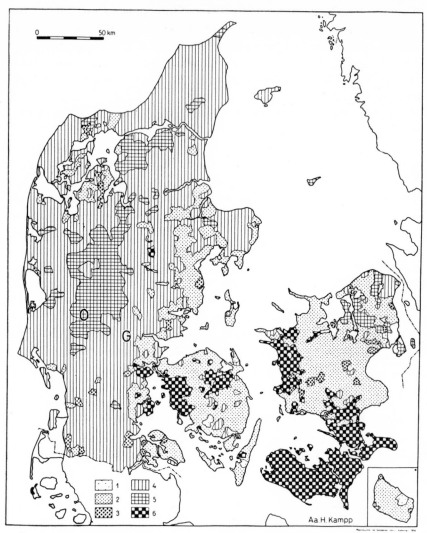

Fig. 5. The principal roots by area in 1951: 1. mangel; 2. fodder-sugar-beet;
3. sugar beet for fodder; 4. swedes; 5. potatoes, and 6. sugar beet for
sugar production.

barley, the preference of oat is now limited to a smaller number
of localities. Until 1938 oat was the predominant Danish cereal.
Rye has ceased to be dominating in a number of North Jutland
parishes, though it still dominates in dry, sandy soils.

The last figure represents the principal roots by area in 1951:
1. mangel; 2. fodder-sugar-beet; 3. sugar beet for fodder; 4. kohlrabi; 5. potatoes; 6. sugar beet for sugar production. Beet roots are

dominating almost everywhere in the isles (except North Sealand), in South East Jutland and, furthermore, in several Jutland parishes, particularly along the coast, especially along the shores of the western Limfjord. Factory sugar beet dominates the root crop in the parishes around the sugar factories; new factories have been established in this century. In the first part of the century mangel dominated the eastern part of Denmark; however, it has now been replaced by fodder-sugar-beet and sugar beet for fodder, which yields much more. It must be borne in mind that even beet for factory is mainly used for fodder: the whole top and about 80 per cent of the root, and it yields more than any other species of beet. Turnip, which at the beginning of this century dominated in a continued Mid-Jutland region, Vendsyssel, North-Djursland and Mid-Djursland, has been replaced especially by kohlrabi, which has now the preference in the principal part of Jutland; potatoes have also acquired an increased importance as root crop (though, botanically, it is not a root crop at all), not only around Copenhagen (for consumption), but also in the Jutland potato-region for fodder and factories for spirits and flour.

LITERATURE

Kampp, Aa. H. (1939 a): Geografisk Grundbog.
- (1939 b): Forarbejder til et dansk landbrugsatlas. Tidsskr. f. Landøkonomi.
- (1952): Lidt frugtavlsgeografi. Erhvervsfrugtavl. 2. edition.
- (1956 a): Hvor gror det, og hvorfor? 3. edition.
- (1956 b): The field rotation in different regions in Denmark. Tidsskr. f. Landøkonomi.
- (1958): Some types of farming in Denmark. The Oriental Geographer, East Pakistan.
- (1959): Some agro-geographical investigations of Denmark. (Thesis).

Danish Agricultural Subdivision and the Majorats

By Aa. H. Kampp

Abstract

According to an Act dealing with the conversion of feudal estates into fee simple the 75 Danish majorats were partly parcelled out, into 2.300 tenant farms 1919-1932. As an example showing a total parcelling-out of a manor a subdivision plan for Hvedholm is commented.

For more than four millenniums agriculture has been the leading industry of Denmark, and through the ages the farm has been the predominant form of exploitation; however, as long as the Danish soil has been under cultivation the size of the farms has, no doubt, been varying. The prehistoric finds do not seem to indicate that Denmark had landowners of any importance (*Hatt*, 1935, 128-129); it may be that in some cases one farmer owned several farms; however, there is nothing which points to profound social distinctions within the prehistoric village.

Later, the distinction became more accentuated between the farms, on one side, and, on the other side, the manors, whose owners in return for war duty enjoyed various privileges, first of all tax-free ownership of big areas *(Steenstrup,* 1874, 112; *Erslev,* 1898, 202). It is probable that the development of the army in the first half of the Middle Ages was the principal cause of the separation of a group of the population to form a class of squires (»herre-mænd«). The squires are first mentioned in »Jutland Law« (Jyske Lov 1241, 3rd volume, XIIII, XV). In the Middle Ages the manors were »just common, sometimes double farms« *(Christensen,* 1886, 18). However, *Nørlund* (1927, 167) has shown that there were exceptions.

An ordinance of 14th May, 1523, decided that a copyholder who had fulfilled his obligations could not be expelled from his farm.

In its application this recess proved to imply a considerable restriction of the squires' liberty to include farmland in the domaine of the manor and, on the whole, contributed to rendering difficult the amalgamation of land to form big estates *(Jensen, 1943, 15—16)*. Rather big parts of the country were Crown land and had but few manors *(Mathiassen, 1931, 11)*.

However, during the first half of the seventeenth century the number of manors was increasing, and after the introduction of the absolute monarchy in 1660 they included in their domaine land of farms which had been abandoned after the devastations of long-lasting wars. Sometimes, whole villages were absorbed; for instance, in 1696, Nislevgaard included in its land a village which came to life again after a total parcelling-out of Nislevgaard in 1925 (45 holdings and 11 supplementary allotments (see later). Lindersvold, which was founded in the seventeenth century, issued from two abandoned villages and was parcelled out, in 1922, into 44 holdings and 12 additional allotments. In the years around 1680 Denmark had about 2.700 derelict farms *(Pedersen, 1913, 125)*. However, the political power of the nobility was submitted to restrictions; so was their exemption from taxation and their special obligation to do war service *(Clausager, 1943, 195)*. The Crown sold half of its landed property *(Jensen, 1943, 23)*, and in order to secure to the King a rich and high-born nobility at the Court, Christian V founded, the 25th May, 1671, the feudalism: when a landowner had acquired as much as 1.000 tdr. htk.[1]) he could be granted a barony (»friherreskab«) or a feudal barony (»baroni«) (§§ 1, 17 and 19) and, if being the owner of 2.500 tdr. htk., a larger estate (»grevskab«) (§§ 1, 19 and 21). Further, it is stipulated in »Danske Lov« (1665) that estates of 400 tdr. htk. may be transformed into entailed estates (»stamhuse« and »fideikommisgodser«). Such estates should be majorats, i e. their succession should be undivided. If the family died out such feudal estates should devolve upon the Crown. In the course of time were founded 21 »grevskaber«, 14 baronies, 45 entailed estates (34 »stamhuse« and 11 »fideikommisgodser«).

In 1688 a few hundreds of landed proprietors possessed more than three fourths of the Danish land; the greater part of the remainder was church land and Crown land, and there were only a little more

---

1) "Td. hartkorn" is a Danish standard of land valuation based on the normal yield of the soil; 3.575 hectares of the most fertile soil constitute 1 "td. hartkorn". In average, however, 1 td. hartkorn requires 5.995 hectares in the islands, 14.630 hectares in Jutland, and 9.900 hectares in the entire country.

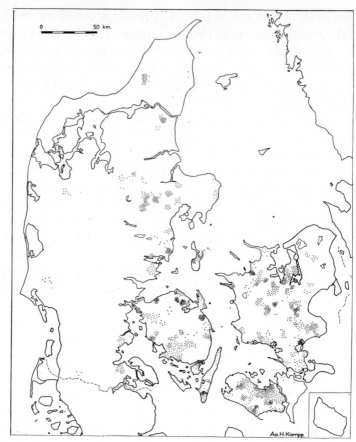

Fig. 1. State-subsidized tenant farms established on former majorats.
Each dot = 1 farm.

than 1.000 freehold farms *(Pedersen,* 1928, 360); the other farmers were copyholders. The taxes increased, and the corn prices decreased *(Falbe-Hansen* and *Scharling,* 1888—1889, II, 109); therefore, the landed proprietors claimed protection, which they obtained by the introduction of the Adscription (1733-1788). After the cattle plague in the years around 1740 the conditions of the Adscription were tightened.

Since the Iron Age the population of Denmark has to a great extent been domiciled in villages. In the village societies the cultivation was founded on community principles with scattered distribution of the land and regularly alternating rotations of crops. According to an Act of 1769 the farmers were allowed to have their part in the community separated and allotted, and after the abolish-

Fig. 2. Aerial photo, 1939: Centre of the split-up area of the former estate of Spanager. Scale: 1:1.500. Geodetic Institute, copyright (M 3927/8764).

ment of the joined ownership of land in 1781 it became possible for them — thanks to the high corn prices — to become freeholders. During the economic conditions favourable to agriculture in the years around 1800, an extensive transition from copyholding to free-holding took place. When the joined ownership of land, centuries old, was split, the small-holder possessing a little land in the village field lost his grazing rights. Some of the small-holders were allotted small parcels, the placing of which, however, was inconvenient to the farmers; others got a piece of common for new cultivation *(Christensen,* 1891, 17—18). During the subdivisions the land-owners established thousands of small-holdings in order to procure man-power; many of the small-holders paid the copyhold-rent for their house by obligatory service to the squires. The notion »houses with land« is primarily a product of the agrarian reforms *(Jensen,* 1936, 208). Thus, the farmers' »villeinage« was replaced by the small-holders' »villeinage«, which was only brought to an end by the adoption of the Act of 23rd May, 1902.

In the period with joined ownership of land more than 90% of Danish farmers had their home in villages of varying size, a fact which was one of the very conditions for this form of ownership. Between the villages the open land was covered with bushy or swampy fields, heaths, bogs, meadows and common, with dying wood at all stages of ruin. In a country with an agricultural area as big as that of Denmark the topographical consequences of the subdivision affected inevitably the character of the landscape, to such a degree that it seems justified to speak of a metamorphosis. Normally, the fields of the villages grew together on top of the former common. The outlying farms came to occupy an outstanding role in the landscape, and at many places houses and villas became predominant in the former villages, whose economic life changed considerably. No doubt, the landscape has rarely undergone so conspicuous an alteration as in the years when the rural habitation from the former villages was scattered over the land. Swamps and morasses were drained off in order to be transformed into meadows, and in the fields resulting from the parcelling-out the soil was cultivated as never before; in growing number the small-holdings appeared in the previously open land, now scattered, now in small colonies.

The lack of man-power in the rural districts in the years about 1890 after the big oversea emigration gave rise to the adoption of the first »Act of State Small-Holdings« of 24th March, 1899 — a result of the work executed in the Land Commission of 13th April, 1894. In this »Act for the purpose of procuring parcels for agricultural workers« the size of the holdings was fixed at 1-4½ hectares according to the quality of the soil. This Act was renewed in 1904 and again in 1909; the purpose of the latter was the independent small-holding. To this effect it was made possible for already existing small-holdings to obtain additional loans. In these years the small-holders' associations came to life and grew to become strong. The small-holders' movement reflected a prevailing need for economic and social independence and aimed at bigger holdings, on the assumption that the holdings which gave full occupation offered the possibilities of the most intensive exploitation. The Act of 24th March, 1899, with later additional laws remained in force jointly with the Acts of 4th October, 1919 (cf. fig. 4), which entitled the government to purchase land and to convey it to the user as copyholding, against the payment of a special duty, the rent, fixed on the basis of periodical reassessments for land.

The Acts of 4th October, 1919, contained regulations about the sale of glebe for parcelling-out, about the conversion of the majorats into absolute property against cession of certain areas of land for subdivision (the Act dealing with the conversion of feudal estates

Fig. 3. Aerial photo, 1939, of the estate of Gaunø. Scale: 1:1.500.
Geodetic Institute, copyright (M 3925/8120).

into fee simple) and about the conditions for sale of land owned
by the State. Already the Constitution of 1849 held out the prospect
of the abolition of the privileges attached to part of the Danish land.
The October Acts established that the farms should be big enough
to assure a family their livelihood. The 25th March, 1933, an Act
was voted according to which holders of rented land were allowed
to have their rent converted into duties conditioned by the economic
fluctuations. The »Act of State Small-Holdings« of 1948, united about
40 older land-laws into one Act, comprising the principles of both
the 1899-Acts and the 1919-Acts. It was a question of two different
main principles, which, though amalgamated into one law, could
not form a synthesis.

Out of the approximately 8.000 state-subsidized tenant holdings
which were established until 1958, a number of 2.300 are distributed
on 18.000 hectares of majorat land, giving an average size of 7,2
hectares. The subdivision resulting from the Act dealing with the
conversion of feudal estates especially took place in 1921-24 and
came to an end in 1932 (fig. 4).

A few majorats avoided, totally or partly, to cede land during the
conversion, either by buying compensation land in other locality,
their landed property thus remaining undivided, or by being exempt

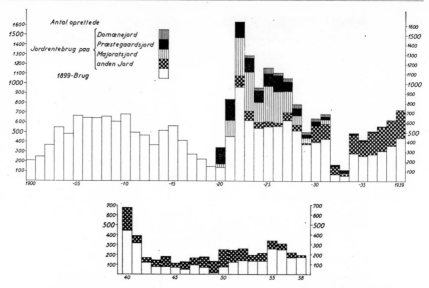

Fig. 4. Chart showing the establishment of state-subsidized tenant farms and holdings 1900—1958: state-subsidized tenant farms on state land, church properties, majorats and other areas; also farms established under the 1899-Act. Since 1899, 27.000 state-subsidized tenant farms have been established (1 eighth of all existing Danish agricultural properties). A small number of them have been demolished (or amalgamated with other holdings). On the other side, additional parcels have been allotted to thousands of small-holders, who have thus become independant farmers (during the period 1940—1958 more than 6.000). Increased prices and lack of material hampered the parcelling-out, which reached its minimum in the financial year 1945—46. During the period 1940—1958 a number of 1.600 state-subsidized tenant farms were established and about 2.700 farms under the 1899-Act.

from ceding land on condition that they paid a sum to the Central Land Board (»Statens Jordlovsudvalg«), enabling this to buy substitute land. On the other hand, other majorats have been compelled to sell land in excess of the land which they had to cede for the conversion. The development of the majorats existing in 1919 is as follows: 18 have been completely parcelled out; 18 have ceded more than the statutory area, while 22 only have ceded the stipulated land, and 17 have remained almost unaltered since 1919.

The majorats were situated primarily in the most fertile regions of the country, and generally they comprised some of the best soil of the parish, either because this soil was originally of a better quality than the rest of the parish, or because a better cultivation and increased manuring had improved the quality of the soil. Consequently, as appears from fig. 1, the majorat subdivision has especially taken place in agricultural region VII (*Kampp*, 1959), where, formerly, it was difficult to purchase land for subdivision, and where the parcelling-out was so strongly counteracted by amalgamations and discontinuations that in numerous regions the total number of farms has undergone a not inconsiderable decrease; thus, as far as Lolland is concerned, the number of state subsidized holdings established on former majorat land alone is 427, while the total increase of agricultural properties only amounts to 382.

The average size of these state-subsidized tenant holdings was: 1920-30: 7 hectares; 1930-40: a little more than 10 hectares; 1940-58: 17 hectares. Within the individual colony the differences of the sizes of the holdings are essentially caused by the different qualities of the soil; they are less caused by the shape which it has been necessary to give the parcels with a view to the terrain conditions, big water courses, roads, the transformation of which would be too expensive, and the orientation of the limits of woods and parishes.

It is attempted to give these holdings, as far as possible, a regular rectangular shape (fig. 2). When, at the conversion, the farmers divided the land of the villages they found it most practical, in view of the labour traffic across their fields, to place the buildings in an almost central position on the farm, while the roads were of secondary importance. In the colonies of state-subsidized tenant holdings the roads were first projected, and then the situation of the buildings in proximity to the road (here are left out of consideration the lanes serving the local labour traffic between the buildings and the field).

The small-holders which were considered as being in greatest need of additional land had occasion to buy a supplementary allotment, or they could obtain it on land-rent conditions; thus, it was not a question of parcelling-out in the sense that the number of farms was augmented, but of an increase of the so-called »dwarf-holdings« (»dværgbrug«); this made the holdings more remunerative and enabled the holders to become independent (fig. 5). Sometimes, these additional parcels were conveyed to already existing holdings on the same majorat land; in other cases to small-holders outside the colony. They served for increasing the rotation area in cases where this was smaller than usual in that period; however, the efforts often tended to supplementing the land by a meadow-parcel, provided that the holding did not already comprise such a parcel. During a very long time the meadows have played a primordial role to the Danish farmer, not least in regions with poor soil, where, especially in dry summers (as 1959), there is a risk of lack of grass.

In no other place of the country the noblemen's estates were

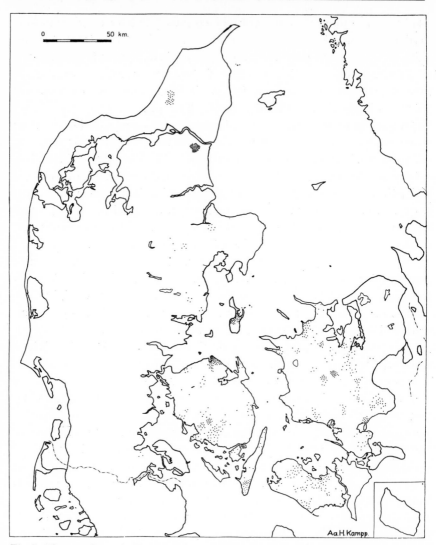

Fig. 5. The number of allotments established on former majorats as a supplement to the farms shown in map 1. Each dot = 1 allotment.

situated so densely as in the southern part of Funen. At the time of the conversion, the Svendborg county had no less than 15 majorat properties; therefore, in the ordnance survey map no. 4014 (measured in 1922, corrected in 1925) has been sketched, as an example, a subdivision plan for the Hvedholm manor under the estates Brahesminde, situated in Horne parish, Salling district, Svendborg county (fig. 6). (The existence of Hvedholm is first mentioned in

1475). This area has not been parcelled out at a time; at the subdivision of the estates Brahesminde in 1928 (according to the 1919-
Act), 12 state-subsidized holdings were established with a total area
of 74.4 hectares (11 tdr. 4 skp. htk.) and 7 additional allotments
of 25.0 hectares (4 tdr. 2 skp. htk.). Later, the government acquired
the total rest of the manor, and in 1939 eight independent state-
subsidized holdings with a total of 60.5 hectares (12 tdr. 4 skp. htk.)
were established, and 17 additional allotments (first of all supplementing the small-holdings founded in 1928 under the manor of
Hvedholm), totalling 43.7 hectares (9 td. htk.). The central part of
the estates remaining after the subdivision, 153.5 hectares, was
sold against cash as one of the biggest properties ever sold by the
Central Land Board; the farm buildings were in such a good condition that it was considered absurd not to make use of them.
However, the manor-house itself had been sold in advance to the
government, together with 19 hectares of park, and serves as a
hospital.

The Hvedholm land is a strongly undulated, principally loamy
moraine land from the last Glaciation (Würm); however, on the
whole, the relief of the terrain has had no influence on the shape
of the holdings; only towards south steep hill-sides have necessitated
a deviation from the otherwise regular, rectangular form.

During this subdivision an unexpected problem presented itself:
the individual state-subsidized holdings were able to satisfy, it is
true, their water-supply from the superior, water-carrying earth-
layers; however, this made it difficult for the central part of the
estate to procure water enough to the relatively big stock.

18 of the state-small-holders are born in Horne parish, 13 in neighbouring parishes. Only two of them have been workers in Hvedholm
before the subdivision; 5 are farmers' sons, 12 are small-holders'
children, 9 are sons of farm-workers, 2 are children of artisans, 1 is
a fisherman's son and 1 is originating from a town.

The new constructed road is a private lane. All the holders of
government land supply milk to the dairy at Horne. All of them have
land enough (1-1½ d. htk.) to secure them a livelihood. These
holdings do not comprise any special poultry farm; however, the
number of hens is, of course, considerably bigger than before the
subdivision. Further, the rotation of crops has developed on the
basis of an augmented production of domestic animals; for instance,
the root-crop areas and the grass-areas have increased at the expense
of the grain areas. No meadow-parcels are found. The children go

Fig. 6. Part of the ordnance survey map 4014 showing the splitting-up of the former feudal estate Hvedholm. (Geodetic Institute, copyright).

to school in Horne and Bjerne, and, consequently, have a distance to school of a few kilometres, at most. There is a bus from Nyborg to Bøjden; thus, the southern colony is most out-of-the-way.

Other development plans have previously been published (*Kampp,* 1956, and 1959).

The immediate effect of the parcelling-out has been subjected to a statistical examination of 8 manors, comprising the utilization of the area and the size of the animal husbandry before and after the subdivision, compared with surrounding, undivided areas in the same parishes during the same period; the grain areas in the sub-divided land are those which have undergone the greatest reduction, whereas the root-crop areas show the greatest increase in the sub-divided areas, where the grass-areas in the rotation have doubled, in contrast to a very small progress in the remaining properties of the parishes in question. The opposite is the case of the grass outside the rotation. The number of milch-cows has been quadrupled, the number of pigs has doubled, whereas, in this respect, the other properties of these parishes are in regression; as for the poultry, it has been trebled or quadrupled, whereas in the remaining properties it has only been doubled.

In consequence of the abolition of the communal property system most of the land-holders, as mentioned, left the villages. However, as the majorat subdivision generally comprised continuous areas the parcelled-out holdings came, in many cases, to form colonies, which, in many parts of the country, as a modern form of village, left their stamp on the cultivated landscape, not only as a distinct element from a point of view of habitational geography, but also topographically, resulting from an increased division of the farms; thereby, the whole landscape acquired a new aspect (figs. 2-3). The last traces of the finer structure of the natural landscape often disappeared totally or partly as a consequence of the levelling effect of the intensive cultivation on the surface relief. Thus, the subdivision has influenced not least the micro-topographical conditions: small pools have been filled out, fences have been demolished and small hills have been levelled. Denmark is tending to become a country with a trimmed nature; for instance, numerous relics of antiquity have been »changed into bread«, until and Act put an end to this vandalism.

The ancient castles of the parcelled-out majorats and the woods are still contributing to characterizing the landscape. Generally speaking, the woods have remained unaltered, either undivided in private property or transferred to the state forestry, while the main buildings principally have been used for social institutions, schools or museums.

LITERATURE

Betænkning (1896) angaaende Tilvejebringelse af Jordlodder for Landarbejdere, afg. af den i Henh. t. Lov af 13/4 1894 nedsatte Landbokommission.

Christensen, C. (1886-1891): Agrarhistoriske Studier I-II. København.

Clausager, A. (1943): Godsernes Beskatningsforhold, i Majoratsforeningen: Herregaardene og Samfundet. København.

Danmarks Riges Grundlov (1849) af 5. Juni.

Danske Lov (1665).

Erslev, Kr. (1898): Valdemarernes Storhedstid. Studier og Omrids. København.

Forordning af 15/3 1523.

Falbe-Hansen, V. & Scharling, N. (1888-1889): Danmarks Statistik I-II. København.

Hatt, G. (1935): Oldtidens Landsby i Danmark. I »Fortid og Nutid«, Bd. XI.

Jensen, Hans (1936): Dansk Jordpolitik 1757-1919. I. Udviklingen af Statsregulering og Bondebeskyttelse indtil 1810. København.

Jensen, Hans (1943): Godsejerklassen og Herregaardene i historisk Belysning. I: Majoratsforeningen: Herregaardene og Samfundet. København.

Jyske Lov 1241 (1941): Text med Oversættelse, Kommentar og Ordbog ved Peter Skautrup. Aarhus.

Kampp, Aa. H. (1956): Die dänische Agrarreform im 20. Jahrhundert. Geogr. Rundschau.

Kampp, Aa. H. (1959): Landbrugsgeografiske studier over Danmark (Some Agro-Geographical Investigations of Denmark). København.

Lov af 25/5 1671 om Grevernes Privilegier.

Lov af 25/5 1671 om Friherrernes Privilegier.

Lov af 28/7 1769 om Fællesskabets videre Ophævelse.

Lov af 24/3 1899 om Tilvejebringelse af Jordlodder for Landarbejdere.

Lov af 23/5 1902 om Fæste-, Leje- og Tjenestehuse.

Lov af 4/10 1919 om Afhændelse af de til Præsteembeder henlagte Jorder til Oprettelse af Husmandsbrug.

Lov af 4/10 1919 om Lens, Stamhuse og Fideikommisgodsers Overgang til fri Ejendom.

Lov af 4/10 1919 om Vilkaar for Bortsalg af Jord i offentlig Eje.

Lov af 25/3 1933 om Oprettelse af mindre Landbrug.

Lov af 4/6 1948 om Udstykning.

Lov af 1/11 1948 om udlaan til Statshusmandsbrug.

Mathiassen, T. (1931): Herregaarde og Godser i det 20. Aarhundrede. København.

Nørlund, Povl (1927): Jorddrotter paa Valdemarstiden. Festskrift for Kr. Erslev.

Pedersen, Henrik (1913): Ødegaarde i 1680-erne. Tillægshefte til Hist. Tidsskr. 8. Rk., IV Bd.

Pedersen, Henrik (1928): De danske Landbrug. Fremstillet paa Grundlag af Forarb. t. Chr. V's Matrikel 1688. København.

Steenstrup, Johs. C. H. R. (1874): Studier over Kong Valdemars Jordebog, efter trykte og utrykte Kilder. København.

Agricultural Geography and Regional Planning in a Marine Foreland

By N. Kingo Jacobsen

Abstract

The characteristics of the Tønder salt-marsh are illustrated by fragments of history, and by the physical geography. This is followed by examples from the research work carried out concerning the land ownership, the land use pattern, the soil conditions and the topography, all factors influencing highly a regional planning.

Tøndermarsken, the salt-marsh area along the river Vidå, is situated in the most southwestern corner of Denmark, just north of the Dano-German frontier. Nowadays it is a sparsely populated, an actually extensively utilized region that is technically underdeveloped, in that it is quite insufficiently supplied or totally devoid of such things as roads, fresh water, electricity, detail drainage and much else. Once upon a time it was a pioneer section. The fine old farm-houses, built upon mounds (Danish værfter = man-made elevations on which to build), suggest a certain measure of wealth in times gone by. The region comprises about 10.000 ha. in all, but the following remarks are confined to its western half. In several respects there is a marked difference between the early polders to the east, reclaimed in 1556, and the three outer, westernmost polders. The difference is manifested by the soils, the levels and the ages, but in addition the two regions are divided distinctly in an occupational- and a cultural-geographical sense. This holds good of their forms of settlement and land-use and of their ownership, as well as of their history of course in which the outermost polders form only part of the picture in more recent times (reclaimed 1692—1861). This does not include Trindsand, the ancient foreland to Vidding Herreds Gl. Kog (1436) — in the south-west border zone of Gl. Frederikskog.

Writing a summary of the more important features of this region, its position today and its prospects will necessitate a sporadic selection of certain phenomena. At this juncture I shall recount very briefly some historical facts before quoting examples from the most recent work of De danske Vade- og Marskundersøgelser (The Danish Tidal-Flat and Marsh Survey). The necessity of working out careful plans for developments in the future will also be stressed — plans which as far as possible should give proper consideration to natural factors (at any rate they should not be unknown) and also to the prevailing cultural and occupational structure which is greatly in need of modernization and change in step with the new possibilities. In Denmark today the marine foreland, of which this marsh region is but an insignificant trifle, is the only landscape complex embodying any future possibility of intensification and new cultivation. Reclamation in Denmark today is urgently necessary but the possibilities are limited. On this background the planning work of De danske Vade- og Marskundersøgelser is of particular interest as the approaches to the problems in fiord and meadow areas along every Danish stretch of coast can and should be analyzed along similar lines, so that we may be more or less ready when the thumb-screws of intensification receive another twist or two.

Tøndermarsken lies in the western part of the valley of the Vidå. Together with the tidal area and the range of dunes it forms the westernmost of the main geomorphological types that trisect South Jutland from north to south. Centrally in the region are extensive outwash plains with islands of older moraines. Rising near the east coast is the main Würm stationary line and the east coast itself is characterized by late-moraine deposits. The river Vidå with tributaries rises just west of the main stationary line. The total area drained through the sluice at Højer comprises 1225 km². of which ab. 125 km². are placed on the German side of the frontier.

The marsh is entirely of recent origin, created by the postglacial transgression which is still in process of development (1960, p. 78). Its situation on the south-east side of the North Sea signifies a tide of about 2 metres as well as passing of cyclones with wind changes from SW—NW as the predominating type of weather, in fact almost the sole type in gales (forces above 4 Beaufort). Such conditions cause the accumulation of water masses accompanied by disastrous floods, such as those which in 1362, 1634 and 1825 left permanent traces. Even present day technics are unable yet to give guarantees against recurrences, as was clearly demonstrated in Holland in 1953.

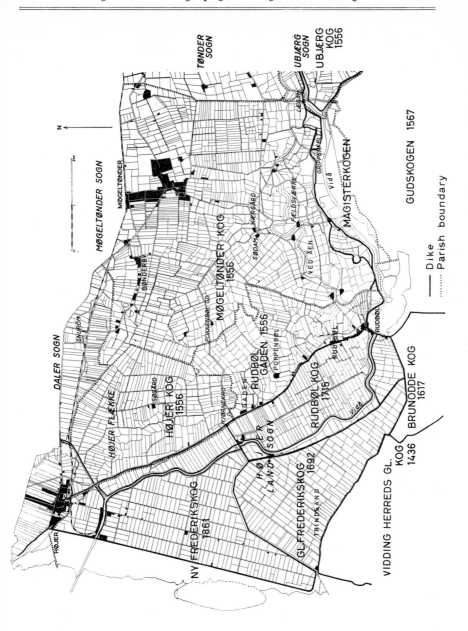

Fig. 1. Map of the western part of the salt-marsh area of Tønder (Tønder-marsken), indicating the position of the polders in relation to the parish boundaries. The pattern of ditches around the fields (Danish: fenner) differs with the age of the endikements. Further, the map elucidates old rivulets, dike-bursts and retirements of dikes.

As regards historical developments, Slesvig has lived a chequered sort of existence as the meeting place between Danish and German. Furthermore, westwards in the marshland and on the islands one encounters the Frisians, the earliest colonizers in this region. Slesvig is ancient Danish territory, segregated for the first time in 1115 as a duchy for Knud Lavard, the son of King Erik Ejegod. By this was set up the tradition of division among the king's sons which took place in 1241 after the death of Valdemar II, and in 1544 after the death of King Frederik I. In the course of time the Danish duchy of Slesvig was often coupled together with the German duchies of the Danish monarchs, especially Holstein. In periods, such as the first half of the 14th century, the entire region was owned by the dukes of Holstein. Contemporaneously with the changing political affiliations (the Danish king or the Gottorp dukes) Slesvig became more firmly associated with Holstein and Germanization spread, particularly via the Church, from south to north. In 1864 all Slesvig fell to Prussia and thus to the new Germany. In 1920 the northern half voted itself back to Denmark. One special problem of particular importance in the western districts was the monarchical enclaves, somewhat large areas of good strategical situation as regards trade routes on land and sea, which had belonged direct to the Danish crown in the period 1407—1864. Originally these areas belonged to the noble family of Limbek or to the see of Ribe. After 1683 the region was subject to Christian V's Danish Law, whereas the Duchy of Slesvig came under the Jutland Code given in 1241 by Valdemar II.

It was fairly late before man settled in Tøndermarsken. Nothing concrete is known about it, but to judge from the place-names there can have been no colonization before about 800—1000 A.D. (—mark, —bøl). There have been no archaeological excavations of the mounds, but borings have been made (the four types of mound shown in pl. II, sections A and B). Nothing definite has been found in the way of farms built on the flat ground such as those referred to by *van Giffen, W. Haarnagel* and *J. Bantelmann* for the Netherlands and German marshlands, but the mounds Ved Åen (section B) show three habitation strata, in the »hallig«* islands Rudbøl-Gaden two strata and in Gl.Frederikskog one stratum, which corresponds to the assumption that settlement in this region was late in coming and that the earliest habitations were made on artificial earth mounds: »værfter« along the banks of the Vidå (cf. pl. II B), Møgeltønder parish in the region Ved Åen. It is scarcely to be doubted that this colonization

---

* a "hallig" is an undiked salt-marsh island.

was made by Frisians. Between them and the Danish inhabitants of the geest lay miles of marshes in which a few geest blown-sand ridges rose like islands. The upper marsh sediments had not yet been deposited at that time. At about the same time or a little later came the colonization of the »hallig« area.

Rudbøl-Gaden. The first historical information about these settlements is contained in *Saxo Grammaticus'* description of the west coast of Slesvig, Frisia Minor (vol. 14), Bishop *Gunnerus'* account of a tithes dispute (1233) and in Avia ripensis (1340). The latter is a list of churches in the bishopric of Ribe and it contains the entry Anflod church (which must have stood at Rudbøl); subsequently it was deleted with the word; submersa, presumably in the flood of 1436 (*Cl. Rolfs*, p. 9).

It would thus seem that the Frisian colonization of the region comprised settlement on islands large and small along the shores of the Vidå. Apart from securing their dwellings the settlers built small dikes (summer dikes) to protect the cultivated fields around the mounds. It was much later that flood dikes (winter dikes) were put up in this region, and it was on the initiative of both king and duke who were eager to consolidate their access to, which also meant their control of Vidding Herreds Kog to the south, reclaimed in 1436. The inner polders on Tøndermarsken were diked in 1553--56 by a collaboration between the ducal parts and the monarchical enclave of Møgeltønderhus. This dike ran from Højer through Rudbøl eastwards to Grippenfelt, where the Vidå was crossed at Lægan, whereafter the dike continued southwards to Grelsbøl. This reclamation comprised in all nine polders, or about 7.000 ha. By this operation Tønder was cut off from the sea and acquired a port at Lægan. The diking of Gudskogen and Magisterkogen was completed in 1567, whereby Tønder's port was moved to Rudbøl. Till then the inhabitants had lived unprotected from tides and floods on the three hallig islands and in a row of mound dwellings along the banks of the Vidå as well as on small halligs where the marsh areas bordered upon the geest. The situation of these habitations is clear from the sections A and B on pl. II. The location of these settlements must have been determined by the somewhat higher levees and islands and the consequent possibilities of transport via rivers and tidal channels. After the areas were diked in, life was rather more secure, but more especially as regards agricultural utilization and transport by land, the subsequent centuries having records of many disastrous floods with breaches through the dikes, particularly in the area

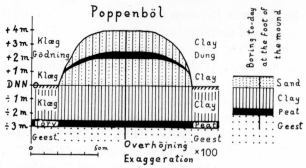

Fig. 2. Section through Poppenbøl "værft" (Cl. Rolf's description p. 234). The top of the mound is situated at ab. + 4 m. DNN, which is the flood-proof height. The previously inhabited stratum, at approximately + 2½ m. DNN, corresponds to a flood-proof height when the settlement was started. Borings at the foot of the mound show sand deposits of about 1 m. on top of the previous marsh surface (N. Kingo Jacobsen, 1956).

south of Højer and north of Rudbøl; at the latter locality when the dike was being restored in 1660 it had to be withdrawn several hundred metres over to the east side of the old hallig islands. This is visible in the course of the dike today and is also expressed through the reclamation rights west of this area, Rudbøl Kog. The following is a summary of the early settlements on the three hallig islands:

Gaden (northernmost hallig, cf. fig. 1)
1695 380 demat (= about 1 acre)
1769 5 bol on 4 mound, 5 houses with 52 inhabitants, $4^1/_{16}$ ploughs
1837 4 farms
1860 4 farms

Poppenbøl (middlemost hallig island, cf. fig. 1)
1695 216 demat
1769 2 bol and 2 houses with 22 inhabitants, $2^1/_5$ ploughs
1837 2 farms and 3 small holdings
1860 2 farms, 4 houses

Rudbøl (southernmost, largest hallig, cf. fig. 1)
1769 8 bol, 21 kaadnere and 12 inderster, in all 229 inhabitants, $4^2/_3$ ploughs
1837 5 farms, 27 kaadnere and 10 inderster, in all 51 houses
1860 6 farms, 51 houses.

Originally one »bol« was equal to one plough, i. e. one farm capable of being worked with one plough. About the year 1800 one plough was reckoned as equal to 100 demat.

Fig. 3. A view of the Tøndermarsken in the region "Ved Åen". The old rivulet is seen on the curving fence-lines of the fields. In the background the dwelling-mound "Fældsværre", the south-easternmost mound in the profile B, plate II.

Although it has entire areas of good farm land Tøndermarsken is only thinly populated today, about 7 inhabitants per km². There are several causes: the character of the land titles, faulty boundary drawing, bad roads, and so on. These phenomena could be clarified only by protracted studies in the field, for the reason that statistical material suffers from two grave defects: 1) where the material is most detailed the information is given parish-wise, whereas what is wanted is to segregate a geomorphological province which for many easily understood reasons lies transversally across the parish boundaries; 2) the actual subdivision and utilization of the lands of each farm cannot be elucidated statistically. In the following I shall give examples of how the details of utilization are charted as well as a single aspect of the very complicated ownership details. Equally important matters such as soils and levels will then be touched upon very briefly before the total picture is outlined in connection with the desiderata if a reasonable regional planning is to be carried through.

Land ownership

An account of the property rights is based upon information secured from the land registry as at 1st January 1954. The area investigated covers about 6.000 ha. in the possession of about 600 title-holders, a pattern which has been arranged in nine categories: five as to the domicile of the owners and four as to the properties held by institutions or the public. Here the marked difference between the earlier polders (1556) and the three outer ones becomes clearly manifest. In the old polders it is plainly to be seen that originally there were only two categories of owners: a) the land owned by people living on the neighbouring geest, a category, comprising all Højer Kog, Daler Sogn and the half of Møgeltønder Kog nearest the geest (peat basins and the blown-sand terrace nearest the geest), b) the land owned by people living in the salt-marsh, this category is consisting of Rudbøl-Gaden and the area Ved Åen as well as isolated blown-sand ridges in Møgeltønder Kog which stood out as hallig islands relatively early in time. Whereas the latter group of owners is chiefly formed of farms with well-designed fields, there is a highly complicated system within the areas owned by people of the neighbouring geest, a system that is most disturbing to a modern form of utilization. Conditions are otherwise in the three outer polders, where there is a veritable labyrinthine distribution of all nine title categories. This will be realized from the following description of the endowment-owned land (fig. 4), which is an excellent type specimen of the cultural-geographical peculiarities prevailing in these parts, peculiarities that are rooted in natural factors and today represent the chief reason why this particular part of the Tøndermarsk must be described as an extensively utilized region.

»Gold may perish but marsh land persists« is a familiar saying round Tønder way, and one of deplorably apt significance when one recalls the contributions made by public benefactors (of which there have been many at Tønder, Møgeltønder and Højer in the course of time) but squandered in the State bankruptcy of 1813, the Great War of 1914—18 and the subsequent inflation. It is only in cases such as the P. Struck Foundation, established in 1713 and consisting of 91 demat of marsh land, that the capital has been maintained and indeed doubled by the reclamation of Ny Frederikskog in 1861, and furthermore by the interest being secured against market fluctuations. It is clearly evident from fig. 4 that the endowment lands are to be found almost solely in the three outer polders: Gl. Frederikskog, reclaimed in 1692, Rudbøl Kog in 1715 and Ny Frederikskog in 1861. On the whole these lands are distributed among 23 endowments comprising 125 »fens« (fields fenced by ditches) totalling 355.1 ha. In the inner polders the only endowment lands are two fens in Rudbøl-Gaden, 3.8 ha., and 8 fens in Højer Flækkekommune of in all 14.4 ha., and these lands are either athletic grounds or small, newly established endowments made since 1920. The rest of the land has the following distribution: Rudbøl Kog, 35 fens of in all

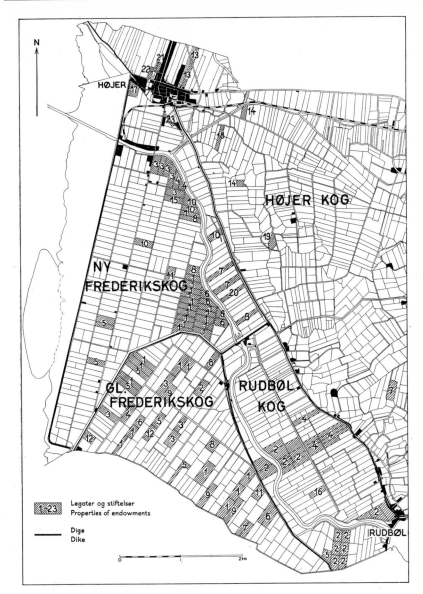

Fig. 4. Property rights as at 1st January 1954 in the Tøndermarsken, exemplified by endowment lands. Dikelines have been drawn to indicate the location of polders, of which most of the inner ones, diked in 1556, have been omitted, as no endowment lands are found here. The figures indicate the individual properties. The few small scattered units of different properties are seen in the inner polders. Further, Rudbøl Kog appears as a unit with other properties than those found in the Frederikskog's. Here, the properties in Gl. Frederikskog (1692) are similar to those in Ny Frederikskog (1861); however, in the old one the properties are scattered.

88.7 ha., Gl. Frederikskog, 34 fens totalling 125.9 ha., and Ny Frederikskog, 46 fens of 122.5 ha. in all.

The following brief enumeration of particulars *(Cl. Rolfs, 1926)* will illustrate the course of events which inter alia led to the appearance of the endowment lands and their special location:

The inner polders (Møgeltønder Kog, Højer Kog and Rudbøl-Gaden) were diked in 1556.

Gammel Frederikskog, in all 641 ha., was diked in 1692. The charter for Gl. Frederikskog was issued on 15th October 1690 by Duke Christian Albrecht, Gottorp, who afterwards transferred to the participants the property and reclaiming rights to the forelands north of Vidding Herreds Kog and the right to the diked lands free of charge for 17 years after the dike was finally completed. Thereafter the sum of a half rixdollar per demat was to become payable to the ducal treasury. Furthermore the participants and their heirs and descendants were granted complete occupational liberty. All participants with more than 60 demat of land, are principal participants with free hunting and fishing rights both within and without the dikes. Through an inspector they exercise the functions of police and administration in the polder and have the right to build their own church with advowson. Originally there were 5 principal participants, in 1859 there were 7 and in 1891 the number was increased to 10, among them being Tønder Orphanage and Tønder Hospital (see Ny Frederikskog).

Rudbøl Kog, 570 ha. in all, diked 1715. Charter issued by the ducal Bishop Christian August at Gottorp on 30th January 1712, giving the same rights as the charter for Gl. Frederikskog. The cost of diking was defrayed by Councillor Joh. Claussen (one third), Province Clerk Christian Bahr, County Clerk N. Hansen, Commissar Heinemann and Dike-Reeve Sibbers the second third, and the participants in the old Højer Kog the last third. The charter transfers to them Rudbøl foreland »vom Friedrichenkoog-Deichhörn westwärts und dann nach Hoyer Deich«. All the principal participants own more than 50 demat of land. They were nine originally: Councillor Claussen, County Inspector Bentzen, County Clerk Hansen, County Clerk von Sallern, Bailiff von Gunderoth, Commissar Heinemann or Dike-Reeve Sibbers, Estate Bailiff Muhl at Rodenæs, Andreas Todsen and Sønnich Nissen, Freesmark. In 1859 there were three principal participants and in 1891 only two, one of which was the Gunderoth Foundation at Aabenraa.

Ny Frederikskog, in all 863 ha., diked in 1861. On 24th March

1859 it was announced that the Gl. Frederikskog charter issued in 1690, in so far as it was unchanged or had been amended by later common laws and decisions, was to be regarded as applying in the same measure as to Gl. Frederikskog, so that the foreland now lying beyond the polder was to become the property of the polder participants. The debt incurred by diking was repaid in the 17 years during which the polder was free of taxes under the charter. Thus the Gl. Frederikskog charter also applies to Ny Frederikskog and both polders are also joint owners of the foreland which, however, has now been transferred to the Danish State (by agreement in 1956). In 1891 there were the following principal participants of the Frederikskog's: 1. Crown fiscal, 2. H. R. Angel, Hohenwarte, 3. Julius Brodersen at Frederikskog, 4. Staatraat Thomas Todsen at Flensborg, 5. J. Hinrichsen at Østerterp, 6. N. A. Paysen at Vimmelsbøl, 7. J. A. Lund at Ballum, 8. Cl. Clausen at Svenstrup, 9. The Orphanage at Tønder, 10. The Hospital at Tønder.

These few particulars make it evident that land titles in these parts are extremely complicated. This is further exemplified by the fact that the chartered polders were subject to the Eiderstedt tribunal up to 1854, whereas the Jutland Code applied to the ducal parts of Højer rural parish and Højer urban commune and the law of Christian V to the monarchical enclaves including Møgeltønder parish. This played a part for instance in the settlement of the action regarding the Kannikhus entailed estate, when it was decided that the paragraphs to be applied were those of the Eiderstedt tribunal.

A statistical investigation of the utilization of the lands in Tøndermarsken was made for the years of 1948, 1949, 1954 and 1957, by means of counts in each fenne (field). For the endowment lands it appeared that they were used solely for grazing, with the exception of 5—10 ha. (the fens in Rudbøl-Gaden and the easternmost ones in Rudbøl polder). The grazing is utilized by about 600 beef cattle and about 600 sheep as well as 25—30 horses and 25—30 dairy cows. In this connection it must be stated that Tønder Commune, which has the administration of large parts of the endowment lands, decided in February 1955 that in future the fens were to be let out for four-year periods.

Particulars of some of the foundations are:

1. *Peter Struck Foundation.* Peter Struck was a lace dealer and councillor at Tønder, he died in 1713. He was brought up as a semi-orphanage child in poor circumstances. The foundation comprises

27 fens totalling 91 ha., 11 of them being in Gl. Frederikskog (45.2 ha.) and 16 in Ny Frederikskog (45.8 ha.). Associated with the orphanage at Tønder which also possesses 7 fens of in all 17.6 ha., of which 3 are in Gl. Frederikskog (9.6 ha.) and 4 in Ny Frederikskog (8 ha.).

2. *The Günderoth's Dwelling-house Foundation and the Günderoth School Foundation, Aabenraa.* Set up in 1743 and 1747 by Captain H. von Günderoth, his wife Sophie née von Saldern, and his brother Master of the Stables E. C. von Günderoth. This land, in all 23 fens totalling 65.7 ha., is mostly situated in Rudbøl Kog: 22 fens aggregating 62.1 ha. and in Gl. Frederikskog: 1 fen of 3.6 ha. The land in Rudbøl Kog was conveyed to H. von Günderoth on 14th January 1752 from Councillor Joh. Claussen, who had defrayed one third of the cost of diking Rudbøl Kog.

3. *Tønder Hospital.* Founded in 1527 by King Frederik I. Proprietor of in all 9 fens of 31.7 ha., of which 4 are in Gl. Frederikskog (15.9 ha.) and 5 in Ny Frederikskog (15.8 ha.).

4. *The Leo Foundation.* H. F. Leo, dealer in spices at Tønder, died 1812, bequeathed 60 demat of land to the hospital. The foundation comprises in all 14 fens of 28.6 ha., mostly in Rudbøl Kog: 11 of in all 21.4 ha., one of 3.9 ha. in Gl. Frederikskog and two of 3.3 ha. in Ny Frederikskog.

5. *The Kannikhus entailed estate.* Kannikhus Farm is situated in the west part of Bønderby (Møgeltønder parish). The trust was set up in 1787 by Peter Andersen and wife and comprised a number of areas in the marsh-land, and two-thirds of these were left to the direct heirs of the Andersen family, whereas the heirs of Hans Brodersen, Mrs. Andersen's brother, were to have one-third. The estate to be wound up when the third generation of the family is extinct. The last person of the third Andersen generation died in 1947. The courts have now decided that the will of 1787 also applies to the third generation of the Brodersen family, of which five persons are still living, all in Germany. It must be observed, however, that the total area of the estate within the Tøndermarsken has decreased from 81.9 ha. in 1876 to 25.7 ha. in 1954, comprising 8 fens, of which four are in Gl. Frederikskog (14.3 ha.), one in Rudbøl Kog (2.5 ha.) and three in Ny Frederikskog (8.8 ha.).

These five examples illustrate the character of the endowments and their purpose. It should be added that some of these endowments own extensive areas in the marsh-lands south of the present frontier. Some of this land is occasionally exchanged for German-owned land in Tøndermarsken; for instance, the Popsen Foundation in 1954 acquired a further 10 ha. in exchange, 4½ ha. in 1955 and 3 ha. in 1956, and that the Richtsen Foundation also received 10 ha. in exchange in 1955.

Utilization of the land

The area investigated covers about 5000 ha., of which 2500 ha. were diked in 1556 and about 2000 ha. in the new polders. Outside the 1861 dike is a marine foreland of about 500 ha. How the land is utilized was mapped on the spot in July 1949 and included the following crops: oats, barley, wheat, rye, mixed grains (oats and barley) or (oats, barley and rye), root crops, flax and a little potatoes and other crops. The grass fields are used as pasture land, hay fields or grass in crop rotation. On the day when the registration was made every head of cattle in the fields was included.

In *the old polders,* diked in 1556, about half the area is ploughed land. About 75% of this is occupied by oats, followed by barley, wheat and root crops (7% each), the rest having flax and horsebeans. The pasture land occupies the other half with 1800 head of beef cattle, 100 horses, 1500 sheep and about 500 dairy cows. *Gl. Frederikskog* (1692), about 641 ha., has only 5 ha. of ploughed land (oats and flax). The rest is pasture: 1100 head of beef cattle, 60 horses, 300 sheep and a few dairy cows. *Rudbøl Kog* (1715), about 570 ha., ploughed land about 50 ha. (oats 35 ha., barley 5 ha., wheat 5 ha. and root crops 5 ha.). The rest, about 520 ha., is pasture land with 600 head of beef cattle, 50 horses, 500 sheep and a few dairy cows. *Ny Frederikskog* (1861), about 863 ha., with about 25 ha. ploughed land (oats). Most of the area is used for pasture: 1400 head of beef cattle, 100 horses, 550 sheep and 25 dairy cows. *The foreland* is utilized partly as hay fields and partly as pasture. It covers about 500 ha. with 1650 sheep and 22 head of beef cattle.

The general impression is of extensive agriculture, especially in the new polders; a more intensive system is employed in the area close to the geest (the older moraine), as may be seen from the choice of crops (reflecting a rotation system) and the keeping of dairy cattle. The isolated farms in the middle of the old polders have a rotation system of crops mixed with grass land for sheep. Fig. 5

illustrates this distribution of the crops by means of a section north of Rudbøl, comprising parts of Gl. Frederikskog, Rudbøl Kog and some parts of the inner polders. It will be seen from this and the figures given above that the marsh-land is utilized mainly for grazing, especially in the outer polders and other areas with badly marked-out boundaries and owners living at a distance. Here the utilization must be described as extensive with a low hectare yield: 20—30 crop units per annum compared with 60—100 crop units per hectare in rational pasturing *(S. Tovborg Jensen, 1956)*. Moreover, areas under field culture have too small a yield on account of the poor drainage while simultaneously the system of open ditches takes up a disproportionately large area. A drive along the Højer-Rudbøl dike (1556) gives a very clear impression of the difference in the land use in the old and the new polders, and of the intermediate position of Rudbøl Kog, due especially to the soil conditions. One will also notice the entire different designs of the ditch and canal system in the two regions. East of the Højer-Rudbøl dike the whole picture is characterized by old channels and creeks (loer), whereas in the outer polders the system is regularly rectangular. This touches upon one of the most delicate of the marsh-land problems: drainage. Since the very first diking this problem has been in the forefront, solved only partially by the construction of sluices. Contributory factors have been and still are the rising sea level with the consequent sedimentation at ever increasing levels. This is clearly evidenced by the relatively high location of the new polders compared with the earlier diking. The problem was only solved effectively by the artificial drainage of 1929; but the four pumping stations: Lægan, Hjørnekro, Snurom and Højer, only provide for the main drainage, making use of the river Vidå and the lake Rudbøl Sø as reservoirs when the sluice at Højer is closed owing to bad weather. This sluice is regulated automatically. Smaller areas along the Vidå, for instance west of the stream in Rudbøl Kog and east of the stream in Ny Frederikskog, are protected by lower river dikes in order to act as emergency reservoirs during protracted gales in periods of heavy rain. The basin of the Vidå extends right over to Aabenraa on the east coast and it takes only two to four days for the run-off to appear in the lower course of the Vidå. What is more, the German pumping station Verlath (Rudbøl Sø) also uses the Vidå as an outlet for the Gudskog area south of the frontier. The detail draining still proceeds chiefly through open ditches, supplemented in the western, high part of the inner polders and in the outer

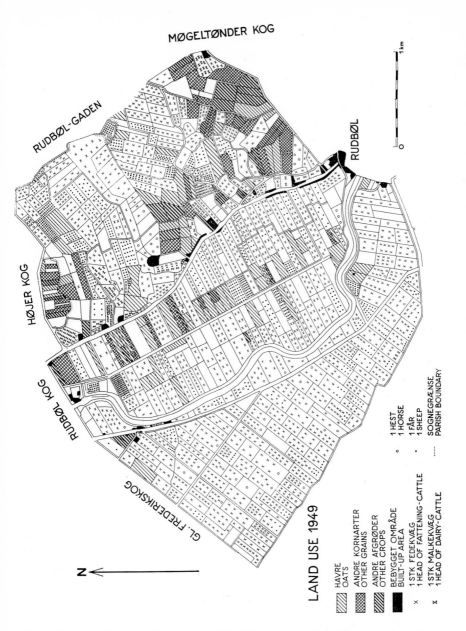

Fig. 5. Section of the land-use map 1949 of Tøndermarsken. The area comprises parts of Gl. Frederikskog (1692), Rudbøl Kog (1715), and the old polders Rudbøl-Gaden—Møgeltønder Kog (1556), west and north of the village Rudbøl. The quite different types of land-use are clearly seen.

polders by surface channels corresponding to the ditches (grøble-render) of the foreland. The cattle are also watered through the ditches, which prevents the drying of the soil in the winter months with the result that spring sowing is delayed three or four weeks. Soil improvement work, taking due regard to local levels and the character and spread of the sedimentary deposits, is therefore necessary. Cultivation experiments in connection with it is already being carried on by the State Marsh Experimental Station at Hohenwarte (Højer).

Soil types and area morphology

Soil types.

It was stated above that soil types and surface topography have been mapped. About 30.000 borings have been made for the purpose of investigating problems relating to the structure, stratification and genesis of these soils *(N. Kingo Jacobsen, 1956, 1960)*. As a result it has been ascertained that the salt-marsh consists of basins to varying depths containing deposits of a variety of types, for instance fat clays are encountered, as well as sand of different characters, mud and peat. This all combines to make the area a mosaic of different landscapes, even if to the student in the field it looks almost the same. It is of practical importance to know about this, because it has a bearing upon the use of the land, the construction of roads, the foundations of farm houses etc. Another important thing is that drainage and cultivation of the salt-marshes result in the immediate shrinking of the soil. Other problems include sodium soils of bad structure and acid soils due to oxidation of FeS which gives ochre and sulphuric acid. In this connection it is important to realize that the salt-marshes are young soils composed of sedimentary strata of varying age, depths and origin, i. e. different facies types. The physico-chemical characteristics of these soils are determined partly by the content of organic matter, partly by the content of $CaCO_3$, chloride, salt cations, pH values and partly by the particle sizes and the packing of the sediments *(Kjeld Rasmussen, 1956)*. These characteristics are further influenced by climate and drainage conditions as are the biological factors working too.

Surface topography.

Levellings have been carried out to an accuracy of about 1 cm. Surface spot heigts have been determined at each 25 m. in a net, and contour lines have been drawn. In the topography the high-lying geest stands out very distinctly, as do the dikes and the mounds.

The river Vidå is also a clear feature, as well as the old rivulets
along which are the mounds with the old farms. Other very low
areas are to be seen in the south-east section, caused by breaches in
the old dike of 1556. In Rudbøl Kog the old course of the Vidå is
also low-lying, as are the small former lakes at Søgård and north of
Nørregård farm.

Most of the old polders and Rudbøl Kog lie between 0 and + 1 m.
DNN. Very clear is a low basin north of Pokkenbøl farm, which is
one of the peat basins where shrinkage has started after the pumping of the Tønder salt-marsh in 1929. Pokkenbøl stands high on a
prominent islet in the sub-surface, easily to be seen in the contours to
the south-east of the farm. The old 1556 dike running from Højer
to Rudbøl has been breached several times north and south, as may
be observed on the contour lines west of the dike and also from the
turns in connection with the retirement of the dike. The northernmost part south-east of Højer is high-lying according to intruding
sand masses during storm floods. Gl. Frederikskog has a high part
close to the German frontier. This is a very old foreland from the
polder just south of the frontier. The rest of Gl. Frederikskog lies
rather low as a result of the influence of the river. Ny Frederikskog
lies very high, + 1½ m. — + 2 m. DNN. Along the high parts running
N-S through the middle of the polder an old coastline comes into
view. The foreland lies high too, + 1.2 m. — + 1.5 m. DNN.

It is a common experience that new polders lie higher than old ones
as a consequence of the relative subsidence of the land. In this area
the range of the tide is about 2 m., normally from — 1 m. to + 1 m.
DNN. In bad weather water masses may be stored in the wadden sea
and high water may reach about + 4 m. DNN. The height of the sea
dike is + 6.5 m. DNN. With a topography such as this the drainage of
the area is as mentioned rather difficult.

Regional planning

In the foregoing I have indicated by example and implication some
of the problems which will need searching investigation if the salt-
marsh areas along the estuary of the Vidå are to become the colonization territory with intensive cultivation and dense habitation to
which its natural potentialities entitle it, by application of present-
day science and technics. The realization of such an aim will necessitate long-term planning based upon a thorough-going analysis of
conditions today in every respect. As also appears from the examples
figs. 4 and 5, the legislature must be empowered to cause a re-

organization of the prevailing systems of ownership and use. Such an organization should proceed gradually, as indeed is already being done; but the drawing up of a general plan provides possibilities of taking convenient advantage of any change, great or small, in the existing conditions, whereby the aim will be attained with the least possible delay. In actual fact plans are already in existence for the safety of the houses, the elaboration of the road system, the parcelling-out of areas owned by the State and for further reclamation. The next step should be plans for detail drainage, cultivation and rounding off of property borders — of course in conjunction with general financial plans. Geographical researches of the kind outlined above can enable several of the above detail plans to be realized. The material from Tøndermarsken has not been fully worked up as yet and certain problems need further elucidation; but all in all it should be possible before long to assemble satisfactory long-term plans for the development of the region.

LITERATURE

Andresen, Ludwig (1940): Bäuerliche und landesherrliche Leistung in der Landgewinnung im Amte Tondern bis 1630. Westküste 2:2/3, pp. 85–149. Heide.

Fink, Troels (1941): Udskiftningen i Sønderjylland indtil 1770. København.

Jacobsen, N. H. (1937): Skibsfarten i Det Danske Vadehav. Kulturgeogr. Skr. 2. Medd. f. Skall.-Lab. V. København.

Jacobsen, N. H. (1938): De gamle kongerigske Enklavers Oprindelse. Geogr. Tidsskr. 41:2, pp. 171–189. Medd. f. Skall.-Lab. VI. København.

Jacobsen, N. Kingo (1953): Mandø. En klit-markø i Vadehavet. Geogr. Tidsskr. 52, pp. 134–146. Medd. f. Skall.-Lab. XIV. København.

Jacobsen, N. Kingo (1956): Jordbundsundersøgelser i Tøndermarsken. Geogr. Tidsskr. 55, pp. 106–146. Medd. f. Skall.-Lab. XV. København.

Jacobsen, N. Kingo (1960): Types of Sedimentation in a Drowned Delta Region. Examples from the Salt-Marsh Area at Tønder. Geogr. Tidsskr. 59. København.

Jensen, S. Tovborg (1955): Om Nordsømarsken og dens landøkonomiske udnyttelse. Tidsskr. f. Planteavl 59:2, pp. 1–37. København.

Rasmussen, Kjeld (1956): Investigations on Marsh Soils and Wadden Sea Sediments in the Tønder Region. Geogr. Tidsskr. 55, pp. 147–170. Medd. f. Skall.-Lab. XV. København.

Rolfs, Cl. (1926): Geschichte des Kirchspiels und Fleckens Hoyer. Aus dem Baltischen Historischen Forschungsinstitut. Kiel.

Schröder, Johs. v. (1837): Topographie des Herzogthums Schleswig I–II. Schleswig.

Trap, J. P. (1864): Statistisk-topographisk Beskrivelse af Hertugdømmet Slesvig. I–II. København.

URBANIZATION

The population of Denmark

By Aage Aagesen

Abstract

*The population geography of Denmark to-day is dominated by the
urbanization. The cultivation of the former heath-areas was accomplished
about 1920, and the agricultural population is decreasing in almost all
parts of the country. The economic structure of the population and the
various types of employment in the Danish towns and urban agglomerations are further dealt with.*

According to the latest estimate Denmark has 4.565.054 inhabitants, out of which a number of 28.298 lie in Greenland, 32.456
in the Faroe Islands and 4.504.300 in Denmark proper. The average
density of the population is as follows:

Denmark proper .... 103.3 inhabitants per sq. km.
Faroe Islands .... 22.7 inhabitants per sq. km.
Greenland: .... 0.01 inhabitants per sq. km.

The following text only deals with Denmark proper.

In Jutland, inclusive of the neighbouring isles, the number of
inhabitants is 1.902.093 (44% of the total population), out of which
205.167 live in North Slesvig. The Danish isles have a total population number of 2.379.182, out of which 1.800.176 live in Zealand and
in the neighbouring small isles; 395.535 live in Funen, 135.337 in
Lolland-Falster and 48.134 in Bornholm. Denmark proper comprises
in total 100 inhabited and 348 uninhabited isles.

No less than 3.070.318 of the Danish population live in towns or
in other urban agglomerations. Copenhagen proper (not identical
with the municipal-administrative Copenhagen) has 1.227.126 inhabitants = 27.6% of the total population. Other big towns are:
Århus (165.522), Odense (120.525) and Ålborg (111.726). In Jutland
should further be mentioned the following towns: Randers (53.314),

Esbjerg (52.877), Horsens (38.720), Vejle (37.619), Kolding (34.211)
and Fredericia (27.910). In Zealand the predominant position of
Copenhagen prevents the development of other big cities. However,
Roskilde (29.556) and Helsingør (28.973), which must be considered
as remote suburbs of the Capital, are of a certain importance. In
Funen, the town of Odense, with has a central position, plays the
same role as does Copenhagen in Zealand. The second largest town
of Funen, Svendborg (24.058), has part of its hinterland in the isles
situated to the south of Funen. Neither Lolland-Falster, nor Bornholm have towns with more than 25.000 inhabitants.

The great average density of population (251.0 per sq.km.) in
Zealand and in the neighbouring small islands is a natural consequence of the fact that Copenhagen is situated in this area. In the
regions outside the influence of the sphere of the Capital, however
the density in Zealand is not greater than elsewhere in East Denmark.

In Bornholm the average density is 82.8 inhabitants per sq.km., in
Lolland-Falster 74.5, in Funen 116.2 and in Jutland 66.4

Map no. 1 shows *the average density in the smallest units:* the
parishes, based on a census of 7th November 1950.

This map gives a striking impression of the distinct difference
between the isles and East Jutland on one side and Central Jutland
and West Jutland on the other side.

In the eastern part of the country the extremely varied densities
compose a very disturbed picture. Outside the towns only a few big
urban agglomerations have densities of more than 200 inhabitants
per sq.km. The influence of a big number of small agglomerations
situated in close proximity to the traffical junctions causes big
differences in the density. The total picture of the western part of
Denmark is much more stable, the country districts having generally a density of between 20 and 40 per sq.km.

The frontier zone between these two regions is, for the greater
part, identical with the ice-border of the last glaciation (Würm).
Thus, the region of East Denmark with the heterogeneous, though
mostly rather great density, is almost completely coinciding with
the extent of the young morainic areas.

The smallest densities are found in the dune area along the
western coast of Jutland and, further, in the diluvial heath plains
to the west of the main stationary line of the ice from the Würm
glaciation. Along the most important arterial roads the density
increases, for instance between Copenhagen and Roskilde, in Funen

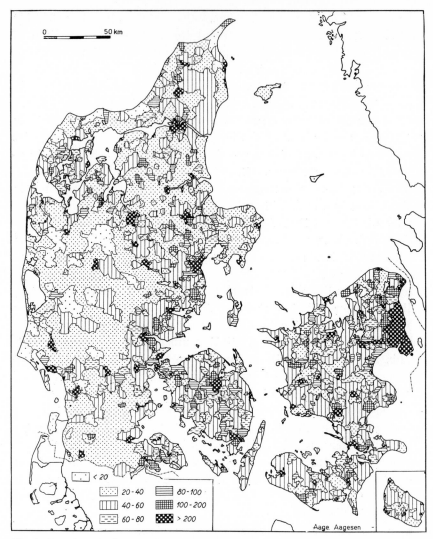

Fig. 1. Density of the population in Denmark 1950. Inhab. per square km. in each parish.

between Odense and Middelfart and in Jutland between the towns situated at the eastern firths.

From a geographical point of view the population of Denmark has undergone so great changes during the last hundred years, as never before; the causes of this are chiefly to be sought in the alterations of the economic structure.

From 1860 to 1880 the Danish population grew from 1.608.362 inhabitants to 1.969.039 = 22.5%, and from 1880 to 1901 it grew to

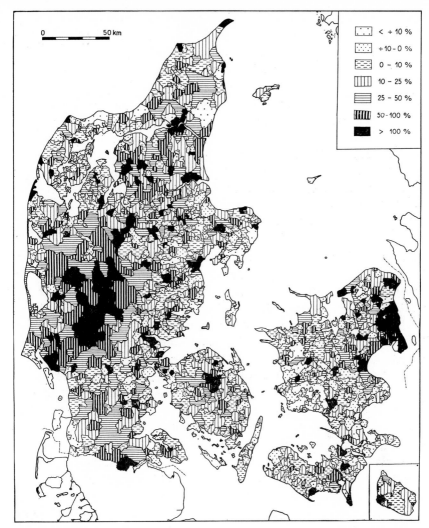

Fig. 2. Net population-increase or -decrease 1901—1950 in Danish parishes.

2.449.540 = 24.4%. However, this growth was not uniformly spread; Copenhagen increased by 60% in the first period and by 74% in the second; for the other towns the corresponding figures are 36% and 66%. This considerable increase of the population in the towns is primarily a result of the industrial development, which was first perceptible in the Capital, later on in the small towns. During the period from 1860 to 1880 the improved economical conditions also resulted in an increase of the rural population, particularly great on the heath in Jutland (about 50%). This growth must be attributed to the activity of Det danske Hedeselskab (the Association for the Cultivation of the Heath). However, several parishes in East-Denmark have in this period a decreasing population as a consequence of the mechanization of agriculture, the adoption of new commercial and industrial lines in the towns, the agricultural crisis in the transition period from export of grain to export of milk products and, finally, the emigration to overseas countries. This tendency was intensified during the subsequent period, where the majority of the parishes in the isles and in East Jutland showed a decreasing population figure, whereas the cultivation of the heath conditioned a continued growth of population in Central Jutland and partly in West Jutland.

Map fig. 2 shows *the population changes in the period 1901-1950.* For each parish the net increase or the net decrease is represented. The regions marked in black have, during the first half of the century, more than doubled their population. This is true of Copenhagen inclusive of its suburbs, the greater part of the big towns and of Central Jutland, where the cultivation of the moorland has developed agglomerations of a certain importance. An increase to more than the double of the population has also taken place in various rural parishes, especially in those which in their capacity of junctions in the railway network offered particularly great possibilities of economic and industrial activity. The new agglomerations which have arisen at these junctions have gradually developed as local centres for the commerce and for the small industry and, as a natural consequence of this, have been charged with certain urban functions. However, the fact that these new urban agglomerations are densely situated and the restricted size of their hinterland set a natural maximum limit to their number of inhabitants. The increase of their population figure gradually comes to a standstill, first in the islands and in East Jutland, where the growth could be noticed already about 1860-1870, and now also in the other parts of Jutland.

Meanwhile, in some of these agglomerations various industries have risen, the products of which are sold in the whole of Denmark and even for export; in such cases the rise of the population figure is bound to continue. Thanks to their growing industrial importance, some of these new agglomerations have now advanced to become towns (Herning, Silkeborg, Brønderslev, Skjern, Struer); others are now town-like agglomerations with 3.000 to 5.000 inhabitants (Brande, Grindsted, Hadsund, Ikast, Odder, and Vejen in Jutland, Haslev and Hundested in Zealand); 19 others have reached 2.000 to 3.000

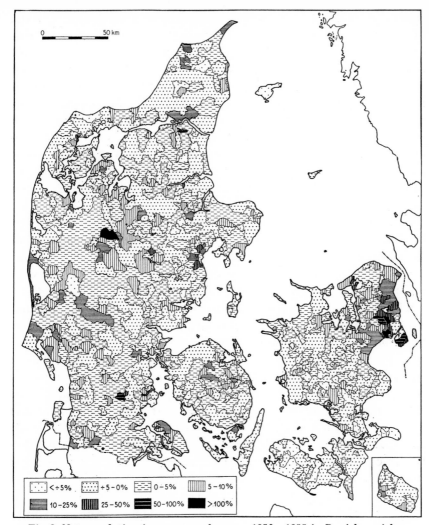

Fig. 3. Net population-increase or -decrease 1950—1955 in Danish parishes.

inhabitants, and 90 of these agglomerations now number 1.000 to 2.000 inhabitants.

Map fig. 2 further shows *the growth of the population at the German-Danish frontier,* where, after 1920, the increase of the number of civil servants occupied in the frontier services and the new employment possibilities have brought about this augmentation of the population figure.

An interesting factor is *the decrease of the population in the greater part of the small islands,* peninsulas and certain other coastal zones, where the traffic conditions are poor. This reduction is, at places, very important, for instance in the North Frisian Islands (Fanø and Mandø 18%; Rømø 17%); in Ærø 15%, (in the town of Marstal 37%). This decline becomes even more noteworthy when compared with the augmentation of the total population from 2.4 millions in 1901 to 4.3 millions in 1950. The above-mentioned tendency has been encouraged by the mechanization of agriculture, which makes the youth in the rural districts available for other activities — especially the industry — concentrated along the traffical roads and particularly in the junctions. The majority of the small islands, the peninsulas and many coastal regions have very modest traffic facilities and do not play any part — anyhow only a small — in the general commercial and industrial progress in the twentieth century. In Denmark the rural exodus often has character of a *flight from the coast*. An increase of the coastal population is only noticeable at places situated in proximity to the ports and in connection with fishing hamlets or other commercial centres.

The increase of the population in the heaths of Central Jutland, which has still been going on, also in the twentieth century, is only to a small extent attributable to immigration from other parts of the country; it is rather a question of a considerable reproduction of the local population, of which the youth had so abundant commercial end economic possibilities at their home place that the majority of them stayed there; therefore, it is evident that this part of the population has not contributed to the rural exodus. However, since about 1940 the growth of the heath-populations seems to be gradually coming to a standstill. This fact allows to suppose that the future development of the population living on the old heath plains will hardly differ from the other agricultural regions.

This assumption is confirmed by the development which has been going on since 1950. Map. fig. 3 shows the population changes in the period 1950-1955. During these five years the total population of Denmark proper increased by 3.9% = 167.126 persons. Some municipalities have more than redoubled their population in this period: Herlev and Brøndbyerne in *the outer suburbs* of Copenhagen, and Grove, with a military airport, on the heath plains in Central Jutland. Other regions showing a considerable increase are those around the Capital and other big towns, such as Århus, Ålborg, etc., while the town-districts proper are stagnating or decreasing. Other regions with increasing population figure are found in localities with an economic activity of a certain importance, such as the northern part

Fig. 4. The economic structure of the population in Danish communes.
Signatures: see the text page 318.

of the islands of Als, around Grindsted, and at other places. The
districts which are essentially rural have a rather stable population
figure, sometimes a slow decrease. Those which, from a traffical
point of view, must be regarded as remote, such as small islands,
peninsulas and some coastal regions, very often show a decrease of
more than 1% annually. It is typical of the population changes 1950-
1955 that in a given region the development is common to a number
of parishes and municipalities, because the modern transport fa-

cilities make the choice of the place of dwelling rather independent of the place of work. The construction of a new factory, harbour or airport inevitably causes an increase of the population, not only in the municipality in question, but also to a great extent in the surrounding area.

Denmark is often, among foreigners, cited as a typical example of an agricultural country; this statement is correct in so far as about 60% of our export is composed of agricultural products. However, if we regard the compositions of the Danish population under economic and commercial aspects we get quite a different impression. In 1950 the distribution of the population in the various branches was as follows: Only 23.7% were employed in agriculture (inclusive of gardening, forestry and fishing), whereas 34.7% were occupied in industry (inclusive of building activity 7.7%), 13% in commerce, 7.1% in traffic and 8.5% in the Administration or in private enterprises; 11.4% are »unemployed«; i.e. they live on their fortune, on their pension or on government subsidy.

This economical structure is new in the classical agricultural Denmark. As late as in 1901, 40% of the population earned their living in agriculture, and as late as in 1930 the figure of the agricultural population (31.2%) was higher than the industrial population (28.6%). In 1940 this picture had changed to such a degree that only 27.7% of the total population were employed in agriculture, whereas 33.4% worked in industry. At the same time the farm-population, which in 1930 had reached a maximum (1.109.093), began to decrease, giving a figure in 1950 as low as 1.013.800.

Map fig. 4 shows the economic structure of the population with the commune as a basis:

Sign 1: parishes of a pronounced agricultural structure, where more than 75% of the active population are employed in agriculture.

Sign 2: parishes of an agricultural structure, in which 50-75% of the active population work in agriculture.

Sign 3: mixed agricultural parishes, in which agriculture still plays the predominant role, though it only employs less than 50%.

Sign 4: mixed industrial parishes, where industry has the predominance, though only employing less than 50% of the active population.

Sign 5: industrial parishes with more than 50% employed in industry.

No sign: other types, such as commercial-traffical parishes (for instance the navigation parishes in Fanø, the ferry-towns Korsør

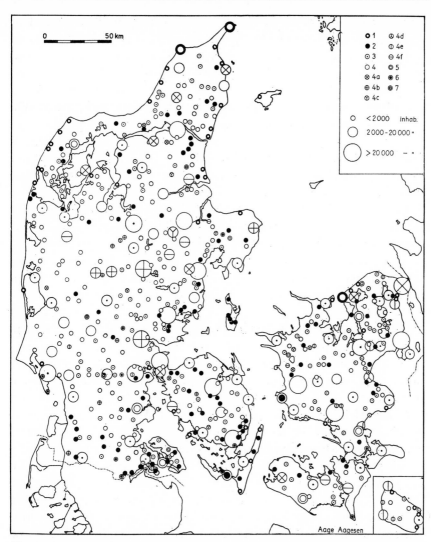

Fig. 5. The economic structure in Danish towns and other urban agglomerations. Sign. 1: fishing towns, 2: agricultural towns, 3: mixed towns, 4: mixed industrial towns, 4a: iron-industrial towns, 4b: textile-industrial towns, 4c: wood-industrial towns, 4d: chemical-industrial towns, 4e: stone and clay-industrial towns, 4f: foodstuff-industrial towns, 5: commercial towns, 6: traffical towns, 7: administrative towns etc.

and Nyborg at the Great Belt; the commercial commune Gentofte, a suburb of Copenhagen), or administration-parishes.

The predominantly agricultural parishes are found first of all in West Jutland, in particular to the north of the Limfjord and in the old cultivated land along the west coast, where there is a certain

tendency of preserving the traditional working methods; this tendency, however, is less common in the former heath plains.

The degree of industrialization is greatest in parishes with favourable traffic conditions, whereas a big number of small isles, peninsulas and other parishes with poor traffic facilities and with a
resulting decrease of the population figure only have reached a
modest degree of industrialization.

Map fig. 5 shows the types of economic structure in the Danish
towns and in other urban agglomerations.

Most of the fishing towns (sign 1) are small; (they are found
at most coastal localities).

The towns characterized by agriculture and gardening (sign 2) are
rather small too; they are rare in the old heath-areas, where the
farms are scattered, whereas they are frequent in East Denmark,
a region with many villages. It is mostly former farmers' villages,
which in their capacity of traffic or railway-junctions have acquired
an urban-like aspect without having lost their agricultural structure.

Sign no. 3 shows mixed agglomerations, in which no special
employment is predominant. This type of agglomeration comprises
first of all middle-size towns in the parts of the country where the
industry is less developed, for instance in West Jutland and in North
Slesvig.

In industrial agglomerations more than half of the active population is employed in trade and industry.

Sign 4 represents mixed industrial agglomerations, where no industrial group is dominating, contrary to the one-sided industrial
agglomerations (sign 4a-4b), in which one particular industry employs more than 50% of the industrial workers. All the Danish big
towns and the greater part of the middle-size towns must be reckoned among the mixed industrial agglomerations. The most important
types of employment in the one-sided industrial agglomerations are:
metal, textile, chemical, wood, and food industries.

In Denmark the agglomerations where commerce and traffic or
the Administration and the schools are predominant are rare. Among
the agglomerations which owe their existence to the traffic, Korsør
at the Great Belt and the old »skipper towns« in Fanø and in the isles
to the south of Funen are standing out.

Finally, to complete the picture of the Danish population, a few
supplementary particulars are given: In Denmark there is an excess
of women (1955: 101.5 women for each 100 men). However, while

this excess of women is of a considerable size in the towns (111.2 women for each 100 men) the situation is opposite in the country, where the number of women only amounts to 93.2 for each 100 men. The migration tendency from the country to the towns is greater among the young women than among the young men, partly because the industrial development within agriculture offers less possibilities for the women than for the men, whereas the opposite is the case in the towns, where many industries prefer the cheaper female labour.

The size of the household is, as an average for the whole country, 3.04 persons. There exists a distinct difference between the urban population (2.83 in each household) and the rural population (3.62 persons in each household). In North-West Jutland there are parishes with an average of 4.30 persons in each household. Since the beginning of the industrialization in the last decades of the nineteenth century the average size of the households has undergone an appreciable decrease.

In the period 1952-1954 the average number of liveborn children for each 1.000 inhabitants was 17.7 with 9.0 deaths; this means that the excess of births amounts to 8.7 $^0/_{00}$ or more than the double of the corresponding figure in Great Britain. After considerable oscillations during the latter decades it seems as if the excess of births, until further, is stable. The infant mortality is low: 2.7$^0/_{00}$ die within the first years.

For each 1.000 inhabitants the marriage figure is 8.1, while the corresponding number of divorces is 1.6 yearly.

The emigration, which before the first World War was very extensive, has had a revival since 1945, though it is far from having reached its former size. During the latter years the Danes have especially emigrated to Sweden and to Canada. At the same time immigrants are coming to Denmark, especially from Scandinavia and from Central Europe. During the decade 1945-1954 the number of immigrants was 200.428, while 235.526 persons emigrated.

LITERATURE

Aagesen, Aa. (1945): Oprindelsen af Esbjergs Befolkning. (Summary: The Origin of the Population of Esbjerg). Geogr. Tidsskr. 47. København.

Aagesen, Aa. (1949): Geografiske Studier over Jernbanerne i Danmark. (Summary: Geographical Studies on the Railways of Denmark). Kulturgeogr. Skr. 5. København.

Aagesen, Aa. (1956): Die Bevölkerung Dänemarks. Geogr. Rundschau. Braunschweig.

Atlas of Denmark. Editor: The Royal Danish Geographical Society.
  I : Schou, Axel (1949): The Landscapes. København.
  II: Aagesen, Aa. (1960): The Population. København.
Kampp, Aa. H. (1959): Landbrugsgeografiske studier over Danmark.
  (Summary: Some Agro-Geographical Investigations of Denmark).
  Kulturgeogr. Skr. 6. København.
Statistisk Departement, København:
  The census-population (various ed.).
  Data of industrial geography from the population ceusus 1950.
  Statistical Yearbook (various ed.).
  The migration of the Danish population (various ed.).
Trap: Danmark (Denmark, a togographical handbook). 4 ed. and 5 ed.
  København.
Unpublished materials on the Geographical Institute of the Copenhagen
  University.
Vahl, M. (1933): The Urban Settlements of Denmark. Geogr. Tidsskr.
  36:1-2. København.

Geography and Economy

By P. P. Sveistrup

Abstract

The author asks for a synthesis and mutual inspiration in the relation-ship between economics and geography as rational decisions of economic questions presuppose a basic knowledge of the regional geography. Examp-les of this are: town planning, regional planning and the problems related to the great market fusions.

The present era is one of specialization, one manifestation of which is that we know more and more about less and less. In many instances this is an advantage, because within their own speciality some people can succeed in advancing our general knowledge a hand's breadth; nevertheless, the advantages of such an evolution are limited, because man as a whole slips more into the background. Consequently, from a humanistic point of view a synthesis of a long series of analyses would often be useful. For example, it is a curious fact that much of our present-day progress is achieved within the border zone of two sciences, in that research workers with different qualifications collaborate and thereby introduce something quite new into the total picture.

I believe that we need such a synthesis and mutual inspiration in the relationship between economics and geography. In the science of economics mention is often made of a function of production, a function of demand and so on in general terms without attaching much weight to the fact that a quite ordinary function of this nature actually is highly abstract, and that what is often needed is to obtain greater clarity about the various concrete functions which must form the background of complete economic comprehension.

In economics there has no doubt always been a need for such a concretization, and in my opinion the need will be greater still in the future, when the economic functions will presumably become more complicated. I shall try to illustrate this by means of three

examples which, I think, show clearly that we shall require more
interaction in future. One is planning, especially planning of means
of communication in large towns, particularly in Copenhagen. Another is regional development and the question of what industries
should specially be promoted in a particular region for which planning has been undertaken. The third is programmes for increased
industrial activity in more or less well-developed parts of the world
where work is often done under varying geographical conditions:
in this connection it is natural for us to mention the expected occupational development in Greenland. All these questions are so
important that within the scope of a short article one cannot do more
than mention them and express the wish that the younger generation
of geographers and economists may imbue each other with a greater
measure of inspiration.

II.

If economics per se is to contribute towards the work of planning
in a large town it will be natural to point out that no single disposition should be regarded as isolated but as part of a wider relation.
Economic resources have their limits and it must be realized beforehand that the economic forces employed in one sector cannot simultaneously be employed elsewhere; a choice must be made, and for
that choice there must be some political ideas. These ideas are set up
by what is done to establish a maximum for the national product.
In principle this is not wholly correct, because other things may have
to be taken into account, for instance the distribution of the national
product between both the present and the future, but also the distribution between the various classes of society. Nevertheless, the argu-
ment is useful as a basis for the following:

Let us assume that as a result of a consideration of the financial
situation there is only a certain sum available for developing one
aspect of a city such as its means of communication. This pecuniary
shortage will mean that there is not money enough to carry out
everything that would be desired. A choice has to be made among
various possibilities and, on the basis of the prepared budget, the
authorities will choose the part of the plan that reaches the limit of
the national product. In any particular town this will depend upon
the geographical conditions. What is economically correct at one
place may be wrong in another because the geographical prerequisites are different. In other words, correct economic decisions
presuppose comprehensive geographical knowledge of the special

conditions prevailing where the new effort is to be made. If geographical conditions and economic conclusions are not closely co-
ordinated, the results will be unsatisfactory as concern sthe object
desired. A proper decision concordant with the standard depends
upon both special and general knowledge. It may be said that in the
development of a city the planners may proceed according to two
principles, centralization and decentralization, and it is quite obvious
that in the long run the consequences would be unfortunate if one
disposition led to centralization (for instance the building of tall
blocks in the business quarter) and another to decentralization
(whereby a large part of the passenger traffic would be carried by
space-wasting private cars). If a large town is to be easy and convenient to live in, each decision must not only be right economo-
geographically, but it must also be a reasonable link within a wider
relation.

Again, the decisions taken must be in accordance with the wishes
of the local population. It is useless to evolve a business quarter
with tall buildings and narrow streets if a large section of the town's
population wish to drive in their own cars to the centre; then parking
problems as an indirect consequence would assume very considerable
dimensions. The questions of centralization or decentralization of a
large town are factors comprised within a very large number of
relations, some of which are economic in character, some geographical and others form part of other, separate sciences.

It is probably very difficult to set up general economic laws for
town development and for deciding whether a centralizing or a
decentralizing development is to be preferred. Every town has its
own conditions, its own type of port, branches of industry and
administration, which it is desirable should be taken into consideration, and this can only be done if the planners have really detailed
information as to the particular town and the present and future
wishes of its population; this calls for interaction among specialists,
with each one making a contribution to the required synthesis.

But if it will be necessary to arrange interaction as a starting point
for the establishment of the main principles, it will also be advisable
to base upon an interaction in connection with many of the concrete
decisions. It may be fairly simple to visualize the purely direct effects
of a single disposition, but as a rule there are also indirect effects
that can be elucidated only from a knowledge of the concrete conditions which often are some distance away. If a wholly new residential
quarter is to be built, the qustioon arises as to how people who will

live in it can get quickly and conveniently to their work. If by means of streets that are already crowded, this one remote disposition may make it necessary to proceed to costly street-widening elsewhere in the urban community.

To put it briefly, the development of a large town, as regards both main principles and individual concrete decisions, is governed by a wide network of relations; and if the individual disposition does not take cognizance of local and distant effects the functions of the town will not work conveniently and without friction and it may involve the local population in many difficulties. True, the final decisions are in the hands of the politicians; but it is very important that they are prepared by means of a synthetic collaboration between the professional groups, each of which is able to make a contribution to the over-all picture.

III.

Another great problem nowadays in most states, not least in Denmark, is the interaction between town and country. It is held to be unsound for large towns to attract business concerns to them as they do. Whether or not this movement is desirable can only be elucidated by the application of comprehensive knowledge, a knowledge which doubtless to some extent is scattered among many specialists, and by a previous clarification of the various possible ways and means.

A lot of people seem to be interested in regional development within certain parts of the country, the scheme being promoted by establishing a new concern of one kind or another in the area to be developed. In many cases it will be possible to estimate the profits on the basis of the concern's own interests and to calculate whether or not the particular plant can be made to pay, but to my mind this is not always sufficient. In addition to the private profits an account must be drawn up of the cost to the community. What will the particular investment involve in the way of necessary costs to other sections of the community, more especially the authorities? Will it be necessary to build new roads? Will it be necessary to build new public institutions, new hospitals, new schools, etc., and is there no available capacity elsewhere in one or more of these respects? In other words, one might raise the question of what effect it will have on the national product to place a new establishment in one or another place. It is not only the public activities that are involved, for consideration must also be given to the matter of suitable housing, new shops, etc. The picture becomes more and more complicated the more indirect effects we add to it. And then it must furthermore be remembered that besides the present the future effects must also be considered. Young families moving to a newly developed area may perhaps be childless when they get there, but there is reason to anticipate a large increase in the number of school-age children in the course of ten years or so — and so on.

Most recently there has been a tendency to regard the chief point of interest as not being the economy of the new establishment itself (observable from its budget and accounts) and of the whole country (as shown through the national budget and accounts), but the economy of the particular province or region which it is sought to improve. The condition for this is that the planners work with the economy of the town or the regions as a whole. If this is to be done satisfactorily, there must be accounts and a budget for the area affected, just as in the case of the single establishment and the entire community. This is a very intricate task, not least because there is nothing to show what is taken into and out of the area. For an individual establishment we have this direct from its payments and receipts, and for the whole community we have the public statistics. But for a particular region or town the material for accounting and budgeting is very difficult to get at. No doubt some information is available, and an attempt has in fact been made to devise a system of accounting for a separate region. All this, however, is merely in embryo as yet and presumably the question will not arise for some years to come, when more people realize that casual regional development dispositions lead only to casual results — a state of affairs that can scarcely be permitted to endure. The information to be acquired must be sought in many different places. Some can be had from official statistics, some again from the municipal or local organizations, but it is apt to be relatively incidental. In this connection the probability is that within a few years the geographers and other specialists will be approached for their support in collecting and working up as much information as possible. Here it is not so much a question of analysis as synthesis. Working on such a synthesis will scarcely come all at once, but in my opinion the march of events will make it imperative. Sooner or later political authorities will formulate their wishes, and scarcely any individual specialist possesses such a general knowledge of all the many relations. Attaining to the best synthesis will require a collaboration between various specialists, not least within economics and geography.

IV.

In all probability the sphere in which an interaction between economics and geography is most needed for understanding the economic and other relations is represented by the great general problems within regions composed of areas of a highly varied character, such as those resulting from the great market fusions. To us in Denmark the most outstanding problem, in which the geographical prerequisites are so different that ignoring geography in the economic considerations will lead to wholly unsatisfactory results, arises out of a parallelization between Denmark and Greenland. No satisfactory results is likely if the fact is ignored that the natural conditions are wholly different, the climatic conditions likewise, and that in many respects the peoples set entirely different values upon things (which is not saying that I commit myself to either the one or the other). Economic dispositions which are considered correct in Funen are not immediately applicable to Greenland. This is a sphere in which it is absolutely necessary to consider the geographical conditions when taking decisions of wide economic range.

There are many more domains in which geographical differences must necessarily be included in the economic picture. If a marketing region which has long been narrowly confined to a state like Denmark is expanded so as to include a large number of states, a number of problems of localization will come into the foreground within these particular communities. Within a partially closed economy such as that which has characterized conditions in Denmark, it has not been important from the angle of national economy whether an establishment meeting this or that demand was located at Odense or Aalborg; some costs of transportation must be included in the picture, but they are not highly important. But there will be problems of quite another order if it is to be decided whether the new establishments planned are to be placed for instance in Denmark, Great Britain or Germany; or perhaps even Switzerland or Holland may come into consideration. In that case there will be many effects as regards employment, currency, capital, etc., of which we shall scarcely be able to take so liberal a view as we now do of the particularly Danish localizing problems. The views and interests of the individual establishment may differ radically from those of the public. In a development of this kind there may be many economic advantages and many economic drawbacks. To my mind it will be unsatisfactory if there are no calculations and investigations made beforehand as a synthesis of the individual knowledge of a number of specialists.

I consider it of importance that, before the political decisions are taken, the powers included should become familiar not only with the direct but with the indirect effects and the whole interplay of factors in the forthcoming development. It will be agreed that this is a task that will require a considerable time for completion, and that it is a border zone where team-work will be more valuable than a series of individual efforts by geographers, economists or other specialists.

Strictly speaking, the economic relations which we must have clarified in order to understand the economic problems of today extend beyond the bounds of economics proper. It is easy enough for an economist to say that if the prices of raw materials fall, as they have been doing these last few years, there are likely to be political tensions in countries overseas, especially in Africa. To me, however, a general economo-political view of this sort is not fully satisfactory. It would be of much greater interest to know just where these political tensions will be manifested and how strong they will be. On a purely economic basis there is not much possibility of forming an opinion on such matters; for the ultimate evaluation of such a question we must have a knowledge of the whole mentality of the peoples concerned, and whether they are relatively well off in advance or they are living on the verge of starvation. In order to make an economic evaluation we must have such information from geographical and other specially expert quarters; specialists who have studied the people concerned can make a valuable contribution towards our understanding of the general relations within future developments.

One might go a step further and raise the question of whether the economic laws devised by the economic theorists on the basis of an empirical material originating chiefly in Europe and North America, can simply be applied to the other continents where people are often apt to react differently. At the moment we can have no opinion on how this question is to be answered; but perhaps it would be useful if specialists in other subject-groups were asked to join in a collaboration for arriving at an understanding of the wider relations.

V.

To summarize, in my opinion there is quite a number of problems lying within the border zone between economics and geography and often several other sciences, in which the individual specialist is relatively uncertain and often is inclined to close his eyes to the questions because they are beyond his own particular province.

Doing so has indeed been possible to a considerable extent hitherto, because the questions were of little current interest and there were problems enough of other kinds to tackle. I believe that this will be more and more difficult in the future, for the reason that in all probability these border problems between the various sciences will gradually become more pressing, so that sooner or later they will have to be taken up with more determination.

The easiest and most direct course to follow will doubtless be for each of the various groups of specialists to endeavour to learn from other specialists' domains and apply this new knowledge to their own work, whereby the uncultivated regions between the groups will become smaller. No-one can prevent an economist or a geographer from trying to expand his knowledge to other spheres; but I imagine that each subject is already so large that only very few can cover such a wide span and thereby fill the entire border zone.

In addition to this actually simple procedure, would it not also be profitable to try another by establishing a team-work, with each member contributing from his own line to an intimate co-operation of this kind? I doubt if this suggestion is one that can be carried out quickly, but I wonder if there are not some, especially among the younger workers, who will recognize that this is a fertile line and will therefore take it up and successively build a collaboration capable of achieving valuable results in the course of time.

Greater Copenhagen
An urbanized area and its geographical environments
By Niels Nielsen

Abstract
    An outline of the urbanization of Greater Copenhagen. The rural rem-
nants are a very characteristic element of the fully developed city, but
equally typical are the far advanced signs of city influence. Details are
given concerning the population, the industries, the green belts, the agri-
cultural area and the coping with distances.

In a natural-geographical sense the region belonging to the urban
communes of Copenhagen and Frederiksberg, the Copenhagen County Council area and the Roskilde County Council area forms a combination of normal East Danish landscape types representing one
harmonious unit. A cultural-geographical summary is rather more
difficult to arrive at because the difficulties are considerable, much
more than in any other part of the country. The explanation of this
is that in addition to the normal combination: scattered habitations,
villages, railway-station towns, boroughs, there is still another type
of habitation, the great City of Copenhagen, which in various ways
makes its own impression on the cultural-geographical pattern.

Drawing an *unequivocal boundary for Greater Copenhagen* is no
easy matter. Administratively the town area is divided into a large
number of units with local, communal government. For example,
a distinction is made between Copenhagen, Frederiksberg and Gentofte communes, which grouped together are called *the capital;* but
in addition there are a large number of suburban communes, in all 22,
some within the Copenhagen county area and some in Frederiksborg
county, all with a certain organic relationship to the capital and geographically closely associated with it.

However, it would not be right to consider these communes solely
as administrative bodies, for many of them have the character of
local, independent urban organisms with a subdivision into »quar-

ters« which in the aggregate contain the various elements normally found within an urban community of similar size: residential quarters, business (shopping) quarters, and quarters for administration, industry, traffic, recreation and so on. The communes of Greater Copenhagen, and parts of these too, are thus possessed of a certain urban individuality, but also fit into the city organism as a whole.

The geographical boundary between Greater Copenhagen and the surrounding rural districts is often quite sharp, urban habitations and urban living conditions verging upon purely rural areas along a very narrow transitional zone. In other cases the boundary is more a matter of opinion, vague. For example, in the city's foreland there are isolated, built-up areas separated from the compact city by a zone of rural habitations, but so closely associated with Greater Copenhagen that functionally they may be considered part of it. There are examples of these in the more distant suburban communes, and others again beyond them. Conversely, within areas that are distinctly urban in their development one encounters islands of rural habitation and occupational structure.

Attempts have been made in various ways to find more exact expressions of the strength of the peripheral areas' association with the city, such as by means of determining the working places of the active population, and also by an evaluation of the travel distance measured in time from the outer zones to the central parts of the city. It seems that one hour may be employed as the approximate limit of the city's area.

The chief feature of the region is the rapid growth of the city as regards area and population. The process of a countryside changing in character and wholly or partly acquiring an urban form of habitation, occupational structure and general social function is called *urbanization;* a study of the history of Copenhagen reveals its various phases, partly recognizable even now in some of its features, especially by the presence of small remnants of earlier geographical traits, for example old village churches in the outskirts of Copenhagen: Brønshøj, Brøndbyerne, Gentofte, Lyngby, Tårnby; remainders of village settlements: Utterslev, Valby, Gladsakse, Husum, Rødovre; old roads, traces of bygone land distribution: Bellahøj; former country palaces and summer residences: Frederiksberg Castle, Sorgenfri Palace; local harbours and their buildings: Dragør, Skovshoved; military installations, woods, parks, cemeteries and the like. In other words, the rural remnants are a very characteristic element of the fully developed city, but equally typical are the far advanced

Fig. 1. The meeting of countryside and city. Aerial photo of Brøndbyøster from the south, 1958. In the centre the old village surrounded by the stellar system of exchange strips of the common. The outlines of the farm lots are still discernible, the apices in towards the farmsteads in the village. The properties on the west are still worked as farms, whereas those on the east and north are marked out for building — with tenement blocks northwards nearest the S-railway station.

signs of city influence, away from the compact, urban habitation. This influence affects the countryside fields, its scattered farms and villages as well as railway-station towns and market boroughs. One might in fact speak of different grades or urbanization. There are examples to be found in many parts of Sjælland, but more particularly in the northern and eastern districts. The whole of the region to the north and east of a line from Køge via Roskilde and Frederiksværk to Helsingør (Elsinore), in other words the greater part of the counties of Copenhagen and Frederiksborg, may in many ways be regarded as solidly connected, but in such a manner that the urbanization is hightly unequal in its distribution.

As will be seen, the limit of Greater Copenhagen's intensive urbanization coincides more or less with the Copenhagen county boundary, but wedges of urban-like character are extending slowly outwards into the counties of both Frederiksborg and Roskilde. On the other hand, the less intense and more sporadic growths can be discerned far out over Sjælland.

In some cases the village is the starting part for urbanized expansion and gradually changes into urban habitation and occupational structure. In other cases urbanization proceeds in the way that a large agricultural area is captured by the city by a brief, but violent process of street-laying, factory building and the erection of houses and public premises.

Such a protracted and complicated process as the growth of the Greater Copenhagen city organism took place under the influence of changing factors. The main lines of the earliest town structure were determined by the harbour and the highways in conjunction with the location of ancient villages. Later the defence fortifications became of vital importance as town limits, but from about the middle of the nineteenth century it was other factors that chiefly determined its growth, and today both the shape of the town area and its inner differentiation are governed by an intricate system of forces, some traceable to the conditions of now departed times, others integral with the economic and traffic situation of the present day. In addition, however, *the natural-geographical basis* exerted a remarkably clear influence on the direction and character of the urbanization.

This is exemplified by the coast to the north and south of Copenhagen. The coast northwards from Hellerup (Tuborg harbour) at an early stage attracted first the building of summer houses, later more and more permanent dwellings. The south coast between Vallensbæk and Køge was late in being captured and still consists largely of dwellings of summer-house type. A somewhat similar development has taken place in the lake-and-forest land northwest of Copenhagen, where a number of local towns grew steadily for about a century and in our own time they have advanced so rapidly that the farm lands once lying between them have practically disappeared. In this region woods and lakes are still a most characteristic element of the landscape and have been responsible for the rich mosaic of fully developed urban areas and extensive lots with self-contained houses, separated by woods, lakes, bogs and valleys.

This scenically and aesthetically oriented section of Copenhagen's development gives a special character to the entire northern part of the town organism.

Another and quite characteristic region is the south of Amager. Whereas the northern part of the island is a genuine branch of the city both administratively and functionally, there are parts in the

Fig. 2. Part of the old town around Vor Frue Kirke (the cathedral) in the centre. Extreme right: the main street, "Strøget" (vertically in the picture) and Gammel-torv. Note the curved street lines and the subdivision of the buildings into small plots.

west and south of a different character altogether; the western area is an empty military ground, whilst in recent years the south coast has been drawn into the Copenhagen system through the building of a summer-house settlement. The Copenhagen Airport covers an area of about 685 ha. to the southeast and forms an obstacle to the city's development along Amager's east coast. In St. Magleby parish and part of the parish of Tårnby, however, there are still large areas used for market gardening and farming.

The situation of the principal traffic lines decided the placing of the zones with the greatest growth. Strandvejen, Lyngbyvej, Frede-rikssundsvej, Roskilde Landevej and Gl. Køge Landevej, together

Fig. 3. Store Kannikestræde, bearing the visible impress of its situation in the university quarter. On the left Borch's College, and, at the foot of the Round Tower, "Regensen".

with the railways: Kystbanen, Nordbanen, Slangerupbanen, Frederikssundsbanen and the line between Copenhagen and Roskilde form the skeleton of communications on which Copenhagen has developed. Along them the city sends out arms from 10 to 25 km. long into the surrounding country. In the northern sector between the coast and Furesøen the rural character has disappeared almost everywhere, or it remains only in patches. Along Roskilde Landevej and the Copenhagen—Roskilde line the older habitations Glostrup, Tåstrup and Hedehusene have become welded together, and along the Køge Bugt too there is an almost continuous settlement, but of another character.

In the sector bounded on the north by Frederikssundsvej and Frederikssundsbanen, and on the south by Gl. Køge Landevej, the city influence except for the Copenhagen—Roskilde railway is of an entirely different character to that in the northern sector and the island of Amager. In places the urban element is very slight; at Ejby, Herstedvester, Herstedøster, Sengeløse and still further westwards the old village structure has been retained. There is little industry and only a very small number of the population have work outside the

Fig. 4. Vimmelskaftet, the narrow, winding and busy shopping street, looking towards Nikolai Church.

parish. The population density in the region between Ejby and Ros-Kilde Fjord is surprisingly low, about 60 per sq.km., that is to say a very small figure for a Sjælland agricultural community, one that moreover is surrounded north and south by a very dense population and on the east borders right upon the metropolitan area.

The part of Roskilde county lying southwest of the Copenhagen—Roskilde line, between this and the valley of Køge Å, is of a different type in its form of settlement. This part of the county is more dense-ly populated, the villages are larger, the scattered houses and buildings are more numerous, and both railway-station towns and highroad towns are well developed (Viby, Borup, Havdrup, Skensved and Tune). As regards population, the western part of the county, comprising the south part of Hornsherred peninsula and a strip about 10 km. wide running from there southwards to the county's southern boundary, has a character all of its own. The configuration of the ground is broken, with wide valleys interspersed with plateaus, the area is well wooded, and a large part of the land is owned by large estates and medium-sized farms. The one well-developed station town is Hvalsø. In the northern half of the area village settlement is the predominating form, in the southern half there are more scattered houses. The influence of Greater Copenhagen is perceptible in many ways, even in remote parts of the county, particularly in its built-up areas. Along the Copenhagen—Roskilde line a considerable number of the occupationally employed have their work in the city area. Even in Roskilde and Hillerød this group represents about 10 per cent, whereas Køge and Helsingør have only about 5 per cent. A number of industrial plants connected with Copenhagen establishments have been built, and an increasing number of people working in the capital are moving out to permanent and summer houses in all parts of the county, but more particularly in places adjacent to woods and seaside. Many institutions, such as sanatoria, hospitals, schools and research stations have moved out to rural surroundings (Avnstrup, Skt. Hans, Boserup, Tune etc.), and also the Risø plant on Roskilde Fjord in the western margin of the thinly populated zone north of the Copenhagen—Roskilde line.

The rich variation in the forms of settlement within the counties of Copenhagen and Roskilde is thus partly a result of the geographical conditions, especially in the course of the coastlines and in the contrast between the fertile, unbroken moraine flat in the triangle between Copenhagen—Roskilde—Køge, the extensive hilly country on the north with its lakes and woodlands, and the very complicated fiord and valley landscapes west of Roskilde.

Out of this scenic profusion Greater Copenhagen has grown into *a highly differentiated cultural landscape,* the largest of its kind in Scandinavia, an enormous mosaic of residential, industrial and traffic areas interspersed with green polygons or zones and with a rich variation between overpopulated town areas with more than 50.000 people per sq. km., regions with self-contained houses, »colony» allotments, modern tenements with from 12 to 15 storeys of apartments, city areas with an enormous day population and an extremely small one at night, distinctly industrial areas, harbour quarters, railways, motor roads and airports.

And in contrast, at Ejby — about 10 km. from Copenhagen's city hall — there is practically undisturbed countryside. And still within the Copenhagen corporation area on the west side of the island of

Fig. 5. The "point blocks" at Bellahøj, built in the 1950's.

Amager there is empty land, while 5—6 km. from the large establishments along the east coast of the same island lies Saltholm's 16 km². with about a score of human beings and a few summer-grazing cattle.

It will be seen that an important factor in the urbanization development emanating from Copenhagen is the radial expansion along especially favoured lines and zones (for instance the Copenhagen-Roskilde line). This expansion explains the town's stellate form. For certain reasons Amager has only partly been incorporated into the town's development, and Saltholm not at all; as a result the star is awry, with its strongest growth determined by the terminal points, Helsingør and Køge, of a line running from the north westwards to the southwest.

This stellate system of urbanization, however, is traversed by another form, a ring-shaped zonal system which, although broken here and there, stands out rather clearly and is easily recognizable. One typical example in a state of full evolution today is the large industrial area that can be traced from Lyngby via Buddinge, Gladsakse, Herlev, Skovlunde and Glostrup to Brøndbyvester. In between are residential areas — though these are also in course of development — and it is all linked up by the great circular artery from Buddinge to Herlev—Glostrup—Køge Bugt. Analogous ring formations can be demonstrated in the parts of the city which have grown up since the year 1900. Another industrial and traffic zone can be traced from Valby and Sydhavnen across Islands Brygge, the shipyards, over to the Free Port and Tuborg, from where a branch runs down the east coast of Amager to Kastrup and the airport. The siting of the earlier industrial areas was largely dependent on the shipping facilities and the railway goods yards; to a great extent the latter ones were able to take advantage of the increasing importance of the motor lorry to liberate themselves from that dependence.

One special feature or urbanization from Copenhagen is the development of *the industrial area along Mølleåen.* This represents an old phase of the time prior to the era of steam power. From Lyngby to Strandmøllen was a sequence of originally water-driven mills and factories, now either closed down or converted into more modern and effective power supplies; on the other hand this entire area no longer holds an important place in the city's organism and nowadays is something in the nature of a relic.

The outer zones of Greater Copenhagen acquire at any rate part of their character from *modern industrial enterprises,* and the local population may be divided into a locally employed and a commuting group, employed either in the capital or in the establishments of the marginal zone. There are typical examples in Hørsholm, Birkerød, Lundtofte, Ballerup—Måløv, Tåstrup and Hedehusene. One particular group of widely advanced industries is represented by the brickworks (Nivå, Lillerød, Birkerød), the gravel industry (Farum and Hedehusene) and the lime-works (Skensved), all closely connected with the metropolis, but sited according to the situation of the raw materials.

Moreover, the industries at or near the towns in Northeast Sjælland (Køge, Roskilde, Frederiksværk, Hillerød and Helsingør), especially the large establishments, are intimately associated with Greater Copenhagen and with some justification may be regarded as an outer ring-zone in the large population and production region of North Sjælland.

Greater Copenhagen is relatively well supplied with areas which afford the population an opportunity of getting out into the open, there being easy access to *woods, lakes, beaches and sea.* Even disregarding the parks properly so called, chiefly within the metropolitan area, there are many ways of reaching »green zones« by public or private means of communication in less than an hour's travelling. In this respects the districts north of Copenhagen have a great advantage for most of the large woodland and lake areas lie to the north of a line from Måløv to Klampenborg. South of this line the countryside is almost devoid of woods, and there are no lakes. Amager has nothing more than Kongelunden and the partly abandoned military ranges. Westwards there are no open-air areas like those in north Sjælland until one is past Roskilde Fjord and at Køge.

Øresund (The Sound) is ideal for yachting and boating of every kind and in fact is utilized intensively. But here again there is something distorted i nthe conditions. The coast between Copenhagen and Køge has very shallow water and is not used much. On the other hand, along a line from Dragør to Helsingør the conditions are fairly unique and, together with points on the coast of Scania in Sweden form a base for open-air life at sea, such as is rarely found elsewhere in the world. On the other hand bathing beaches are not quite so accessible, though the south shore, the south and east coasts of Amager and especially the coast north of Hellerup are extremely popular seaside resorts in summer; but the best conditions lie somewhat more remote, e.g. along the north coast of Sjælland. Most important of all are the green areas north and northwest of Copenhagen, especially those that can be reached by »S« (electric) trains to Klampenborg, Holte and Ballerup. Most of these adjacent green areas are within the boundaries of Copenhagen county, but the north-Sjælland railways and bicycle traffic make it easy to reach woods, lakes and shore in a more distant zone from Farum through Hillerød to Helsingør; and finally, the motor-car has opened up a rather intensive utilization of outdoor areas up to a distance of about 100 km.

The summer houses (bungalows) properly so called are chiefly intended for the holidays, so it is a type of dwelling that has proved capable of spreading over large parts of the Sjælland archipelago; Bornholm also plays a considerable role as a summer place for the residents of Copenhagen. The types of landscape chiefly preferred are the coasts and the hilly woodland and lake districts. A large proportion of the summer houses lie within a travelling distance of 1—1½ hours from Copenhagen and therefore are convenient for use well outside the actual vacation period.

The many groups of »colony« gardens, or garden colonies, form a very characteristic element of the Copenhagen summer form of dwelling. They are to be found almost exclusively within the west

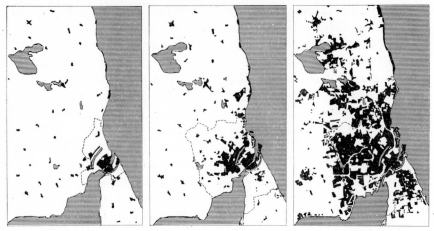

Fig. 6. Building up of the Copenhagen area in three stages. Left: 1850, where apart from some slight suburban building there were nothing but village settlements outside the ramparts. Centre: the situation about 1900, when the suburbs as well as Frederiksberg and quarters in Hellerup, Charlottenlund and Kongens Lyngby were developing. Right: 1950, showing the wide expansion on the north side but also west of Copenhagen at Rødovre, Hvidovre and Glostrup. The stippled line shows the communal boundary between Copenhagen and the suburban communes.

borders of the suburban communes. These gardens are utilized very effectively, most of them being in use throughout the summer on account of the short distance away from home. Summer houses in the proper sense are usually private properties, whereas the garden colonies generally are formed on rented land. In a good many instances older, more centrally situated colonies have had to make way for permanent houses, compensation being secured in the form of new ones at a somewhat greater distance from the metropolitan centre. By this means a displacement is proceeding out to the city's periphery.

The 19 suburban communes belonging to the County of Copenhagen have a total area of about 468 km² and they house 309.999 people (1955). There are considerable uninhabited areas with woods, parks, lakes, bogs and military grounds, and even if *the agricultural area* is rapidly decreasing, there are large stretches here and there occupied by farms and market gardens. In 1955, for instance, the 19 communes still had 200 km². of agricultural land or about 43 per cent; but it is most unequally distributed: in the communes of Rødovre and Hvidovre the farm land is less than 10 per cent of the total area, but it is as much as 80—90 per cent in the least urban of them (Ledøje—Smørum and Torslunde—Ishøj).

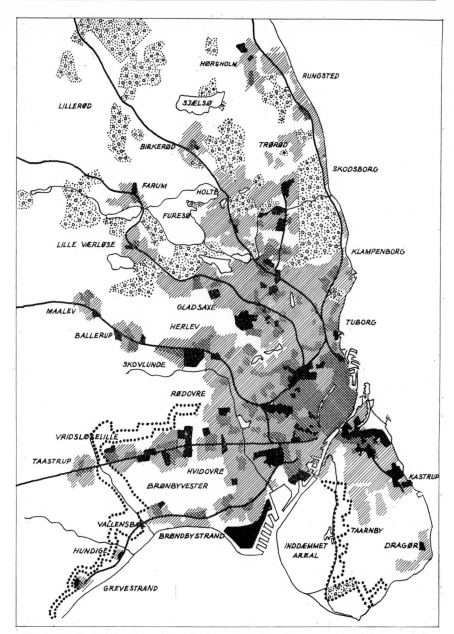

Fig. 7. Draft sketch of a regional plan, 1948. The future residential areas indicated by hatching and the industrial areas by black. The areas inside the
stippled lines (west of Copenhagen and on Amager) were suggested as woods.

The agricultural area is also on the decline in the Roskilde county area, but it represents more than 70 per cent of the whole.

In both counties about half the agricultural area is sown with cereals, 10—15 per cent with root-crops. On the whole the crop yield is high. It is a characteristic feature of the Copenhagen county area that about a tenth of the agricultural land is utilized for market gardening, especially for vegetable growing, but with other special crops of importance too. On the other hand livestock in the Copenhagen county area is somewhat low, 0.9 head of cattle per ha., whereas Roskilde county has 1.6. For Copenhagen the figure is rapidly decreasing whereas the Roskilde county figure has increased a good deal, in recent years too.

cattle	1945—49	1955
Copenhagen cty	26.100	18.500
Roskilde cty	71.500	84.500

These figures and evidence of many other kinds indicate that the urbanizing effect of Greater Copenhagen is fairly sharply delimited. Throughout the whole of the Copenhagen county area (with the exception of the few communes of rural character) the effect is well marked. In the Roskilde county area exactly the reverse is the case: a few communes have become more or less affected by urbanization, whereas much the greater number in practically all respects act as »normal« rural communes. In the case of many other cities the situation is that the surrounding country districts within a radius of 30—60 km. are organized for supplying food to the city population. This is so only to a small extent in the environs of Greater Copenhagen.

Greater Copenhagen, i.e. Copenhagen and Frederiksberg, the Copenhagen County area and the communes of Birkerød, Farum and Hørsholm in Frederiksborg county, today contain about 29 per cent of Denmark's aggregate *population,* viz. 1.311.000 on 1st October, 1957. According to the 1955 census the metropolis, i.e. Copenhagen, Frederiksberg and Gentofte, had 960.319 inhabitants; 309.047 were living in the remainder of the Copenhagen County area, and on the same day the population of the Roskilde County area was 82.223, with about half in the towns. Up to about the year 1950 the metropolitan population was growing, but now it seems to have come to a standstill, whereas population increases are still being recorded in the suburban communes. The huge population of the capital is concentrated within a moderate area, about 117 km²., of which however large parts are practically empty of people, such as reclaimed areas, parks, cemeteries, water areas, traffic areas etc. The built-up area, which includes streets, roads and squares, is thus reduced to 60—70 km². This makes the mean population density of the capital about 8000 per km²., but in places it is much greater. In the urbanized communes in the neighbourhood 500—1000 people per km². is the usual, but a few communes within the Copenhagen County area are purely or almost purely rural in character with a density of about 50 per km². (Ledøje—Smørum and Sengeløse). These figures clearly illustrate the deep contrast between the city and the adjoining rural areas.

In the rural districts within the Roskilde County boundaries there are wide variations in the size and distribution of the population. Several communes, like so many other island—Danish areas in the period 1901—55, have had fairly constant populations — a few indeed a slight decrease. This type includes communes such as Ejby, Nr. Dalby, Roskilde Vor Frue, Rye—Sonnerup, Tune and Ørsted—Dåstrup, whereas other rural communes in the same period have recorded a moderate growth of 10—20 per cent. Others again, those where there has been a growth of the closed, town-like settlements, have increased in population by about 50 per cent (Hvalsø—Særløse and Osted). Six communes bordering upon Køge Bugt between Greater Copenhagen and the town of Køge: Greve—Kildebrønde, Havdrup—Solrød, Højelse, Jersie—Skensved, Karlslunde, Karlstrup and Ølsemagle, are outstanding in that the local population in the years 1901—1955 grew from 6010 to 12.550 (about 104 per cent), whereas the other rural communes in the county area grew only from 19.245 to 23.341 (about 21 per cent). It is a feature of the communes along Køge Bugt that there is a great seasonal variation, the summer population far exceeding the winter population in numbers. However, both the heavy increase in the local population and that in the summer population are mostly associated with the coast itself and the Copenhagen—Køge high road. The other Køge Bugt communes as regards population seem to have kept pace with the developments in the other rural communes within the county.

Whereas the station towns on the Copenhagen—Roskilde line have a strong Copenhagen impress, those on the far side of Roskilde along the railways to Køge, Ringsted and Holbæk are much more »normal« in character. The station town of Hvalsø alone has a population exceeding 1000. In the more densely populated parts of the county there has been much ribbon development, of which the best example is Ny Osted, on Main Line No. 1 between Roskilde and Ringsted, where there is now a double row of modern houses, 2—3 km. long, whereas nearby Osted Kirkeby has retained its old village stamp.

There is a paucity of manor houses in both counties, but west and south of Roskilde there are several estates such as Svenstrup, Ledreborg, Ryegård and Lindholm, all one-time majorats, whose extensive fields and woods characterize the landscape; in Køge parish is Gammel Køgegård.

Industry in Roskilde County area is closely related to that in Greater Copenhagen. It is particularly associated with the neighbouring towns Køge and Roskilde and their immediate environs, whereas the smaller urban formations in the rural districts only exceptionally contain industrial enterprises of any size. The building industry is the most important, employing over a fourth of the industrial population, but in addition there is an important food and beverage industry, as well as metal and chemical industries. Roskilde has large slaughterhouses, a distillery, tannery, engineering works and a paper-goods factory. Lying in the part of Roskilde commune that extends in a narrow zone to Hedehusene are several large industrial plants, and north of Køge, in Højelse and Ølsemagle commune, is the largest rubber factory in Denmark with its workers' dwellings.

North of the very urban-like zone Copenhagen—Roskilde are six parish communes where, so far, urbanization has been surprisingly slight. The changes in the populations during the period 1901—55 have been as follows:

	1901	1955
Ledøje—Smørum	1259	1556
Sengeløse	1197	1266
Agerup—Kirkerup	1067	1071
Jyllinge—Gundsømagle	1100	1510
Hvedstrup—Fløng	960	1975
Himmelev	606	1560

The first four of these parish communes have preserved their ancient structure so to say completely, whereas since 1940 the last two have increased their population at a relatively quicker rate. From the point of view of population and occupations this region has followed lines of development quite different from those of the surrounding areas which in the present century have recorded a heavy population growth, increased industrialization and an evolution in its trade structure that indicates close contact with Greater Copen-

Fig. 8. Asylgade at Lyngby. In the outer districts of the city there still remain
old dwellings, relics of the original village settlement.

hagen. This small enclave has retained its countrified character not-
withstanding the growth of the city. Nevertheless, in the last two
communes in the above list, bordering upon Roskilde—Hedehusene,
an incipient urban influence is now perceptible, for Fløng is coales-
cing with Hedehusene and Himmelev with Roskilde.

It is characteristic that the southeast section of Roskilde County
area, i.e. south of the Copenhagen—Roskilde line and east of the
Lejre—Ringsted line, has large villages, well-developed station towns
and a considerable, scattered population. The west section of the
county is not so thickly settled. The villages of the southeast zone
are generally of the size 200—500, those in the other part being
much smaller. To some extent the larger villages have lost something
of their original character, more and more of the populations being
employed in work of an urban type; in most the parish communes,
however, the occupational distribution is strongly agricultural, 17 of
the 28 having more than 40 per cent of their populations engaged in
farming. On the other hand, in 17 parish communes the number of
those employed in industry and handicrafts is larger than those

working in agriculture. For comparison, only 4 parish communes in the Copenhagen County area have over 40 per cent occupied in farming and market gardening; these are Ledøje—Smørum, Sengeløse, Store Magleby and Torslunde—Ishøj, with altogether 5761 inhabitants of whom 2738 work on the land. Thus there is a very distinct population boundary which runs almost along by the border between the two county areas. The figures of the occupational distribution are as follows:

	farming etc.	industry handicrafts building
Copenhagen County	14.348	104.942
Roskilde County	17.683	27.560
Purely rural districts in Copenhagen County	4.733	3.195
Purely rural districts in Roskilde County	15.842	8.065

Coping with distances is a vital factor in the life of Greater Copenhagen city organisms. Most important are the problems that are associated with the distance between home and working place, though of course distances to centres of education and culture, outdoor areas, shopping centres and places of amusement are also very important and determine traffic requirements and their variation.

As regards Copenhagen, conditions are complicated by the circumstance that the long-distance transit traffic by land is of relatively large volume, because almost all railway traffic between Scandinavia and the rest of Europe has to make use of Copenhagen's railway network, and because a very large part of the motor-cars running between Scandinavia and Western Europe pass through Copenhagen County. The total number of Scandinavian cars crossing the frontiers at Helsingør and Copenhagen inwards is over 100.000 per annum.

The average distance between dwelling and work place seems to be lengthening, i.e. because industrial plants are moving out from central parts of the city to suburban communes, and because since the war it has been difficult for people to remove. Investigations at the more recent industrial quarters suggest that about a fifth of the male workers have more than 12 km. between home and their work, and a half have over 6 km. A considerable section of the population of Greater Copenhagen have to spend between one and two hours daily in travelling to and from their work, and this unproductive employment of time and transportation fares is one of the city's serious problems. For this reason the development of the traffic system within the Greater Copenhagen area is a matter of the highest importance, and urbanization is intimately bound up with that development.

In the inner zones of the city the tramways form a dense network serving the fully built-up city area and also providing a very considerable part of the conveyance along the shorter distances.

The electrified railways (»S«) attend principally to the traffic between the central parts of the city and the far-outstretched branches of the suburban quarters. There the »S«-railway stations are the terminals of a very well developed network of bus services, and the same applies to the terminals of the tramways. Private conveyances, bicycles and motor cars, have not nearly the same important role as the public means of conveyance.

Motor-car traffic is largely connected with a stellate system of large radial streets and roads which are intersected by ring-roads. Modern motor roads such as the Hørsholm road, the Motor Ring road and Roskilde Highway are growing in importance, and others are projected or in course of construction.

The characteristic feature of Copenhagen County is a very large local traffic, which is indicated simply by the fact that 75 millions or 69 per cent of all train journeys in Denmark in 1956—57 proceeded within the Copenhagen local system (about 25 millions on the »town line«, a section of the electric railway system) i.e. on the lines between Copenhagen and Helsingør, Ballerup, Farum and Roskilde. In addition, a large network of motor-coaches, chiefly in the suburban communes, in 1956 carried about 42 million passengers, whereas the tramways, which run chiefly within the city area, Copenhagen—Frederiksberg—Gentofte, had 206 million passengers. Thus the total number of journeys by public means of conveyance comes up to 320 millions per annum. It is difficult to form a fairly exact idea of the use af private means such as bicycle, power-cycle, motor cycle or car, but about 70.000 cars are registered in the capital as well as about 28.000 motor-cycles and scooters, about 15.000 power-bikes and half a million pedal bicycles.

About 80 per cent of *the city's vegetable requirements* come from market gardens in the vicinity. The glass-house producing establishments are located principally west and southwest of the city area between Køge Bugt and Bagsværd, more particularly in the region south of Roskilde Highway. The outdoor establishments are also important in the west and in the south of Amager, whereas fruit supplies come from a much larger radius, some from the islands south of Sjælland and from Fyn. There is also a fruit-growing section in the area along the northern edge of geographical Copenhagen, i.e. along the stretch between Værløse, Vedbæk and Hørsholm. Fruit growing is also connected with the hilly area to the north, whereas the market gardens proper are to be found on the flat, very fertile regions in the west and on Amager.

At the present moment water supplies are of some importance to future developments. The stretch between Roskilde Landevej and Gl. Køge Landevej has large reserves of water, so that a further extension of market gardening is to be anticipated there. On the other hand, the reserves in the wedge between Roskilde Landevej and the Husum—Måløv line are not large, a circumstance that argues in favour of retaining the area as normal farm land, which indeed would also be desirable from a scenic point of view.

LITERATURE

J. P. Trap: Danmark 5. Ed. Vol. I, 2 and II, 1–2. G. E. C. Gads forlag, København 1959–60.

Illustrations and permission to translation of this article into English by courtesy of G. E. C. Gads forlag.

The Copenhagen District and its Population

By Aage Aagesen

Abstract

Thanks to its position at the most important waterway between the Baltic and the oceans, Copenhagen has developed to become an urbanized area. It is characterized by the normal division in zones of the modern big town, ranging from the almost depopulated »City« to dormitory towns and satellite towns in the outermost zones. The population figure of Greater Copenhagen is about 1.3 millions. It is foreseen that the anticipated development will create an »Øresund urban area«, a conurbation situated partly in Sweden, partly in Denmark.

The development of Copenhagen (København)

The origin of Copenhagen, the capital of the kingdom of Denmark, is not exactly known; already in the Stone Age small settlements existed, where to-day the Capital, its ports and suburbs are situated. Traces of a farmers' village from about the year 1000 are found in the city of to-day, and at the coast a small fishing-settlement arose with ferryconnections to Scania. By and by the port acquired an increasing importance, which was favoured by the sheltered position at the narrow water between the islands of Sealand (Sjælland) and Amager.

In 1167, Absalon, Bishop of Roskilde and Archbishop of Lund, built a castle on a small island (Slotsholmen) at the port of the town, thence called Havn (= harbour). In 1248 a Hanseatic fleet captured the town. Later, it was given over to the king, and from 1416 Copenhagen has been the residence of the Danish kings.

Until about the year 1620 Copenhagen only covered the area which to-day is occupied of the so-called »City«. The town, at that time counting about 30.000 inhabitants, was — after 1290 — surrounded by moats and ramparts. In 1618 a new town, Christianshavn, was founded from Dutch model on some small islands between Sealand and Amager. For about a century Christianshavn was considered as a town independent of Copenhagen, although, already in 1619, a bridge was built between Christianshavn and Copenhagen.

From the year 1629 the fortifications of Copenhagen were extended northwards, and during the subsequent decades the area of the town expanded in that direction. At the northeastern end of the fortifications a citadel protected the entrance to the harbour. Later, the fortifications around Christianshavn were enlarged. About 1660 the number of inhabitants of the total city of Copenhagen was in the neighbourhood of 60.000. In the course of the next half of this century a new quarter arose inside the latest ramparts.

In 1660 Denmark adopted the absolute monarchy. This political system resulted in a pronounced centralisation of the administration and of the economic and commercial life. A consequence of this was an increasing prosperity in the Capital, whereas the population did not increase as much as could justifiably have been expected. In 1769 Copenhagen had 80.000 inhabitants, in 1801 101.000. In the meantime, suburbs had grown up outside the ramparts. About 1850 the greater part of the habitation was still found within the intact fortifications. However, already a few years later this area could no longer hold the rapidly increasing population. The commencing industrialization offered the capital such variety of new prospects of occupation that the suburbs grew enormously. The population number increased from 130.000 in 1850 to 261.000 1880 and, in 1901, reached 454.000.

The geographical delimitation of Copenhagen

In this century the traffic has undergone a radical development. One of the most conspicuous consequences of this is that whereas the employees, a hundred years ago, were domiciled in the immediate neighbourhood of the place of their work, this is no longer the case. It is possible to-day, within ample limits, to choose the domicile independent of the place of work. The strongly reduced time of transport has caused a scattering of the population, primarily in the regions surrounding the big towns. This development is accompanied by a dispersion of the urban occupations; for instance, many industries which work direct for a big town are placed in the environs of the town.

All these factors combined have made the geographical delimitation of Copenhagen a problem, for the solution of which different methods are tried. This question may be considered under different

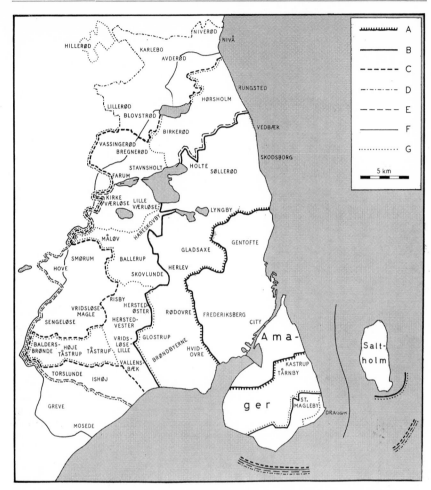

Fig. 1. The delimination of Copenhagen. Frontier lines of A: The "Capital".
B: „Greater Copenhagen" according to The Statistical Department. C: "The
Metropolitan Region" according to The Statistical Office of Copenhagen. D:
The Custom-district of Copenhagen. E: The county of Copenhagen. F: The tele-
phone local district of Copenhagen. G: Municipalities with more than 200
inhab. pr. sq. km.

aspects; for instance, an administrative point of view may be adopted. The municipality of Copenhagen comprises but a small part of
the region denominated »Storkøbenhavn« (Greater Copenhagen). It
encloses the municipality of Frederiksberg, which, since 1860, has
been officially regarded as a suburb of Copenhagen. The municipalities of Copenhagen, Frederiksberg and Gentofte are, in the official conception, considered as the »capital« (fig. 1.). The Statistical
Department reckons 9 municipalities in the environs to be suburbs.

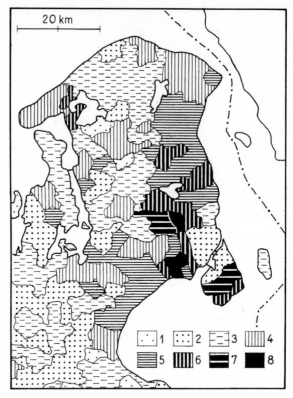

Fig. 2. Net increase and decrease of the population in the municipalities 1950-1955. 1: decrease more than 5 %, 2: decrease 0-5 %, 3: increase 0-5 %, 4: increase 5-10 %, 5: increase 10-25 %, 6: increase 25-50 %, 7: increase 50-100 %, 8: increase more than 100 %.

The Statistical Office of Copenhagen applies the term of suburbs to 19 (environs) municipalities. According to the first-mentioned delimitation (fig. 1.), Copenhagen and its suburbs counted, in 1955, 1.227.126 inhabitants; if using the second division as a base, the so-called »metropolitan region« counted, in 1955, 1.287.491 inhabitants and, in 1958, 1.310.740 inhabitants. Other demarcations of practical importance appear from fig. 1. With a point of departure in the average time of transport with public means of transport and bicycles, a delimitation was made on the basis of the conditions reigning in 1939; a certain conformity appeared between the 1-hour mean-isochrone and the delimitation now used by the Statistical Department.

The distribution of the population in Copenhagen is identical with the typical distribution in modern big towns. In the 1st zone: *the*

centre (the »City«), which almost corresponds to the total area of
Copenhagen in 1850, and which, to-day, almost exclusively has *City-
functions,* live (1957) only 35.480 persons = 14.700 per sq.km..
Even more sparsely populated are Christianshavn (5.400 per sq.km.)
and the quarters between the City and the lakes (9.600 per sq.km.).

The 2nd zone: *the inner quarters* from the latter part of the
nineteenth century have population desities varying from 13.000 to
25.000 per sq.km.; however, the most densely populated parts of
Vesterbro and of the interior Nørrebro have about 90.000 inhabitants
per sq.km.. Al these parts of the town show a decreasing population
figure.

In the 3rd zone: *the outer quarters* (Vanløse, Brønshøj, Valby
Husum, and others) the population figure is, on the whole, constant,
however, at many places with a feeble tendency of decrease. Here,
the population density is 6.000-13.000 per sq.km.

In the 4th zone: *the inner suburbs,* which are primarily residential quarters and dormitory suburbs, the density varies from 3.000
to 8.000 per sq.km., and here the population is greatly increasing,
not rarely by more than 20% a year (see fig. 2).

At a bigger distance from the centre the 5th zone: *the outer
suburbs,* the density varies from a few hundreds till about 8.000
inhabitants per sq.km.. Here, the increase of the population, though
important enough, is somewhat slower that in the suburbs situated
in close proximity to the town.

Outside the last-mentioned regions, which are undeniably to be
considered as integrating parts of the Capital, a transition zone is
stretching, where habitation and industrial and commercial life
are more or less depending on the Capital. This dependence, which
is varying strongly from one locality to another, is most often greatest in the vicinity of the most important lines of communication;
this contributes to throwing in relief the stelliform characteristic
of the outskirts of the modern city. Ancient provincial towns like
Helsingør (Elsinore), Hillerød, Roskilde and Køge, all of which are
situated at a distance of 30-45 km. from the centre, have become,
during the last decenniums, residence for a rather big mass of
population working in Copenhagen, amounting to 10-15% of the
able population of these town. Further, they have become the seat
of a number of industries working predominantly or totally for the
market in Copenhagen. However, in addition to these new functions
they are continuosly occupying the role of towns serving the catch-
ment areas: local commercial and industrial centres for the sur-

rounding rural districts. Contrary to this there are districts of a purely rural character — situated between the rays of communication lines — which stretch far in the direction of Copenhagen, and where the urbanization and other influences exercised by the metropolis are feeble or even nil; this is true of the regions around Sengeløse-Ledøje and Vallensbæk, etc.

In this connection it should be mentioned that according to the prevailing systems of delimitation the isle of Saltholm (in 1955: 16 sq.km., with 22 inhabitants) in the municipality of Tårnby constitutes an integrating part of the Copenhagen district; this isle is a plain with a maximum height of 2 m. above sea-level; the soil consists of limestone and is covered with salt-meadow vegetation.

The present-day population-development in the Copenhagen district

The development of the population within the two most current demarcations of the Copenhagen district (B. and C. in fig. 1) appears from the following table:

	Delimitation B.	Delimitation C.
1st February 1901	515.879	532.057
1st February 1921	742.970	768.844
5th November 1930	843.618	874.980
5th November 1940	1.007.993	1.044.464
7th November 1950	1.168.340	1.216.654
1st January 1959	1.251.832	1.326.422

The figures up to and including 1930 indicate the population which was present at the time of the census; the figures from and including 1940 the domiciled population.

The population of the Copenhagen municipality reached its maximum in 1950; since, a decrease has taken place and is now continuing at a rate of ¾-1 % annually. The population of Frederiksberg, which also culminated in 1950 is now feebly declining, while the population of Gentofte is stationary. These three municipalities compose the »Capital« (delimitation A. in fig. 1), whose population figure is now decreasing by 7-9 °/oo annually. The cause of this development is the fact that a continuously increasing part of the »Capital« adopts a »City-character«, and that young families settle and get their children in new habitation quarters, surrounding the old quarters. Concequently, the environs of the Capital include municipalities in strong growth (fig. 2); among these, Brøndbyerne and

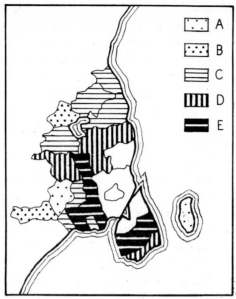

Fig. 3. Percentage of the active population in the municipalities of the Metropolitan Region working in Copenhagen proper. A: less than 20 %. B: 20-30 %.
C: 30-40 %. D: 40-50 %. E: more than 50 %. (The isle of Saltholm considered
as a unit apart).

Herlev have more than doubled their population figure during the
quenquennium 1950-1955, and a number of other municipalities in
the environs have also undergone a strong growth in this period.
After 1955 the environning municipalities have shown a tendency
of a more uniform growth.

The intensive urbanization which has developed in proximity to
the railway stations seems to have been transformed into a more
general, less pronounced urbanization of more extensive areas; this
is a natural result of the fact that the importance exercised by motor-cars and other motor-vehicles on the daily transport is constantly
increasing. Another consequence is that there are almost no limits
to the choice of residence; this allows to give the preference to
esthetic considerations by choosing the site in coastal regions, in
undulating land, at the edge of a wood or of a lake. A combination
of these factors has caused the expansion of the Copenhagen district
towards north, in the sub-glacial stream-trenches of North Sealand
filled with lakes and woods. To the west and to the southwest of
Copenhagen, in a flat and fertile moraine-land, the relief of the
landscape is far from being as attractive and, therefore, has not
invited to an expansion of the same dimensions.

The „Øresundsstad" (The Øresund urban area)

The continued growth of the Copenhagen district has rendered possible a fusion with the surrounding towns. The coast of the Sound, from Køge until north of Helsingør, is to-day lined with an almost uninterrupted row of habitations, and towards Hillerød and Roskilde we find dormitory towns and commencing satellite towns along railways and roads. On the east coast of the Sound, in Sweden, a corresponding development takes place and, further, an interchange within habitation and industrial and commercial life is going on between these two coasts. This interchange is most distinct at Helsingør — Hälsingborg: at thise place of the Sound, which here is only 3½ km. broad, and where the passage only takes 20 minutes, a considerable daily traffic takes place between domiciles in Denmark and places of work in Sweden, and vice versa. A totality of all the crossings of the Sound to-day gives about 13 million persons per year; this figure is increasing rather much.

Danish and Swedish town-planning experts are to-day foreseeing, in their plans, the »Øresundsstad« (see fig. 4) as a future reality A relevant factor in this connection is that the importance of the frontier between Denmark and Sweden is decreasing. From all responsible parts it is recognized that a bridge across the Sound is necessitated by the greatly increasing traffic between Scandinacia and Central Europe. If the »Øresundsstad« develops as foreseen, the local traffic will become so enormous that it will be necessary to build two bridges, one between Helsingør and Hälsingborg and one between Copenhagen and Malmö across Amager and Saltholm. Certain circles go in for the project of establishing Saltholm as a central air-port and the Swedish island Ven as a recreation area or as a centre for the production of energy of the district (for instance an atomic power station).

The greatest handicap of the Sound in its capacity of communication-line is the barrier of limestone which stretches from Sealand south of Copenhagen across Amager and Saltholm to the coast of Scania southwest of Malmö, and which only allows the passage of ships of less than 20 feet draught, whereas it is possible for ships up to about 30 feet draught to enter the ports of Copenhagen and Malmö. As the size of the new constructed ships is more and more increasing a deepening of the channels in the Sound will be necessary; otherwise, this area will inevitably loose of the advantages drawn from its position at the shortest passage between the Baltic and the oceans.

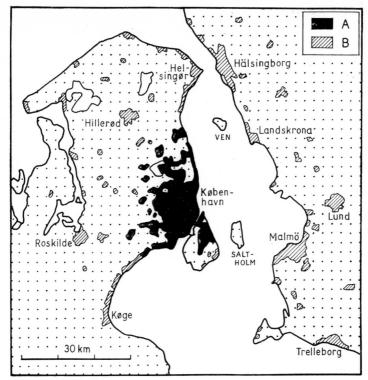

Fig. 4. The Øresund region. A: urban areas inside the Copenhagen Metropolitan
Region. B: other urban areas in the Øresund region.

Within the area planned to form part of the »Øresundsstad«, the
most important agglomerations are the following:

In Denmark: *figures in every 1.000 persons*		*In Sweden:* *figures in every 1.000 persons*	
Greater Copenhagen	1.326	Malmö	236
Helsingør	31	Hälsingborg	76
Roskilde	31	Lund	40
Hillerød	17	Landskrona	29
Køge	12		

This combination would give an estimated population of 1,8
millions of inhabitants about 1960. The most optimistic town-planning experts are foreseeing an »Øresundsstad« with 2,5 millions of
inhabitants in the year 2000.

LITERATURE

Aagesen, Aa. (1942): Om Københavns geografiske Afgrænsning. Geogr. Tidsskr. 45. København.

Atlas of Denmark II. *Aage Aagesen* (1960): The Population. Editor: The Royal Danish Geographical Society. København.

Bruun, Daniel (1921): Danmark.

Copenhagen Statistical Office: Stastistical Yearbook (annual).

Reumert, Johs. (1929): The Commercial-Geographic Importance of the Situation of Copenhagen. Supplement to Geogr. Tidsskr. 1929.

Statistical Department, København: The census-population, etc. various ed.

Trap: Danmark. (Denmark, a topographical handbook). 1st–5th ed. København.

Some characteristics of a growing suburban region.

By Viggo Hansen

Abstract

A rapidly developing suburban area to the west of Copenhagen is studied. The migration in and out of the area as well as the composition of the population is discussed, and it is shown how the adoption of a town plan leads the local development along certain fixed lines.

The growth of the Danish capital outside its municipal boundaries has at various times followed different lines, and the purpose of this paper is to show how development took place in an area covering about one hundred square kilometres to the west of the city and extending from four to fourteen kilometres from the previous line of walls.

The history of the modern growth of Copenhagen begins after 1850, when the fortifications from Mediaeval times were demolished and restrictions against building outside the walls cancelled. As the crowded city for many years had felt the urgent need for more space, the result was the rapid growing up of the so-called »bridge-quarters« (Vesterbro, Nørrebro, Østerbro, Sønderbro), which to begin with extended only to a normal walking distance from the City, even after the first horse-drawn street cars had appeared in 1865.

But all this happened much nearer to the City than can be shown on the four maps, fig.s 1-4 (A-D). From fig. 1 (A) it is evident that the City at that time (1855) had made no mark on the area to the west, even if a railway has been built in 1847 from Copenhagen to Roskilde. The settlements in this area were purely rural, mostly in the form of green villages, surrounded by flat and fertile land. Sixty years after enclosure the farms still lay in villages as a result of the farmers' preference for drawing the boundary lines between their possessions like spokes in a wheel. Only a few farmers had broken away from village life and moved into the middle of their fields. Scattered farms were also to be seen on the land of the former dismantled village of Islev.

While the years previous to the First World War had seen a

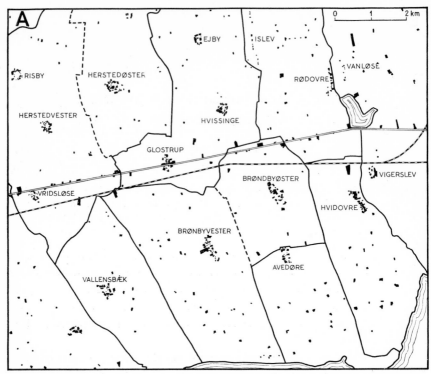

Fig. 1. In 1860 the villages west of Copenhagen are still quite undisturbed by the expanding capital.

uniform and continuous spreading of the capital until it had reached the easternmost parts of the map area, where the old villages Vanløse and Vigerslev had been incorporated in the municipality of Copenhagen, the changes outside the new boundaries were still only few by 1913, fig. 2 (B). Two new railway towns had grown up on the great western railway, Glostrup and Vridsløse. Of these two only Glostrup (2231 inhabitants in 1911) had some suburban traits, while Vridsløse had growth up round a state prison. The other habitations were mostly unchanged except for a certain filling up of the villages by small houses. Agriculture was still the main occupation, but market gardening was beginning to spread into the area, influenced by the rapid growth of industrialization in Copenhagen.

By 1930, fig. 3 (C) the areas inside the municipality of Copenhagen are built up with only a few exceptions, some of which are in horticulture. From here the continuous built-up areas have spread into the neighbouring parishes (Hvidovre and Rødovre). As often happens these new outer areas grew up as week-end gardens with a

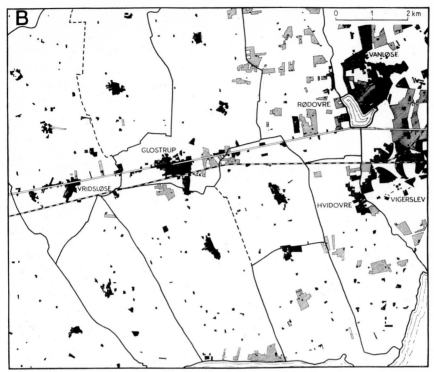

Fig. 2. In 1910 the suburban development has reached the boundary of the parishes mentioned in the paper. A small town has grown up round Glostrup railway station. Market gardening (grey) is gradually spreading in the area.

semi-permanent housing, where people lived during week-ends or even through the whole summer. By 1930 a great part of these suburban settlements still had a semi-permanent character and were only served by a few and infrequent bus lines. The same semi-permanent housing characterizes the habitations along the coast (Brøndbystrand), here partly in connection with new market-gardering areas that now had spread still more over the whole area, the lorries having replaced the horse-drawn cars.

This spread of market-gardering is perhaps an important reason why the old village structure is preserved as soon as we are off the main roads, besides of course the lack of transport facilities in the same area.

The most notable feature is the urbanization of Glostrup, and of that habitation alone, by now with more than 4000 inhabitants. But this development is only partly suburban. Local industries have grown up, while at the same time its function as a local service and

Fig. 3. In 1930 suburban development has penetrated into the area, mostly along the eastern boundary, at the coast and at Glostrup. Market gardening (grey) and week-end gardens (dotted areas) are growing.

trade centre is of some importance. The trains now run daily at an interval of one hour, but in the rush hours every half hour.

The last map, fig. 4 (D) shows how the continuous built-up area has spread far beyond the municipality of Copenhagen. Not only have new housing areas completely filled up the two nearest parishes (Hvidovre and Rødovre), but have also crossed the boundary into the neighbouring parish of Brøndbyerne and stretch uninterrupted to a distance of 8,5 kilometres from Copenhagen. But there is a marked difference in housing before and now. Until 1930 and partly up to the Second World War most outlying areas were built with small private houses in gardens of their own, while now, after the war, most building activity has become company building, often tall blocks of 12-16 storeys, mingled with small tenement houses of 2-3 storeys and with park area and greens between. Outside the fully built-up areas building activity is mostly concentrated upon only two parishes, Glostrup and Brøndbyerne. Only

Fig. 4. In 1960 the eastern part of the area is fully developed, Glostrup is growing rapidly and has got extensive industrial areas (coarse hatching) while the outer zones more and more turns into market gardening (grey).

these two suburbs show an accelerated growth, mainly after the opening in April 1953 of a new suburban railway line from Copenhagen to Glostrup, the consequences of which are shown in the population figures. Thus Glostrup grew from 13,490 in 1952 to 18,288 in 1958, and Brøndbyerne from 6,402 in 1952 to 13,014 in 1958. Now Brøndbyerne is really two suburbs. One is centered round the railway station of Brøndbyøster, while the other one, Brøndbyvester, forms part of Glostrup railway town, and more correctly said Brøndbyøster has about 8000 inhabitants, and Glostrup (including Brøndbyvester) has 25,000 inhabitants.

The opening of a new suburban railway is often seen to influence a much larger area than immediately adjacent to the railway itself, but this is not the case here because of the acceptance of a city plan for the suburban parishes. According to these plans only so-called »Inner Zones« are allowed to be developed. Inner Zones are areas that, besides being technically fully equipped, have a public system of transport means which give a rapid and frequent service of great capacity direct to the centre of Copenhagen. »Middle Zones« are areas that are reserved for future development, while »Outer Zones« are not supposed to be developed. The Outer Zones comprise purely agricultural land including villages and similar old habitations which will always lie as green »islands« between separate suburbs.

The adoption of this great zonal division has a marked effect in many ways. Among the immediate results is the rapid growth of the market-gardening areas in the Outer Zones, even if this growth is also affected by the latest enlarging of the Copenhagen airport (Kastrup) on the flat lands of Amager, where market-gardening has been a traditional occupation for hundreds of years. Another effect is the establishment of new colonies of week-end gardens on leases limited in time. These are situated in the Outer Zones as well as in the Middle Zones, where they will be surrendered in time of development.

The old village structure is still mostly intact, partly because the villages lie in the Outer Zones and partly because the old farm houses can be used unchanged by the gardeners, who now have succeeded the farmers in most places.

The adopted boundaries between Inner and Middle Zones, and between Middle and Outer Zones, are liable to change, but normally it may be said that areas wanted for the Inner Zone must lie within »Walking distance« from a railway station, which in practice will mean »Cycling distance«. This condition has been made in order to avoid a net of bus lines with terminals at the suburban railway station.

Industrial development. Copenhagen has always been the manufacturing and industrial centre of Denmark, and up to 1940 it was still possible to find suitable industrial areas in the town itself. But since 1945 vacant lots for new industries have no longer been available, and industry had to seek out areas outside the municipality, either in the suburbs or somewhere else in the country where facilities were present. As a results of this demand for more space new industrial areas were laid out in some of the suburbs, where transport facilities were already at hand or could be supplied. Glostrup became a natural choice, because it had a big railway area, where more trails could be added if required, and besides the town had an industrial tradition even if on a smaller scale, and it had a rather large population to satisfy the demand for an additional number of hands; and if this should prove unsufficient, then there was a satisfactory train service to Copenhagen to bring workers to and from. In less than ten years Glostrup grew from a merely trade and service centre to an industrial town. Among the new industries are some very big ones in metals and in electric equipment, like a factory for making coin metals, one for making cables and wires, a telephone factory and another for office machinery (typewriters), and the manufacturing includes such divers commodities as chocolate and automobiles.

Only a few of the establishments, mostly among the smaller ones, are newly founded firms ,the greater part being more or less branches or extensions of already existing companies, which circumstances have forced to move from their old sites in Copenhagen.

The question has often been asked why they did not move into the country, where land is cheaper and the number of hands more stable. The answer has newly been given in an interrogation of a sample of 155 enterprises of different kinds. From this it seems obvious that nearness to the customers, especially with regard to semi-manufactured or consumers' articles, is of great importance; next: abundance of educated and qualified workers, and thirdly: better transport facilities by sea and air, in the interest of foreign customers and wholesale tradesmen.

On the other hand, no one mentioned raw materials as a location factor, which is quite reasonable, because neither raw materials nor power can possibly influence location when they are not present anywhere in Denmark, while it is stressed that transport facilities by sea are still of importance (Copenhagen is the most busy seaport in Denmark). New is the information that a busy airport is something to reckon with, because traffic by air brings the salesmen and the foreign customers nearer. For these reason it is obvious that Copenhagen has an advantage over other Danish towns, and the suburbs must be reckoned as parts of Copenhagen in this sense.

Population. The general increase of population in the six suburban parishes is shown in the following table for the last 25 years.

	1930	1935	1940	1945	1950	1955
Hvidovre	6523	8499	12014	14208	23163	32688
Rødovre	5836	9233	12443	14780	18704	27007
Glostrup	4877	6184	7581	9056	11731	15884
Brøndbyerne	2967	3340	3635	3941	6355	12505
Herstederne	2554	2708	2294	2458	3096	3291
Vallensbæk	550	615	676	717	856	1184
Total	23307	30579	38643	45160	63905	92559

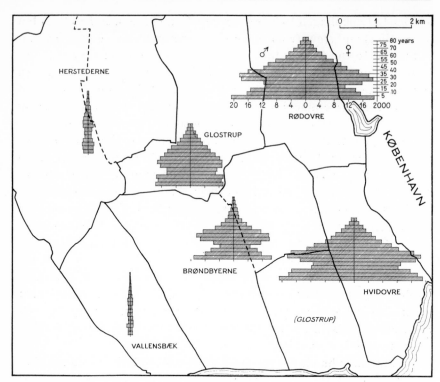

Fig. 5. The age-and-sex pyramids illustrate the characters of the different suburban developments.

While the six parishes in 1930 had only 23.307 inhabitants, this figure by 1955 had grown to 92,559, nearly four times as much. In 1958 the total population had passed the hundred thousands and was 103,423.

The rapid growth of these suburbs of course began in the ones nearest to Copenhagen (Hvidovre and Rødovre). A little later they were joined by Glostrup, while the increase in population in Brønd-byerne only began after 1945. Details of this population increase are shown in fig. 5. In Hvidovre the increase seems to have passed its maximum speed, meaning that the parish is filled up. Another group comprises Glostrup and Brøndbyerne. Being a railway town for more than a hundred years has favoured Glostrup with an earlier population increase, but after 1952 (the new suburban railway came in April 1953) Brøndbyerne shows a more rapid growth, and there are no indications that these two new towns will stop growing for the first ten years. The third group, containing Herstederne and Vallensbæk, seems completely unaffected by the presence of a mil-

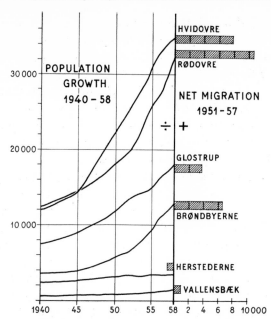

Fig. 6. Population development 1940-1958 in the six parishes and (to the right) the migration 1951-1957 for the same communities.

lion-town less than 15 kilometres to the east. Herstederne has even a slightly decreasing population. But this condition will not last much longer (see below). Vallensbæk shows signs of a slow wakening from its magic sleep, after it has become the junction of two main roads. But in a few years two new suburban railways will be built, one of which will pass through Vallensbæk, following the coastline to the southwest, while the other one will be an extension line to the west of Glostrup. That the latter one will affect Herstederne has been foreseen: a detailed town plan has been made for some years and the new town has even got its name (Albertslund).

Fig. 5. also gives the net migration figures in the six suburban parishes for the years 1951-57, showing once more the rapid immigration in the upper four, while it is only small for Vallensbæk, and Herstederne even has had a surplus emigration. The gross migration figures for the same period show for Rødovre an immigration of 25.831 persons against an emigration of 15.281, for Hvidovre an immigration of 29.768 against an emigration of 21.869 persons, while the respective figures for Glostrup are 13.581 and 9.850 and for Brøndbyerne 13.011 and 6.813.

While the yearly emigration does not deviate much from 10 per cent. of the actual population in any of the four parishes, the immigration has so far been more or less directly proportional to the distance from Copenhagen. The only exception to this rule is Hvidovre, and only for the last year (1957), when immigration and emigration balanced each other, this being another sign that the parish is nearly built-up. In Hvidovre 64 per cent of the population increase is still due to migration. This figure seems rather high, but not in comparison with Brøndbyerne, where immigration amounts to nearly 80 per cent of the population increase.

Even if only a lesser share of the increase is due to surplus births, the birth rate is still very high in relation to all Denmark. The number of live-births per thousand inhabitants for the years 1951-57 varied from 28 to 33 for Brøndbyerne and from 20 to 22 for Glostrup. The rate is increasing in Rødovre, but decreasing in Hvidovre.

Many of the variations get their explanation from the age-and-sex pyramids (fig. 6.). These give the different age groups superimposed in layers, each layer representing five years, beginning with the age group 0-5. Males are represented to the left of the centre line, and females to the right. The length of each horizontal layer expresses the total number of the age groups in hundreds.

The four bigger pyramids (Rødovre, Hvidovre, Brøndbyerne and Glostrup) are representative of communities affected by immigration towards a town. The profiles swell in the middle, meaning an immigration of young adults, but as most of the immigrants are married couples, the predominance of females over males is not pronounced, as might have been expected. The many young married couples are also responsible for the swelling at the bottom of the pyramids because of many small children. This last swelling is not so distinct for Glostrup because of a different age composition, wherein the great share of the older adults reflects its past as a railway town. The pyramid does not narrow so much towards the apex, as is the case with the other three bigger parishes.

Contrary to the above pyramids, the ones for Herstederne and Vallensbæk show a constriction in the middle and at the bottom. In these small communities there are fewer small children and fewer young adults, while the age groups 35-50 years and again 10-20 years dominate, a very common profile for rural areas with an emigration of young adults. From this it is evident that the composition of the population in Vallensbæk and Herstederne is not suburban at all.

No exact statistics are available to show where the immigration into the suburbs originated, except that about two thirds came from the metropolitan area and only one third from the rest of the country, but it would not be erroneous to suppose that many of the immigrants came from all over the country, but stopped for some years in Copenhagen before they married and settled in the suburbs. The reason for believing this is the difficulty for young married couples to get hold of an apartment in Copenhagen, because the town favours its own. Most Copenhagen apartment are occupied by middle aged and older people who have no wish to move from their old and cheaper apartment to live in a more modern, but also more expensive one, the rent of which will often require that both man and wife have a regular income.

The immigrants into the suburbs fall into two groups: I. Those who live in the suburbs, but have their income in Copenhagen, and II: those who have their income from their new municipality of domicile. The proportion between the two categories differs somewhat from one parish to another. In 1948 60 per cent. of the taxpayers in Rødovre had an income from Copenhagen, but in 1957 this share had fallen to 57 per cent. The same figures were for Hvidovre 68 per cent and 59 per cent respectively. If one goes from these older suburbs to the newer ones, there is a marked difference. While only 24 per cent of the taxpayers in Brøndbyerne had their income from Copenhagen in 1948, this figure in 1957 had risen to 54 per cent., thus showing a typically residential town. For Glostrup once again its past as a railway town is evident from the source of the income. In 1948 38 per cent of the taxpayers had their earnings from Copenhagen, and the corresponding figures for 1957 show hardly any alteration (39 per cent). This rather low portion of earnings from Copenhagen is of course owing to the increase of manufacturing industries in Glostrup.

On the other hand there is a considerable number of people who are taxpayers in Copenhagen but have their income in the suburbs. This is the case for 3.560 persons in Rødovre, 2.800 in Hvidovre, 1.770 in Brøndbyerne and 1.560 in Glostrup, totalling about 10.000 people who live in Copenhagen, but work in the suburbs. This seems rather peculiar, until it is made clear that many of the newly erected factories in Glostrup used to lie in Copenhagen, where also the employees lived. When the factories moved to Glostrup, the employees remained in their old and cheap apartments, because this was cheaper, even if they had to pay the daily fare to their work.

The total number of taxpayers in the six parishes with an income from Copenhagen amounts to about 30,000, and if we add another

10.000 people who have their income in the six suburbs but live in Copenhagen, we get a total of about 40.000 people who are forced to travel twice the day between their homes and their place of work. To these may be added some thousands of children and young people who must travel to and from Copenhagen for educational purpose.

This of course means an enormus traffic on roads and streets and a similar pressure on the public means of transport, particularly in the rush hours. Those who live in Hvidovre and in the southern part of Rødovre have easy access to Hvidovre suburban railway station from where they can use cheap urban railway fare. For these journeys no figures are available, but from the other four parishes it is possible to get the number of journeys to and from the suburban stations of Brøndbyøster and Glostrup. They amount to 1,8 million journeys (1957/58) for Brøndbyøster and 2,4 million for Glostrup, or totally 5.000 respectively 7.000 journeys every day. It each person travels twice a day it means that 6.000 people use the suburban railway, and this is a little more than half of the people in Brøndbyerne and Glostrup who have to travel to and from the same parishes on account of their daily work. The other half then must make use of buses or private means of conveyance (car, motorcycle, bicycle). This is why the town planning committee has insisted on the building of more suburban railways in order to avoid more pressure on existing roads and streets and to lead the daily stream of people along the narrowest possible channels.

Another way out of the traffic dilemma was of course an interchange of people between Copenhagen and the suburbs, in order to make the municipality of domicile also the municipality of income; but this would require an equalization of the level in rent, which is hardly possible. Besides, only a minor part of the dwellers in the suburbs are manual workers, while most of them are engaged in public services or are office personnel or shop assistants, for whom there are no means of income in the suburbs.

LITERATURE

Betænkning vedrørende Partiel Byudviklingsplan, Nr. 2: for København-Egnens Byudviklingsområde, 1951.

Stadsingeniørens Direktorat: København, skitser til en generalplan, 1954.

Statistisk Årbog for København, Frederiksberg og Gentofte samt Omegnskommunerne. København 1951-58.

Københavns statistiske Kontor: Statistisk Månedsskrift. København.

Storkøbenhavn, Økonomisk månedsoversigt for hovedstadsområdet.

Statistiske Efterretninger (Weekly statistical review). København.

Danske Statsbaner: Årsberetning. (Annual report). København.